FUNCTIONS OF A COMPLEX VARIABLE

THE PRINDLE, WEBER & SCHMIDT
COMPLEMENTARY SERIES IN MATHEMATICS

Under the consulting editorship of

HOWARD W. EVES

The University of Maine

TITLES IN THE SERIES:

Howard W. Eves, Functions of a Complex Variable, Volume One
Howard W. Eves, Functions of a Complex Variable, Volume Two
Edward H. Barry, Introduction to Geometrical Transformations, Volume Three
Richard E. Johnson, Vector Algebra, Volume Four

Functions of a
Complex Variable

HOWARD W. EVES

VOLUME TWO

PRINDLE, WEBER & SCHMIDT, INCORPORATED

Boston, Massachusetts

TO B_1

AND THOSE WONDERFUL HOPATCONG DAYS

THAT B_2 WILL NEVER FORGET

Preface

The following notes are those of an advanced undergraduate and first-year graduate course in functions of a complex variable given by the author over a period of several years almost a couple of decades ago. At the time, essentially the only texts available in the subject were those of Burkhardt, Copson, Durège, Goursat, Harkness and Morley, MacRobert, Osgood, Pierpont, Titchmarsh, and Townsend. Since none of these texts, though grand for their day and still often useful, quite fit the plan of the course, the following notes were evolved. A goodly number of students learned their complex function theory from these notes and were kind enough to express an admiration of them. The admiration spread to some other instructors who, in turn, also used the notes. And to this day there are many students who borrow copies of the notes to supplement a present-day course in the subject. The result is that there has been an urging on the part of a number of students and instructors that these notes be published, and after various misgivings and considerable reluctance the author has consented.

The misgivings and reluctance arose from the classical nature and the skeletal form of the notes. Of course the hard core of the subject still resides in the classical development, but over the intervening years there have been embellishments and refinements in function theory and several fine modern texts have appeared. Not only have a number of proofs and approaches been improved over the years, but in a course in complex function theory today one can make much wise and excellent use of concepts of both topology and abstract algebra. A course in complex function theory given by the author today leans heavily on the work of Carathéodory and differs materially from the course he started almost two decades ago. But to rewrite the notes toward updating them, or even toward padding their skeletal form to make a finished book of them, would involve much more time and energy than the author has at his disposal. Moreover, it has actually been urged that the notes be left essentially in their original classical and skeletal form—that these are features the users wish preserved. So here they are, pruned and altered a little, but very much as formulated in the beginning. May they possibly furnish mathematical pleasure to some and supplementary material and approach to others.

The author's love of function theory was aroused and nurtured by the masterful expositions given by Professor David Vernon Widder of Harvard University. Any worthy features of these notes undoubtedly owe something to those remarkable lectures of yesteryear.

The material in this second volume continues the notes started in the first volume. When teaching from these notes several years ago, the author covered the material of Volume One in one semester and most of that of Volume Two in the following semester. Sometimes in the second semester Chapter 22 was omitted and sometimes both Chapters 20 and 22 were omitted and replaced by an introduction to conformal mapping and the Schwarz-Christoffel transformation.

HOWARD EVES

Contents

CHAPTER 12

Singularities

SINGULARITIES

12.01. DEFINITION. $f(z)$ has a *singularity* at $z = z_0$ if $f(z)$ is not analytic at $z = z_0$.

12.02. DEFINITION. $f(z)$ has an *isolated singularity* at $z = z_0$ if it is analytic in a neighborhood of z_0 except at z_0.

12.03. DEFINITION. $f(z)$ has a *pole* at $z = z_0$ if z_0 is an isolated singularity and if $\lim_{z \to z_0} f(z) = \infty$.

Note: This definition includes our previous one made in Article 3.05.

Examples

(1) $\dfrac{1}{z - z_0}$ has a pole at z_0.

(2) $\dfrac{1}{(z - z_0)^n}$ has a pole at z_0.

(3) $\dfrac{\varphi(z)}{(z - z_0)^n}$, where $\varphi(z)$ is analytic at z_0 and $\varphi(z_0) \neq 0$, has a pole at z_0.

(4) $\tan z$ has a pole at $z = \pi/2$.

12.04. DEFINITION. $f(z)$ has a *removable singularity* at $z = z_0$ if z_0 is an isolated singularity and if $f(z)$ becomes analytic at z_0 after being defined or redefined there.

Examples

(1) $f(z) = 1, \ (z \neq 0)$.

(2) $\left.\begin{array}{l} f(z) = 1, \ (z \neq 0) \\ \ f(z) = 2, \ (z = 0) \end{array}\right\}$.

(3) z^2/z.

12.05. DEFINITION.   If $f(z)$ has a singularity at $z = z_0$ which is neither a pole nor a removable singularity, then it has an *essential singularity* there.

Notes: (1) Essential singularities exist, for consider

$$f(z) = e^{1/z}, \quad z \neq 0.$$

Along the real axis this function becomes

$$f(x) = e^{1/x}.$$

Now,

$$\lim_{x \to 0+} e^{1/x} = \infty \quad \text{and} \quad \lim_{x \to 0-} e^{1/x} = 0.$$

Hence $f(z)$ does not become infinite as $z \to 0$, nor, on the other hand, can the singularity be removed.

(2) All nonisolated singularities are essential singularities.

(3) Suppose $f(z)$ has an isolated singularity at $z = z_0$. Then one of the following cases certainly exists:

(a) $f(z)$ becomes infinite as $z \to z_0$.

(b) $f(z)$ remains finite in a neighborhood of $z = z_0$.

(c) $f(z)$ does neither (a) nor (b).

In case (a) the singularity is always a pole (Article 12.03). In case (b) the singularity is always removable (Article 12.06).

12.06. RIEMANN'S THEOREM.   If $f(z)$ has an isolated singularity at $z = z_0$ and remains finite in a neighborhood of z_0, then z_0 is a removable singularity of $f(z)$.

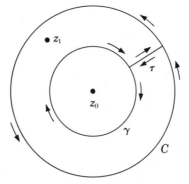

Figure 12.1

Proof: Since $f(z)$ is finite in a neighborhood of z_0, there exists an M and a δ such that

$$|f(z)| < M \quad \text{when} \quad |z - z_0| < \delta.$$

As shown in Figure 12.1, draw circle $C : |z - z_0| = R$ within the domain of analyticity of $f(z)$. Let $z_1 \neq z_0$ be an arbitrary point within C. Draw circle γ:

$$\gamma : |z - z_0| = r, \quad r < |z_0 - z_1|, r < \delta.$$

By Cauchy's integral formula,

$$f(z_1) = \frac{1}{2\pi i} \int_C \frac{f(t)\,dt}{t - z_1} + \frac{1}{2\pi i} \int_\gamma \frac{f(t)\,dt}{t - z_1}. \tag{1}$$

(We treat the regular closed curve $C + \tau + \gamma + \tau$.) But

$$\left| \frac{1}{2\pi i} \int_\gamma \frac{f(t)\,dt}{t - z_1} \right| \leq \frac{1}{2\pi} \int_\gamma \frac{|f(t)|}{|t - z_1|}\,ds$$

$$< \frac{M2\pi r}{2\pi(|z_1 - z_0| - r)}, \tag{2}$$

for

$$|t - z_1| = |(t - z_0) - (z_1 - z_0)|$$
$$\geq |z_1 - z_0| - |t - z_0|$$
$$= |z_1 - z_0| - r > 0.$$

Now take r smaller. Then the integral about γ does not change because of (1). Hence the integral is independent of r. It must then be a constant. But, by (2), since r may be taken as small as we please, this constant must be 0. Hence, from (1),

$$f(z_1) = \frac{1}{2\pi i} \int_C \frac{f(t)\,dt}{t - z_1}.$$

Now define, or redefine if necessary,

$$f(z_0) = \frac{1}{2\pi i} \int_C \frac{f(t)\,dt}{t - z_0}.$$

Then, by Article 11.58, $f(z)$ is analytic at $z = z_0$, and the singularity has been removed.

12.07.   COROLLARY.   Under the conditions of Riemann's theorem (Article 12.06), $\lim_{z \to z_0} f(z)$ exists.

12.08.   THEOREM.   Nonisolated essential singularities exist.

Proof: Consider $1/\sin 1/z$ at $z = 0$. Certainly $z = 0$ is an essential singularity. Moreover, it is nonisolated inasmuch as there are infinitely many poles in any neighborhood of $z = 0$, namely the points

$$z = 1/k\pi, \quad k = \pm 1, \pm 2, \cdots .$$

12.09.   WEIERSTRASS'S THEOREM.   If $f(z)$ has an isolated essential singularity at $z = a$, then in any neighborhood of $z = a$, $f(z)$ comes arbitrarily near any prescribed (complex) value.

Proof: Let c be any prescribed value. Then we wish to show that given $\epsilon > 0$ and $\delta > 0$, there exists a point z_0 such that

$$|f(z_0) - c| < \epsilon, \quad 0 < |z_0 - a| < \delta.$$

Suppose there is no such point z_0. Then

$$|f(z) - c| \geq \epsilon > 0 \tag{1}$$

for all points z such that

$$0 < |z - a| < \delta.$$

From (1), we have, since $\epsilon \neq 0$,

$$\frac{1}{|f(z) - c|} \leq \frac{1}{\epsilon} > 0. \tag{2}$$

Consider the function

$$F(z) = \frac{1}{f(z) - c}.$$

$F(z)$ is certainly analytic in some deleted neighborhood $0 < |z - a| < r$, for $f(z)$ is analytic in some such neighborhood inasmuch as $z = a$ is an *isolated* singularity. Also, by (2), we may take r so small that $F(z)$ has no poles in the neighborhood. Hence we may apply Article 12.07, obtaining

$$\lim_{z \to a} F(z) = A.$$

Two cases arise:
   Case 1. $A \neq 0$. Here we have

$$\lim_{z \to a} \frac{1}{f(z) - c} = A \neq 0,$$

whence

$$\lim_{z \to a} f(z) = 1/A + C.$$

But this is a contradiction of the hypothesis, since the singularity at $z = a$ is *not* a removable singularity.

Case 2. $A = 0$. Here we have

$$\lim_{z \to a} f(z) - c = \infty$$

or

$$\lim_{z \to a} f(z) = \infty.$$

But this is also a contradiction of the hypothesis, since the singularity at $z = a$ is *not* a pole.

Hence the theorem by *reductio ad absurdum*.

Notes: (1) We may state this theorem as follows: Let $f(z)$ have an isolated essential singularity at $z = a$. Then, given any numbers c, $\delta > 0$, $\epsilon > 0$, there is a point z_0 in the circle $|z - a| < \delta$ at which $|f(z) - c| < \epsilon$.

(2) Actually there are an infinite number of such points z_0. For if z_0 is such a point in the neighborhood $|z - a| < \delta$, there must be another in the neighborhood $|z - a| < \frac{1}{2}|z_0 - a|$, and so on indefinitely.

12.10. THEOREM. If $f(z)$ has an isolated essential singularity at $z = a$, and if c is an arbitrary constant, then there exists a sequence $z_1, z_2, z_3, \cdots$ such that

$$\lim_{n \to \infty} z_n = a \quad \text{and} \quad \lim_{n \to \infty} f(z_n) = c.$$

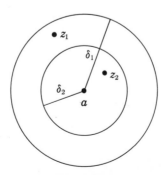

Figure 12.2

Proof: (See Figure 12.2.) By Weierstrass's Theorem (Article 12.09), there exist points $z_1, z_2, \cdots, z_n, \cdots$ such that

$$|f(z_1) - c| < 1, \qquad 0 < |z_1 - a| < \delta_1,$$
$$|f(z_2) - c| < \tfrac{1}{2}, \qquad 0 < |z_2 - a| < \delta_2 < |z_1 - a|,$$

$$\cdot\ \cdot\ \cdot\ \cdot\ \cdot\ \cdot\ \cdot\ \cdot\ \cdot\ \cdot\ \cdot\ \cdot\ \cdot\ \cdot$$

$$|f(z_n) - c| < 1/n, \quad 0 < |z_n - a| < \delta_n < |z_{n-1} - a|,$$

$$\cdot\ \cdot\ \cdot\ \cdot\ \cdot\ \cdot\ \cdot\ \cdot\ \cdot\ \cdot\ \cdot\ \cdot\ \cdot\ \cdot$$

Also, let us suppose that our δ's are chosen so as to be subject to the further condition that

$$\lim_{n \to \infty} \delta_n = 0.$$

Then the sequence $z_1, z_2, \cdots, z_n, \cdots$ is the required sequence.
For certainly, given any $\epsilon > 0$, we may find an n such that

$$|z_n - a| < \epsilon,$$

by choosing n so that $\delta_n < \epsilon$. Hence

$$\lim_{n \to \infty} z_n = a.$$

Also,

$$|f(z_n) - c| < \epsilon, \quad \text{where} \quad 1/n < \epsilon,$$

and hence

$$\lim_{n \to \infty} f(z_n) = c.$$

Example: $e^{1/z}$ has an isolated essential singularity at $z = 0$. Now, $e^{1/z}$ never vanishes, but it may be made to come arbitrarily near to 0 by taking the sequence

$$z_n = -1/n, \quad n = 1, 2, \cdots.$$

Here we have

$$\lim_{n \to \infty} z_n = 0 \quad \text{and} \quad \lim_{n \to \infty} e^{1/z_n} = 0.$$

(See Article 10.36 in connection with showing that $z = 0$ is neither a pole nor a removable singularity of $e^{1/z}$.)

12.11. PICARD'S THEOREM.   If $f(z)$ has an isolated essential singularity at $z = a$, then in any neighborhood of $z = a$, $f(z)$ takes on every value, except perhaps one value, infinitely often.

(We only state this remarkable theorem here. As examples, $\sin 1/z$ and $e^{1/z}$ have isolated essential singularities at $z = 0$; $\sin 1/z$ actually attains every value in $0 < |z| < r$, no matter how small r may be, whereas $e^{1/z}$ attains there every value except 0 (see example, Article 12.10).)

POLES

12.12. THEOREM.   If $f(z)$ is analytic in a neighborhood of a point $z = a$, except for a pole at $z = a$, then

$$f(z) = \frac{\varphi(z)}{(z - a)^k},$$

where

(a) k is a positive integer,

(b) $\varphi(z)$ is analytic at $z = a$,

(c) $\varphi(a) \neq 0$.

Proof: Since, by hypothesis,

$$\lim_{z \to a} f(z) = \infty,$$

there exists a δ such that, given $M > 0$,

$$|f(z)| > M \quad \text{when} \quad 0 < |z - a| < \delta. \tag{1}$$

Consider the function

$$F(z) = 1/f(z).$$

This function is certainly analytic in the deleted neighborhood of a,

$$0 < |z - a| < \delta,$$

because, from (1), $f(z)$ has no zeros in this neighborhood. But, also from (1), we have

$$|F(z)| < 1/M \quad \text{when} \quad 0 < |z - a| < \delta.$$

Hence

$$\lim_{z \to a} F(z) = 0.$$

Let us define $F(a) = 0$. Then $F(z)$ is analytic at $z = a$ also. Hence, by Article 11.61,

$$F(z) = (z - a)^k \Phi(z),$$

where $\Phi(z)$ is analytic at $z = a$ and $\Phi(a) \neq 0$. Hence

$$f(z) = \frac{1}{F(z)} = \frac{1}{(z - a)^k} \frac{1}{\Phi(z)} = \frac{\varphi(z)}{(z - a)^k},$$

where

$$\varphi(z) \equiv 1/\Phi(z).$$

Since $\Phi(z)$ is analytic at $z = a$ and $\Phi(a) \neq 0$, it follows that $\Phi(a)$ is finite. Hence $\varphi(z)$ is analytic at $z = a$ and $\varphi(a) \neq 0$. This proves the theorem.

12.13.   DEFINITION. k in Article 12.12 is called the *order* of the pole at $z = a$.

12.14.   DEFINITION.   The *number of poles* of $f(z)$ in a domain D is the sum of the orders of all the poles of $f(z)$ in D.

12.15.   THEOREM.   If $f(z)$ has a pole of order k at $z = a$, then $f'(z)$ has a pole of order $k + 1$ at $z = a$.

Proof: Since $f(z)$ has a pole of order k at $z = a$, we have (Article 12.12)

$$f(z) = \frac{\varphi(z)}{(z - a)^k},$$

where $\varphi(z)$ is analytic at $z = a$ and $\varphi(a) \neq 0$. Therefore

$$f'(z) = \frac{(z - a)^k \varphi'(z) - \varphi(z)k(z - a)^{k-1}}{(z - a)^{2k}}$$

$$= \frac{(z - a)\varphi'(z) - k\varphi(z)}{(z - a)^{k+1}}$$

$$= \frac{\psi(z)}{(z - a)^{k+1}}, \text{ say.}$$

Since $\varphi(z)$ is analytic at $z = a$, so also is $\varphi'(z)$. Hence $\psi(z)$ is analytic at $z = a$. Moreover, $\psi(a) = -k\varphi(a) \neq 0$. Hence $f'(z)$ has a pole of order $k + 1$ at $z = a$.

12.16. THEOREM. If $f(z)$ is analytic in a neighborhood of $z = a$, except for a pole of order k at $z = a$, then

$$f(z) = \sum_{n=-k}^{\infty} A_n(z-a)^n, \quad 0 < |z-a| < \delta,$$

and $A_{-k} \neq 0$.

Proof: By Article 12.12, we have

$$f(z) = \varphi(z)/(z-a)^k,$$

where $\varphi(z)$ is analytic at $z = a$ and $\varphi(a) \neq 0$. Hence, by Taylor's expansion, we have

$$\varphi(z) = \varphi(a) + \varphi'(a)(z-a) + \varphi''(a)\frac{(z-a)^2}{2!} + \cdots,$$

the series converging to $\varphi(z)$ in some neighborhood

$$|z-a| < \delta.$$

Hence

$$f(z) = \frac{\varphi(a)}{(z-a)^k} + \frac{\varphi'(a)}{(z-a)^{k-1}} + \cdots + \frac{\varphi^{(k-1)}(a)}{(k-1)!(z-a)}$$
$$+ \frac{\varphi^{(k)}(a)}{k!} + \frac{\varphi^{(k+1)}(a)(z-a)}{(k+1)!} + \cdots,$$

the series converging to $f(z)$ in the *deleted* neighborhood

$$0 < |z-a| < \delta.$$

Hence, setting

$$A_{-k} = \varphi(a), \text{ etc.,}$$

and noting that

$$A_{-k} = \varphi(a) \neq 0,$$

we have the theorem.

12.17. DEFINITION. $\sum_{n=-k}^{-1} A_n(z-a)^n$ is known as the *principal part* of $f(z)$ at the kth-order pole $z = a$. (See Article 12.16.)

12.18. THEOREM. If $f(z)$ has a pole at $z = a$ with a principal part $P(z)$ at $z = a$, then $f(z) - P(z)$ has a removable singularity at $z = a$.

Proof: In a deleted neighborhood of a we certainly have

$$f(z) = \varphi(z)/(z - a)^k$$

$$= \frac{1}{(z-a)^k}\{\varphi(a) + \varphi'(a)(z-a) + \cdots + (z-a)^k Q(z)\},$$

where [see (1) of Art. 11.48, Vol. I],

$$Q(z) = \frac{1}{2\pi i}\int_\gamma \frac{f(t)\,dt}{(t-a)^k(t-z)}.$$

That is,

$$f(z) = P(z) + Q(z).$$

Hence

$$F(z) = f(z) - P(z) = Q(z).$$

Hence, if we define

$$F(a) = Q(a),$$

we see (by Art. 11.59, Vol. I) that $F(z)$ is analytic in a neighborhood of $z = a$. Thus the singularity at $z = a$ has been removed.

12.19.   EXAMPLES.   (a) Find the principal parts of $f(z) = 1/\sin z$ at the poles $z = k\pi$, $(k = 0, \pm 1, \pm 2, \cdots)$.

  The pole $z = k\pi$ is of the first order because

$$\frac{d\,(\sin z)}{dz} = \cos z \neq 0 \quad \text{at} \quad z = k\pi.$$

Hence there is some function $\varphi(z)$ analytic and nonvanishing at $z = k\pi$ such that

$$\frac{1}{\sin z} = \frac{\varphi(z)}{z - k\pi}. \tag{1}$$

Clearly, from (1) itself, for $z \neq k\pi$,

$$\varphi(z) = (z - k\pi)/\sin z.$$

Now,

$$\lim_{z\to k\pi}\frac{1}{\varphi(z)} = \lim_{z\to k\pi}\frac{\sin z}{z - k\pi} = \frac{\cos k\pi}{1} = \pm 1, \tag{2}$$

$\pm$ according as k is even or odd. Hence, expanding $\varphi(z)$ at $z = k\pi$ and substituting in (1), we have

$$\frac{1}{\sin z} = \frac{1}{z - k\pi}\{\varphi(k\pi) + \varphi'(k\pi)(z - k\pi) + \cdots\}.$$

Thus the principal parts of $1/\sin z$ at $z = k\pi$ are, by (2),

$$\frac{\pm 1}{z - k\pi},$$

$\pm$ according as k is even or odd.

(b) Find the poles and principal parts of $\cot z$.

The poles are at $z = k\pi$, $(k = 0, \pm 1, \pm 2, \cdots)$, and are of the first order because

$$\frac{d(\tan z)}{dz} = \sec^2 z \neq 0 \quad \text{at} \quad z = k\pi.$$

Hence there is a function $\varphi(z)$ analytic and nonvanishing at $z = k\pi$ such that

$$\cot z = \varphi(z)/(z - k\pi). \tag{1}$$

Clearly, from (1) itself, if $z \neq k\pi$, then

$$\varphi(z) = (z - k\pi) \cot z.$$

Now,

$$\lim_{z \to k\pi} \frac{1}{\varphi(z)} = \lim_{z \to k\pi} \frac{\tan z}{z - k\pi} = \sec^2(k\pi) = 1. \tag{2}$$

Hence, expanding $\varphi(z)$ at $z = k\pi$ and substituting in (1), we have

$$\cot z = \frac{1}{z - k\pi} \{\varphi(k\pi) + \varphi'(k\pi)(z - k\pi) + \cdots\}.$$

Hence the principal parts of $\cot z$ at $z = k\pi$ are, by (2),

$$\frac{1}{z - k\pi}.$$

(c) Find the poles and principal parts of $\csc^2 z$.

The poles are at $z = k\pi$, $(k = 0, \pm 1, \pm 2, \cdots)$, and are of the second order because

$$\frac{d(\sin^2 z)}{dz} = 2 \sin z \cos z = 0 \quad \text{at} \quad z = k\pi,$$

and

$$\frac{d(2 \sin z \cos z)}{dz} = -2 \sin^2 z + 2 \cos^2 z \neq 0 \quad \text{at} \quad z = k\pi.$$

Hence there is a function $\varphi(z)$ analytic and nonvanishing at $z = k\pi$ such that

$$\csc^2 z = \varphi(z)/(z - k\pi)^2. \qquad (1)$$

Clearly, from (1) itself, if $z \neq k\pi$,

$$\varphi(z) = (z - k\pi)^2 \csc^2 z.$$

Now,

$$\lim_{z \to k\pi} \frac{1}{\varphi(z)} = \lim_{z \to k\pi} \frac{\sin^2 z}{(z - k\pi)^2} = \frac{-2 \sin^2 (k\pi) + 2 \cos^2 (k\pi)}{2} = 1.$$

Also, for $z \neq k\pi$,

$$\varphi'(z) = 2(z - k\pi)\csc^2 z - 2(z - k\pi)^2\csc^2 z \cot z.$$

Now,

$$\lim_{z \to k\pi} \varphi'(z) = \lim_{z \to k\pi} \frac{2(z - k\pi)^2}{\sin^2 z} \left\{ \frac{1 - (z - k\pi) \cot z}{z - k\pi} \right\}$$

$$= \lim_{z \to k\pi} \frac{2(z - k\pi)^2}{\sin^2 z} \lim_{z \to k\pi} \left\{ \frac{1 - (z - k\pi) \cot z}{z - k\pi} \right\}$$

$$= (2)(0) = 0.$$

Hence

$$\csc^2 z = \frac{1}{(z - k\pi)^2} \{\varphi(kz) + \varphi'(kz)(z - k\pi) + \cdots\},$$

and the principal parts of $\csc^2 z$ at $z = k\pi$ are

$$\frac{1}{(z - k\pi)^2}.$$

(d) Find the poles and principal parts of $\csc z^2$.

The poles are at $z = \pm \sqrt{k\pi}$, $(k = 0, \pm 1, \pm 2, \cdots)$. The poles at $z = \pm \sqrt{k\pi}$, $(k \neq 0)$, are of the first order because

$$\frac{d(\sin z^2)}{dz} = 2z \cos z^2 \neq 0 \quad \text{at} \quad z = \pm \sqrt{k\pi}, \quad k \neq 0.$$

However, the pole at $z = 0$ is of the second order because

$$\frac{d(\sin z^2)}{dz} = 2z \cos z^2 = 0 \quad \text{at} \quad z = 0,$$

and

$$\frac{d(2z \cos z^2)}{dz} = -4z \sin z^2 + 2 \cos z^2 \neq 0 \quad \text{at} \quad z = 0.$$

Hence, in the case of poles $z = \pm \sqrt{k\pi}$, $(k \neq 0)$, there is a function $\varphi(z)$ analytic and nonvanishing at $z = \pm \sqrt{k\pi}$, $(k \neq 0)$, and such that

$$\csc z^2 = \frac{\varphi(z)}{(z \mp \sqrt{k\pi})}. \tag{1}$$

clearly, from (1) itself, for $z \neq \pm \sqrt{k\pi}$, $(k \neq 0)$,

$$\varphi(z) = (z \mp \sqrt{k\pi}) \csc z^2.$$

Now,

$$\lim_{z \to \pm \sqrt{k z}} \frac{1}{\varphi(z)} = \lim_{z \to \pm \sqrt{k z}} \frac{\sin z^2}{(z \mp \sqrt{k\pi})}$$

$$= 2z \cos z^2 \big|_{z = \pm \sqrt{k\pi}}$$

$$\left.\begin{array}{l} = \pm 2\sqrt{k\pi} \text{ if } k \text{ is even} \\ = \mp 2\sqrt{k\pi} \text{ if } k \text{ is odd} \end{array}\right\}.$$

Hence, expanding $\varphi(z)$ at $z = \pm \sqrt{k\pi}$, $(k \neq 0)$, and substituting in (1), we have

$$\csc z^2 = \frac{1}{(z \mp \sqrt{k\pi})} \{\varphi(k\pi) + \cdots\},$$

whence the principal parts of $\csc z^2$ at $z = \pm \sqrt{k\pi}$, $(k \neq 0)$, are

$$\frac{1}{\pm 2\sqrt{k\pi}(z \mp \sqrt{k\pi})} \text{ if } k \text{ is even,}$$

$$-\frac{1}{\pm 2\sqrt{k\pi}(z \mp \sqrt{k\pi})} \text{ if } k \text{ is odd.}$$

In the case of the pole $z = 0$ there is a function $\psi(z)$ analytic and non-vanishing at $z = 0$ such that

$$\csc z^2 = \psi(z)/z^2. \tag{3}$$

clearly, from (3) itself, for $z \neq 0$,

$$\psi(z) = z^2 \csc z^2.$$

Now,

$$\lim_{z \to 0} \frac{1}{\psi(z)} = \lim_{z \to 0} \frac{\sin z^2}{z^2} = 1,$$

and

$$\lim_{z \to 0} \psi'(z) = \lim_{z \to 0} \frac{2z^2}{\sin z^2} \left\{ \frac{1 - z^2 \cot z^2}{z} \right\}$$

$$= (2)(0) = 0.$$

Hence

$$\csc z^2 = \frac{1}{z^2} \{ \psi(0) + \psi'(0)z + \cdots \}$$

$$= \frac{1}{z^2} \{ 1 + 0 + \cdots \},$$

and the principal part of $\csc z^2$ at $z = 0$ is $1/z^2$.

Note: The limits in the above examples were established by using L'Hospital's Rule. This is justifiable because we know that $\varphi(z)$ is analytic and therefore that the limit exists. Thus we can evaluate it for an approach along the x-axis and use L'Hospital's Rule with a clear conscience.

THE POINT AT INFINITY

12.20. **DEFINITION.** $f(z)$ is *analytic* at $z = \infty$ (has a *pole* at $z = \infty$, has an *essential singularity* at $z = \infty$, etc.) if $f(1/w)$ is analytic at $w = 0$ (has a pole at $w = 0$, has an essential singularity at $w = 0$, etc.)

Examples

(1) $\sin 1/z$ has a simple zero at $z = \infty$.

(2) $(z + 1)^2$ has a double pole at $z = \infty$.

(3) e^z has an essential singularity at $z = \infty$.

12.21. **THEOREM.**   If $f(z)$ is analytic in a neighborhood of $z = \infty$, then

$$f(z) = \sum_{n=0}^{\infty} a_n/z^n,$$

the series converging to $f(z)$ in some region

$$|z| > R.$$

Proof: Making the transformation $z = 1/w$, we have that the function $f(1/w)$ is analytic in a neighborhood of $w = 0$. Hence, by Maclaurin's expansion,

$$f(1/w) = \sum_{n=0}^{\infty} a_n w^n, \quad |w| < R, \tag{1}$$

where

$$a_n = \frac{1}{n!} \frac{d^n f(1/w)}{dw^n} \bigg|_{w=0}. \tag{2}$$

Hence, from (1) and (2), we have

$$f(z) = \sum_{n=0}^{\infty} a_n/z^n, \quad |z| > R,$$

where

$$a_n = \frac{1}{n!} \frac{d^n f(1/z)}{dz^n} \bigg|_{z=0}. \tag{3}$$

12.22. THEOREM.   If $f(z) \not\equiv 0$ has a zero at $z = \infty$, then

$$f(z) = \varphi(z)/z^k,$$

where

  (a) k is a positive integer,
  (b) $\varphi(z)$ is analytic at $z = \infty$,
  (c) $\varphi(\infty) \neq 0$.

Proof: Making the transformation $z = 1/w$, we have $f(1/w)$ is analytic at $w = 0$. Also, $f(1/w) \not\equiv 0, f(1/0) = 0$. Hence, by Art. 11.61, Vol. I,

$$f(1/w) = w^k \Phi(w), \tag{1}$$

where

  (a) k is a positive integer,
  (b) $\Phi(w)$ is analytic at $w = 0$,
  (c) $\Phi(0) \neq 0$.

Therefore, by (1),

$$f(z) = \varphi(z)/z^k,$$

where

$$\varphi(z) = \Phi(1/z),$$

and the theorem is proved.

Note: We may, by expanding $\varphi(z)$ as in Article 12.21, write $f(z)$ as the series

$$f(z) = \sum_{n=k}^{\infty} A_n/z^n, \quad |z| > R. \tag{2}$$

12.23. THEOREM.   If $f(z)$ has a pole at $z = \infty$, then

$$f(z) = z^k \varphi(z),$$

where

      (a) k is a positive integer,
      (b) $\varphi(z)$ is analytic at $z = \infty$,
      (c) $\varphi(\infty) \neq 0$.

Proof: Making the transformation $z = 1/w$, we have that $f(1/w)$ has a pole at $w = 0$. Hence, by Article 12.12,

$$f(1/w) = \frac{1}{w^k} \Phi(w), \tag{1}$$

where

      (a) k is a positive integer,
      (b) $\Phi(w)$ is analytic at $w = 0$,
      (c) $\Phi(0) \neq 0$.

Therefore, by (1),

$$f(z) = z^k \varphi(z),$$

where

$$\varphi(z) = \Phi(1/z),$$

and the theorem is proved.

Note: We may, by expanding $\varphi(z)$ as in Article 12.21, write $f(z)$ as the series

$$f(z) = \sum_{n=-k}^{\infty} A_n/z^n, \quad |z| > R. \tag{2}$$

12.24. DEFINITION.   If $f(z)$ has a pole at $z = \infty$, then the *principal part* of $f(z)$ at $z = \infty$ is

$$\sum_{n=-k}^{-1} A_n/z^n$$

from series (2) of Article 12.23.

12.25. EXAMPLE. Prove that $(1 - z)z^2e^{1/z}$ has a pole at $z = \infty$. Find the order and the principal part.

We have

$$f(z) = (1 - z)z^2e^{1/z}$$
$$= z^3(1/z - 1)e^{1/z}$$
$$= z^3\varphi(z), \text{ say,}$$

where

$$\varphi(z) = (1/z - 1)e^{1/z}.$$

We notice that $\varphi(z)$ is analytic at $z = \infty$ and that $\varphi(\infty) \neq 0$. Hence $f(z)$ has a pole of order 3 at $z = \infty$. The principal part is

$$P_\infty = \sum_{n=0}^{2} \frac{\dfrac{d^n\varphi(1/z)}{dz^n}\Big|_{z=0}}{n!z^{n-3}} \quad \begin{array}{l} \text{by (2) of Article 12.23} \\ \text{and (3) of Article 12.21} \end{array}$$

$$= \frac{(z - 1)e^z|_{z=0}}{z^{-3}} + \frac{(z - 1)e^z + e^z|_{z=0}}{z^{-2}} + \frac{(z - 1)e^z + 2e^z|_{z=0}}{2z^{-1}}$$

$$= -z^3 + (0)z^2 + \tfrac{1}{2}z$$

$$= -z^3 + \tfrac{1}{2}z.$$

12.26. THEOREM. A function which is analytic throughout the extended complex plane is a constant.

Proof: Such a function must everywhere be absolutely less than some definite number M, for otherwise there would exist a point z_0, finite or infinite, in every neighborhood of which $|f(z)| >$ arbitrary $G > 0$. That is, we would have $f(z_0) = \infty$. Since this is impossible, the theorem follows from Liouville's Theorem (Art. 11.35, Vol. I).

MEROMORPHIC FUNCTIONS

12.27. DEFINITION. $f(z)$ is *meromorphic* in a domain D if it is analytic there, except possibly for poles.

12.28. THEOREM. If $f(z)$ is meromorphic in a *closed* region R, then it has a finite number of poles in R.

Proof: If there are infinitely many poles, then there is a limit point of these poles. This limit point must be in R and must be either a pole or a point of analyticity. But it can be neither because (1) a pole is an isolated singularity and the limit point is not, (2) the function is not defined throughout any neighborhood of the limit point.

12.29. THEOREM.   If $f(z)$ is meromorphic in the extended plane, then it has at most a finite number of poles in the extended plane.

Proof: Since poles are isolated singularities, it follows that if $z = \infty$ is a pole, then there exists a deleted neighborhood of $z = \infty$ in which $f(z)$ is analytic. The rest of the plane constitutes a closed region in which, by Article 12.28, there is but a finite number of poles.

If $z = \infty$ is not a pole, then $f(z)$ is analytic at $z = \infty$ and hence in a neighborhood of $z = \infty$, and again the rest of the plane constitutes a closed region, and again Article 12.28 applies.

Example: $\tan z$ has an infinite number of poles in the extended plane. Hence $\tan z$ is not meromorphic in the extended plane. In fact, $\tan z$ has an essential singularity at $z = \infty$.

12.30. THEOREM.   A function is rational if and only if it is meromorphic in the extended plane.

Proof: Suppose the function is rational. Then it is analytic everywhere except at its poles. Hence it is meromorphic in the extended plane.

Suppose the function is meromorphic in the extended plane. Then there is at most a finite number of poles, say

$$a_1, a_2, \cdots, a_k, \infty,$$

with orders, say

$$m_1, m_2, \cdots, m_k, m,$$

and principal parts, say

$$P_{a_1}(z), P_{a_2}(z), \cdots, P_{a_k}(z), P(z).$$

Consider the function

$$F(z) \equiv f(z) - P_{a_1}(z) - P_{a_2}(z) - \cdots - P_{a_k}(z) - P(z). \qquad (1)$$

Now take

$$(1)\ z_0 \neq a_i, \infty.$$

Then $F(z)$ is analytic at $z = z_0$, since $f(z)$ and each principal part is.

$$(2)\ z_0 = a_i, \text{ or } = \infty.$$

$F(z)$ can be made analytic at $z = a_i$, for $f(z) - P_{a_i}(z)$ has a removable singularity at $z = a_i$ (Article 12.18), and the other principal parts are analytic at $z = a_i$.

Thus $F(z)$ is analytic everywhere except for removable singularities. Removing these, we have $F(z)$ analytic in the extended plane. Hence, by Article 12.26,

$$F(z) = c, \text{ a constant.}$$

Therefore, from (1), we have

$$f(z) = \sum_{j=1}^{k} P_{a_j}(z) + P(z) + c, \tag{2}$$

a rational function.

12.31. THEOREM. Every rational function has a unique partial fraction development.

Proof: We have development (2) of Article 12.30, which is unique because the principal parts are unique.

Example: Obtain the partial fraction development of

$$f(z) = \frac{z^2(z + 2)^3}{(z - 1)^3(1 + 2z)}$$

by the method of principal parts.
    We notice that $f(z)$ has poles at

$$z = 1, \text{ third order,}$$

$$z = -\tfrac{1}{2}, \text{ first order,}$$

$$z = \infty, \text{ first order.}$$

Let us calculate the principal parts at the poles.

$$(1) \qquad f(z) = \frac{1}{(z - 1)^3}\left\{\frac{z^2(z + 2)^3}{1 + 2z}\right\} = \frac{1}{(z - 1)^3}\,\varphi_1(z), \text{ say.}$$

Here

$$\varphi_1(1) = 9.$$

$$\varphi_1'(1) = \left.\frac{(1 + 2z)[3z^2(z + 2)^2 + 2z(z + 2)^3] - 2z^2(z + 2)^3}{(1 + 2z)^2}\right|_{z=1}$$

$$= 21.$$

$$\varphi_1''(1) =$$

$$\frac{(1 + 2z)^2[(z^3 + 4z^2 + 4z)(16z + 9) + (8z^2 + 9z + 4)(3z^2 + 8z + 4)]}{(1 + 2z)^4}$$

$$\left. - \frac{4(z^3 + 4z^2 + 4z)(8z^2 + 9z + 14)(1 + 2z)}{(1 + 2z)^4} \right|_{z=1}$$

$$= 32.$$

Therefore

$$P_1 = 9(z - 1)^{-3} + 21(z - 1)^{-2} + \tfrac{32}{2}(z - 1)^{-1}$$

$$= \frac{9}{(z - 1)^3} + \frac{21}{(z - 1)^2} + \frac{16}{(z - 1)} .$$

(2) $$f(z) = \frac{1}{(z + \frac{1}{2})} \left\{ \frac{z^2(z + 2)^3}{2(z - 1)^3} \right\} = \frac{1}{(z + \frac{1}{2})} \varphi_2(z), \text{ say.}$$

Here

$$\varphi_2(-\tfrac{1}{2}) = -\tfrac{1}{8}.$$

Therefore

$$P_2 = -\frac{1}{8(z + \frac{1}{2})} = -\frac{1}{4(2z + 1)} .$$

(3) $$f(z) = z \left\{ \frac{z(z + 2)^3}{(z - 1)^3(1 + 2z)} \right\} = z\varphi_\infty(z), \text{ say.}$$

Now,

$$\varphi_\infty \left(\frac{1}{z} \right) = \frac{\frac{1}{z} \left(\frac{1}{z} + 2 \right)^3}{\left(\frac{1}{z} - 1 \right)^3 \left(1 + \frac{2}{z} \right)} = \frac{(1 + 2z)^3}{(1 - z)^3(z + 2)} ,$$

whence

$$\varphi_\infty (1/0) = \tfrac{1}{2}.$$

Therefore

$$P_\infty = z/2.$$

(4) But also,

$$f(z) - P_1 - P_2 - P_\infty \equiv C, \text{ a constant.}$$

Evaluating C by setting $z = 0$, say, we find

$$C = f(z) - P_1 - P_2 - P_\infty|_{z=0} = 0 - (-9 + 21 - 16) - (-\tfrac{1}{4}) - 0$$

$$= \tfrac{17}{4}.$$

Hence we finally have

$$\frac{z^2(z+2)^3}{(z-1)^3(1+2z)} = \frac{9}{(z-1)^3} + \frac{21}{(z-1)^2} + \frac{16}{z-1}$$

$$-\frac{1}{4(2z+1)} + \frac{z}{2} + \frac{17}{4}.$$

12.32. SUMMARY ON PRINCIPAL PARTS.

A. $z = a$, finite.

(1) Taylor's expansion (f analytic at $z = a$),

$$f(z) = \sum_{n=0}^{\infty} f^{(n)}(a) \frac{(z-a)^n}{n!}.$$

(2) Polar expansion, $z = a$ pole of order m,

$$f(z) = \frac{\varphi(z)}{(z-a)^m}$$

$$= \frac{1}{(z-a)^m} \sum_{n=0}^{\infty} \varphi^{(n)}(a) \frac{(z-a)^n}{n!}$$

$$= \sum_{n=0}^{\infty} \varphi^{(n)}(a) \frac{(z-a)^{n-m}}{n!}.$$

(3) Principal part at pole $z = a$ of order m,

$$P_a = \sum_{n=0}^{m-1} \varphi^{(n)}(a) \frac{(z-a)^{n-m}}{n!}.$$

B. $z = \infty$

(1) Taylor's expansion (f analytic at $z = \infty$),

$$f(z) = \sum_{n=0}^{\infty} \frac{1}{n!z^n} \frac{d^n f(1/z)}{dz^n}\Bigg|_{z=0}.$$

(2) Polar expansion, $z = \infty$ pole of order m,

$$f(z) = z^m \varphi(z)$$

$$= z^m \sum_{n=0}^{\infty} \frac{1}{n!z^n} \frac{d^n \varphi(1/z)}{dz^n}\Bigg|_{z=0}$$

$$= \sum_{n=0}^{\infty} \frac{1}{n!z^{n-m}} \frac{d^n \varphi(1/z)}{dz^n}\Bigg|_{z=0}.$$

(3) Principal part at pole $z = \infty$,

$$P_\infty = \sum_{n=0}^{m-1} \frac{\dfrac{d^n\varphi(1/z)}{dz^n}\Big|_{z=0}}{n!\,z^{n-m}}.$$

C. *Partial fraction development*

$$f(z) = \sum_{j=1}^{k} P_{a_j}(z) + P_\infty(z) + C.$$

CHAPTER 13

Residues

CAUCHY'S RESIDUE THEOREM

13.01. DEFINITIONS.   If $f(z)$ is analytic in a deleted neighborhood N of $z = a$, a finite,

$$N: 0 < |z - a| < \delta,$$

then

$$\frac{1}{2\pi i} \int_C f(z)dz, \quad C: |z - a| = r < \delta,$$

is called the *residue of $f(z)$ at $z = a$.*

If $f(z)$ is analytic in a deleted neighborhood N of $z = \infty$,

$$N: |z| > G,$$

then

$$\frac{1}{2\pi i} \int_C f(z)dz, \quad C: |z| = R > G,$$

is called the *residue of $f(z)$ at $z = \infty$.* (Notice that the direction of integration for $z = \infty$ is opposite to that for $z = a$, but is still *positive.*)

13.02. THEOREM.   If $f(z)$ is analytic at $z = a$, a finite, then the residue of $f(z)$ at $z = a$ is zero.

Proof: By Cauchy's Theorem (Art. 11.10, Vol. I).
Note: This theorem is not true for $a = \infty$. For consider $f(z) = 1/z$. This function is analytic at $z = \infty$; in fact, it has a zero there. But

$$\frac{1}{2\pi i} \int_C \frac{dz}{z} = -1 \qquad \text{by Art. 11.24, Vol. I.}$$

23

13.03 THEOREM. If $z = a$ is a finite pole of order m, then the residue of $f(z)$ at $z = a$ is

$$\frac{\varphi^{(m-1)}(a)}{(m-1)!}, \quad m \geq 1,$$

where $\varphi(z) = (z - a)^m f(z)$.

Proof: We have

$$f(z) = \sum_{n=0}^{\infty} \varphi^{(n)}(a) \frac{(z-a)^{n-m}}{n!} \qquad \text{by Art. 12.32}$$

$$= \frac{\varphi(a)}{(z-a)^m} + \frac{\varphi'(a)}{(z-a)^{m-1}} + \cdots + \frac{\varphi^{(m-1)}(a)}{(m-1)!(z-a)} + Q(z),$$

where $Q(z)$ is analytic in a sufficiently small neighborhood of $z = a$ (Art. 11.59). Hence

$$\int_C f(z)dz = \int_C \frac{\varphi(a)dz}{(z-a)^m} + \int_C \frac{\varphi'(a)dz}{(z-a)^{m-1}} + \cdots$$

$$+ \int_C \frac{\varphi^{(m-1)}(a)dz}{(m-1)!(z-a)} + \int_C Q(z)dz$$

$$= 0 + 0 + \cdots + 2\pi i \frac{\varphi^{(m-1)}(a)}{(m-1)!} + 0,$$

by the alternative of Article 11.24 and Cauchy's Theorem. Hence

$$\frac{1}{2\pi i}\int_C f(z)dz = \frac{\varphi^{(m-1)}(a)}{(m-1)!}.$$

Corollary: If $z = a$ is a pole of the first order, then

$$\frac{1}{2\pi i}\int_C f(z)dz = \varphi(a) \neq 0.$$

13.04. THEOREM. If $z = \infty$ is a pole of order m, then the residue of $f(z)$ at $z = \infty$ is

$$-\frac{\varphi^{(m+1)}(1/0)}{(m+1)!}, \quad m \geq 0.$$

Proof: We have

$$f(z) = \sum_{n=0}^{\infty} \frac{\varphi^{(n)}(1/0)}{z^{n-m}n!} \qquad \text{by Art. 12.32}$$

$$= z^m\varphi(1/0) + z^{m-1}\varphi'(1/0) + \cdots + \frac{z\varphi^{(m-1)}(1/0)}{(m-1)!}$$

$$+ \frac{\varphi^{(m)}(1/0)}{m!} + \frac{\varphi^{(m+1)}(1/0)}{(m+1)!z} + \frac{Q(z)}{z^2},$$

where $Q(z)$ is analytic at $z = \infty$ and $Q(\infty) \neq 0$. Hence

$$\int_C f(z)dz = \int_C z^m\varphi(1/0)dz + \int_C z^{m-1}\varphi'(1/0)dz$$

$$+ \cdots + \int_C \frac{\varphi^{(m+1)}(1/0)dz}{(m+1)!z} + \int_C \frac{Q(z)}{z^2} dz$$

(or, since $dz = -dw/w^2$, where $z = 1/w$)

$$= -\int_C \frac{\varphi(1/0)dw}{w^{m+2}} - \cdots - \int_C \frac{\varphi^{(m+1)}(1/0)dw}{(m+1)!w}$$

$$- \int_C Q(1/w)dw$$

$$= 0 + \cdots - \frac{\varphi^{(m+1)}(1/0)}{(m+1)!} 2\pi i + 0,$$

by the alternative of Article 11.24 and Cauchy's Theorem. Hence

$$\frac{1}{2\pi i}\int_C f(z)dz = -\frac{\varphi^{(m+1)}(1/0)}{(m+1)!}.$$

13.05. THEOREM. If $f(z)$ is analytic in a region R except for a finite number of singularities, and if $f(z)$ has nonzero residues $r_1, r_2, \cdots, r_n$ at these singularities, and if R is bounded by a curve C composed of a finite number of simple regular closed curves on which $f(z)$ is analytic, then

$$\frac{1}{2\pi i}\int_C f(z)dz = \sum_{k=1}^{n} r_k,$$

the integration being taken in the positive sense.

Proof: There are two cases according to whether $z = \infty$ is not or is a singular point:

Case 1. $z = \infty$ is not a singular point. Surround the singular points by small circles $\gamma_1, \gamma_2, \cdots, \gamma_n$ and draw cut lines from each γ_i to the external boundary C_0 of R (see Figure 13.1). Then, by the extension of Cauchy's Theorem,

$$\frac{1}{2\pi i}\int_C f(z)dz + \frac{1}{2\pi i}\sum_{k=1}^{n}\int_{\gamma_k} f(z)dz = 0.$$

$$\frac{1}{2\pi i}\sum_{k=1}^{n}\int_{\gamma_k} f(z)dz = -\sum_{k=1}^{n} r_k.$$

Hence

$$\frac{1}{2\pi i}\int_C f(z)dz = \sum_{k=1}^{n} r_k.$$

Case 2. $z = \infty$ is a singular point. Draw a circle Γ so large as to include all the $n - 1$ finite singular points and all the parts of C. As before, surround each finite singular point by a small circle γ_i and draw cut lines joining these circles to Γ (see Figure 13.2). Then we have

$$\int_\Gamma f(z)dz + \int_C f(z)dz + \sum_{k=1}^{n-1}\int_{\gamma_k} f(z)dz = 0.$$

But

$$\frac{1}{2\pi i}\sum_{k=1}^{n-1}\int_{\gamma_k} f(z)dz = -\sum_{k=1}^{n-1} r_k,$$

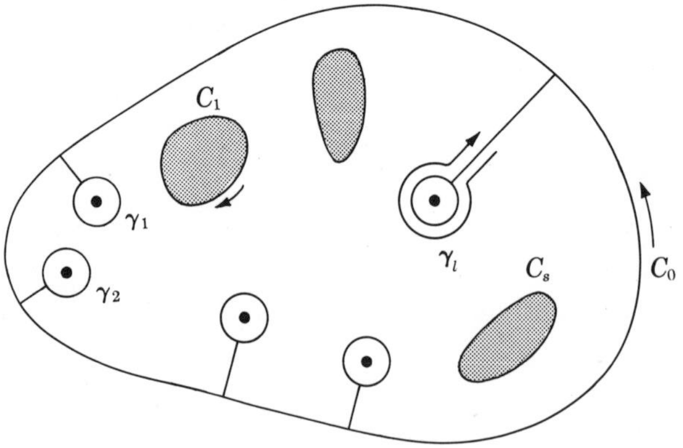

Figure 13.1

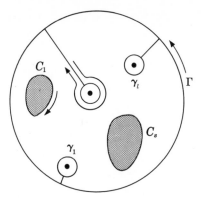

Figure 13.2

and

$$\frac{1}{2\pi i}\int_\Gamma f(z)dz = -r_\infty.$$

Therefore

$$\frac{1}{2\pi i}\int_C f(z)dz = \sum_{k=1}^{n-1} r_k + r_\infty.$$

Note: This theorem is known as *Cauchy's Residue Theorem.*

13.06. THEOREM.   If $f(z)$ is rational, then the sum of its residues is zero.

Proof: Since the function is rational, it has a finite number of finite singularities (by Article 12.30). Hence we may draw a circle γ so large as to include all these points. Then, by Article 13.05,

$$\frac{1}{2\pi i}\int_\gamma f(z)dz = \sum_{k=1}^{n} r_k.$$

But, by definition,

$$\frac{1}{2\pi i}\int_\gamma f(z)dz = -r_\infty.$$

Hence we have

$$\sum_{k=1}^{n} r_k + r_\infty = 0.$$

13.07. SUMMARY OF SOME SPECIAL RESIDUES.

(a) If n is any integer $\neq 1$, then the residue of $(z - a)^{-n}$ at $z = a$ is 0 (alternative of Art. 11.24, Vol. I).

(b) The residue of $(z - a)^{-1}$ at $z = a$ is 1 (Art. 11.24, Vol. I).

(c) If

$$f(z) = A_1/(z - a) + A_2/(z - a)^2 + \cdots + A_n/(z - a)^n + Q(z),$$

where $Q(z)$ is analytic at $z = a$, then the residue of $f(z)$ at $z = a$ is A_1 (alternative of Art. 11.24, Vol. I, and Art. 13.02).

(d) If $f(z)$ is analytic at $z = a$, then the residue of $f(z)/(z - a)$ at $z = a$ is $f(a)$ (Art. 13.03).

(e) If $\lim_{z \to a} \{(z - a)f(z)\}$ is a definite number A, then the residue of $f(z)$ at $z = a$ is A (corollary of Art. 13.03).

(f) If $\varphi(z)$ and $\psi(z)$ are polynomials, and if $(z - a)$ is a nonrepeated factor of $\psi(z)$, then the residue of $\varphi(z)/\psi(z)$ at $z = a$ is $\varphi(a)/\psi'(a)$ [use (e)].

(g) If $\lim_{z \to a} \{-zf(z)\}$ is a definite number A, then the residue of $f(z)$ at $z = \infty$ is A [set $z = 1/w$ and use (e)].

13.08. PROBLEM.　　Find the residues of

$$f(z) = \frac{(z - 1)^3}{z(z + 2)^3}$$

at all points and show that their sum is zero.

Since $f(z)$ is rational, nonzero residues can occur only at the poles of $f(z)$ and at $z = \infty$. The poles of $f(z)$ are $z = 0$ and $z = -2$, of the first and third orders, respectively. Let us calculate the residues at these poles and at $z = \infty$.

(a) *Pole $z = 0$.*

$$f(z) = \frac{1}{z}\left\{\frac{(z - 1)^3}{(z + 2)^3}\right\} = \frac{1}{z}\varphi_1(z), \text{ say.}$$

Now

$$r_1 = \varphi_1(0) = -1/8. \tag{1}$$

(b) *Pole $z = -2$.*

$$f(z) = \frac{1}{(z + 2)^3}\left\{\frac{(z - 1)^3}{z}\right\} = \frac{1}{(z + 2)^3}\varphi_2(z), \text{ say.}$$

Now

$$r_2 = \frac{\varphi_2''(-2)}{2!}.$$

We see that

$$\varphi_2'(z) = \frac{3z(z-1)^2 - (z-1)^3}{z^2} = \frac{(z-1)^2(2z+1)}{z^2}.$$

Hence

$$\varphi_2''(z) = \frac{z^2[2(z-1)^2 + 2(2z+1)(z-1)] - 2z(z-1)^2(2z+1)}{z^4},$$

and

$$\varphi_2''(-2) = 9/4.$$

Therefore

$$r_2 = 9/8. \tag{2}$$

(c) $z = \infty$.

$$r_\infty = \lim_{z \to \infty} \{-zf(z)\} \qquad \text{by (g), Art. 13.07}$$

$$= -\lim_{z \to \infty} \frac{(z-1)^3}{(z+2)^3}$$

$$= -\lim_{w \to 0} \frac{(1-w)^3}{(1+2w)^3}$$

$$= -1. \tag{3}$$

From (1), (2), and (3), we have

$$r_1 + r_2 + r_\infty = -\tfrac{1}{8} + \tfrac{9}{8} - 1 = 0.$$

13.09. PROBLEM.   Show that the only function $f(z)$ analytic for $|z| < \infty$ such that (a) $f(0) = 1$ and (b) $\lim_{z \to \infty} f(z)/z = 1$, is $f(z) = z + 1$.

Since

$$\lim_{z \to \infty} \frac{f(z)}{z} = 1,$$

it follows that

$$\lim_{z \to \infty} f(z) = \infty, \quad \lim_{z \to \infty} \frac{f(z)}{z^2} = 0,$$

and that $f(z)$ has a pole of the first order at $z = \infty$. But $f(z)$ is analytic everywhere else in the plane. Hence $f(z)$ is meromorphic in the extended plane and is therefore rational and is therefore *uniquely* expressible as a partial fraction development. Thus we have

$$f(z) = P_\infty + C,$$

where P_∞ is the principal part of $f(z)$ at $z = \infty$, and C is some constant. Now,

$$P_\infty = z \left\{ \frac{f(1/z)}{1/z} \bigg|_{z=0} \right\} = z \qquad \text{by (b).}$$

Hence

$$f(z) = z + C.$$

But

$$f(0) = C = 1 \qquad \text{by (a).}$$

Hence, finally,

$$f(z) = z + 1$$

uniquely.

13.10. PROBLEM. $F(z)$, $G(z)$ are analytic at $z = a$, $F(a) \neq 0$, $G(z)$ has 2 zeros at $z = a$. Show that the residue of $F(z)/G(z)$ at $z = a$ is

$$\frac{6F'(a)G''(a) - 2F(a)G'''(a)}{3[G''(a)]^2}.$$

Since $G(z)$ has 2 zeros at $z = a$, we have

$$G(z) = (z - a)^2 \Phi(z),$$

where $\Phi(z)$ is analytic at $z = a$ and $\Phi(a) \neq 0$. Therefore

$$\frac{F(z)}{G(z)} = \frac{F(z)}{(z-a)^2 \Phi(z)} = \frac{\varphi(z)}{(z-a)^2}, \qquad \text{say,}$$

where $\varphi(z)$ is analytic at $z = a$. Now, the required residue is given by $\varphi'(a)$ (Art. 13.03). But

$$\varphi'(z) = \frac{\Phi(z)F'(z) - F(z)\Phi'(z)}{[\Phi(z)]^2}. \qquad (1)$$

Now,

$$\Phi(z) = \frac{G(z)}{(z-a)^2}$$

$$= \frac{G(a) + G'(a)(z-a) + G''(a)(z-a)^2/2! + (z-a)^3 R_1}{(z-a)^2}$$

$$= \frac{G''(a)}{2} + (z-a)R_1,$$

where R_1 is analytic at $z = a$ and $G(a) = G'(a) = 0$ because $z = a$ is a double zero of $G(z)$. Hence

$$\Phi(a) = G''(a)/2. \tag{2}$$

Again,

$$\Phi'(z) = \frac{(z-a)^2 G'(z) - 2G(z)(z-a)}{(z-a)^4}$$

$$= \frac{G'(z)}{(z-a)^2} - \frac{2G(z)}{(z-a)^3}$$

$$= \frac{G'(a) + G''(a)(z-a) + G'''(a)(z-a)^2/2 + (z-a)^3 R_2}{(z-a)^2}$$

$$-2 \left\{ \frac{G(a) + G'(a)(z-a) + G''(a)(z-a)^2/2 + G'''(a)(z-a)^3/6 + (z-a)^4 R_3}{(z-a)^3} \right\}$$

$$= \frac{G''(a)}{z-a} + \frac{G'''(a)}{2} + (z-a)R_2 - \frac{G''(a)}{z-a} - \frac{G'''(a)}{3} - 2(z-a)R_3,$$

where R_2 and R_3 are analytic at $z = a$. Hence

$$\Phi'(a) = \frac{G'''(a)}{6}. \tag{3}$$

Hence, from (1), (2), and (3), we finally have for the residue

$$r = \varphi'(a) = \frac{\Phi(a)F'(a) - F(a)\Phi'(a)}{[\Phi(a)]^2}$$

$$= \frac{6F'(a)G''(a) - 2F(a)G'''(a)}{3[G''(a)]^2}.$$

Note: This is an extension of (f), Article 13.07.

LOGARITHMIC RESIDUES

13.11 DEFINITIONS.   If $f(z)$ is analytic in a neighborhood $|z - a| \leq \delta$, except perhaps for a pole at $z = a$, then the *logarithmic residue of $f(z)$ at $z = a$* is the residue of $f'(z) / f(z)$ at $z = a$.

If $f(z)$ is analytic in a neighborhood $|z| \geq R$, except perhaps for a pole at $z = \infty$, then the *logarithmic residue of $f(z)$* at $z = \infty$ is the residue of $f'(z)/f(z)$ at $z = \infty$.

13.12. THEOREM.   If $f(z)$ is analytic at $z = a$, a finite, and if $f(a) \neq 0$, then the logarithmic residue of $f(z)$ at $z = a$ is zero.

Proof. $f'(z)/f(z)$ is certainly analytic at $z = a$.   Hence the residue of $f'(z)/f(z)$ at $z = a$ is zero (Art. 13.02).

13.13. THEOREM.   If $f(z)$ is analytic at $z = a$, a finite, and if $f(z)$ has a zero of order m at $z = a$, then the logarithmic residue of $f(z)$ at $z = a$ is m.

Proof: We have

$$f(z) = (z - a)^m \varphi(z),$$

where $\varphi(z)$ is analytic at $z = a$ and $\varphi(a) \neq 0$. Now,

$$f'(z) = m(z - a)^{m-1} \varphi(z) + (z - a)^m \varphi'(z).$$

Hence

$$\frac{f'(z)}{f(z)} = \frac{m}{z - a} + \frac{\varphi'(z)}{\varphi(z)}.$$

This function has a pole of first order at $z = a$, and therefore its residue at $z = a$ is given by

$$r = \lim_{z \to a} (z - a) \frac{f'(z)}{f(z)} \qquad \text{by (e), Art. 13.07}$$

$$= \lim_{z \to a} \left\{ m + (z - a) \frac{\varphi'(z)}{\varphi(z)} \right\}$$

$$= m.$$

This proves the theorem.

13.14. THEOREM.   If $f(z)$ has at least two zeros at $z = \infty$, then the residue of $f(z)$ at $z = \infty$ is zero.

Proof: We have
$$f(z) = \varphi(z)/z^n,$$
where $n \geq 2$, $\varphi(z)$ is analytic at $z = \infty$, and $\varphi(\infty) \neq 0$. Now set $z = 1/w$. Then

$$\int_C f(z)dz = \int_C w^n \varphi(1/w)(-dw/w^2)$$

$$= \int_C -w^{n-2}\varphi(1/w)dw$$

$$= 0,$$

by Cauchy's Theorem.

13.15.   THEOREM.   If $f(z)$ is analytic at $z = \infty$, and if $f(\infty) \neq 0$, then the logarithmic residue of $f(z)$ at $z = \infty$ is zero.

Proof: Let
$$g(w) = f(1/w).$$
Then
$$g'(w) = f'(1/w)(-1/w^2),$$
or
$$-\frac{w^2 g'(w)}{g(w)} = \frac{f'(1/w)}{f(1/w)} = \frac{f'(z)}{f(z)}. \tag{1}$$

But the left side of (1) has a zero of at least the second order at $w = 0$ [for $g(0) \neq 0$], and hence the residue of this side at $w = 0$ is zero, by Article 13.14. Thus the residue of the right side at $z = \infty$ is zero, and the theorem is proved.

13.16.   THEOREM.   If $f(z)$ is analytic at $z = \infty$, and if $f(z)$ has a zero of order m at $z = \infty$, then the logarithmic residue of $f(z)$ at $z = \infty$ is $+m$.

Proof: We have
$$f(z) = \varphi(z)/z^m,$$
where $\varphi(z)$ is analytic at $z = \infty$ and $\varphi(\infty) \neq 0$. Therefore
$$f'(z) = \frac{z^m \varphi'(z) - m z^{m-1} \varphi(z)}{z^{2m}}$$
and
$$\frac{f'(z)}{f(z)} = -\frac{m}{z} + \frac{\varphi'(z)}{\varphi(z)}.$$

Now, the residue of this function at $z = \infty$ is

$$\frac{1}{2\pi i}\int_C -mw\left(\frac{-dw}{w^2}\right) + \log \operatorname{res} \varphi(z) = m + 0 \qquad \text{by Art. 11.24,}$$

by Art. 11.24, Vol. I, and Art. 13.15.

13.17. THEOREM. If $f(z)$ has a pole of order m at $z = a$, a finite, then the logarithmic residue of $f(z)$ at $z = a$ is $-m$.

Proof: We have

$$f(z) = \varphi(z)/(z - a)^m,$$

where $\varphi(z)$ is analytic at $z = a$ and $\varphi(a) \neq 0$. Therefore

$$f'(z) = \frac{(z - a)^m \varphi'(z) - m(z - a)^{m-1}\varphi(z)}{(z - a)^{2m}},$$

whence

$$\frac{f'(z)}{f(z)} = -\frac{m}{z - a} + \frac{\varphi'(z)}{\varphi(z)}.$$

Now, the residue of this function at $z = a$ is

$$\frac{1}{2\pi i}\int_C -\frac{m\,dz}{z - a} + \log \operatorname{res} \varphi(z) = -m + 0 \qquad \text{by Art. 11.24, Vol. I, and Art. 13.12.}$$

13.18. THEOREM. If $f(z)$ has a pole of order m at $z = \infty$, then the logarithmic residue of $f(z)$ at $z = \infty$ is $-m$.

Proof: We have

$$f(z) = z^m \varphi(z),$$

where $\varphi(z)$ is analytic at $z = \infty$ and $\varphi(\infty) \neq 0$. Therefore

$$f'(z) = mz^{m-1}\varphi(z) + z^m \varphi'(z),$$

whence

$$\frac{f'(z)}{f(z)} = \frac{m}{z} + \frac{\varphi'(z)}{\varphi(z)}.$$

Now, the residue of this function at $z = \infty$ is

$$\frac{1}{2\pi i}\int_C wm\left(-\frac{dw}{w}\right) + \log \operatorname{res} \varphi(z) = -m + 0 \qquad \begin{array}{l}\text{by Art. 11.24, Vol. I,} \\ \text{and Art. 13.15.}\end{array}$$

13.19. SUMMARY OF RESULTS FOR LOGARITHMIC RESIDUES.

	Order of Zero	Order of Pole	Log Res
a	m		m
a		m	$-m$
∞	m		m
∞		m	$-m$

ZEROS

13.20. THEOREM.   If $f(z)$ is meromorphic in a region R bounded by C, where C is composed of a finite number of simple regular closed curves, and if $f(z)$ is analytic on C and $f(z) \neq 0$ on C, and if $f(z)$ has N zeros and M poles in R, then

$$\frac{1}{2\pi i}\int_C \frac{f'(z)}{f(z)}\,dz = N - M,$$

the integration being performed in the positive sense.

Proof: By Art. 11.62, Vol. I, and Art. 12.15, the function $f'(z)/f(z)$ has a simple pole wherever $f(z)$ has a zero or a pole. Elsewhere $f'(z)/f(z)$ is analytic in R. By the Cauchy Residue Theorem,

$$\frac{1}{2\pi i}\int_C \frac{f'(z)}{f(z)}\,dz = \Sigma r_k,$$

where the r_k are the residues of $f'(z)/f(z)$ at its poles. But, by Article 13.19, we have

$$\Sigma r_k = N - M,$$

where, of course, a zero (or pole) of $f(z)$ of order m is counted m times. This proves the theorem.

13.21. THEOREM.   If $f(z)$ is analytic in a region R bounded by C, where C is composed of a finite number of simple regular closed curves, and if $f(z)$ is analytic on C and $f(z) \neq 0$ on C, and if $f(z)$ has N zeros in R, then

$$\frac{1}{2\pi i} \int_C \frac{f'(z)}{f(z)} \, dz = N,$$

the integration being performed in the positive sense.

Proof: This is an immediate corollary to Article 13.20.

13.22 DEFINITION.   We define

$$\Delta_C f(z) = \int_C f'(z) dz,$$

the integration being performed in the positive sense. Thus $\Delta_C f(z)$ denotes the *variation* of $f(z)$ round the contour C. The value of $f(z)$ with which we start is clearly a matter of indifference.

13.23. THEOREM. Δ_C arc $f(z)$ is the algebraic increase in arc $f(z)$ as z describes one complete circuit of C.

Proof: Let $\theta = $ arc $f(z)$. Then

$$\Delta_C \text{ arc } f(z) = \Delta_C \theta = \int_{\substack{z \text{ about} \\ C}} d\theta.$$

Example: Let

$$f(z) = z^2 = r^2 e^{i2\theta}, \quad z = re^{i\theta}.$$

Then

$$\text{arc } f(z) = 2\theta.$$

Now suppose C to be the unit circle about the origin. Then, since in one positive tracing of C by z, θ increases by 2π, 2θ increases by 4π. Hence

$$\Delta_C \text{ arc } z^2 = 4\pi, \quad C \text{ the unit circle about origin.}$$

13.24. THEOREM. $\Delta_C \{f(z) + g(z)\} = \Delta_C f(z) + \Delta_C g(z).$

Proof:

$$\Delta_C\{f(z) + g(z)\} = \int_C \{f'(z) + g'(z)\}dz$$

$$= \int_C f'(z)dz + \int_C g'(z)dz$$

$$= \Delta_C f(z) + \Delta_C g(z).$$

31.25. THEOREM. $\Delta_C \log |f(z)| = 0.$

Proof: Set

$$\log |f(z)| = x, \quad \text{a real quantity.}$$

Then

$$\Delta_C \log |f(z)| = \Delta_C x = \int_C dx = 0 \qquad \text{by Art. 8.91, Vol. I.}$$

13.26. THEOREM. Under the conditions of Article 13.21,

$$N = \frac{1}{2\pi} \Delta_C \operatorname{arc} f(z).$$

Proof: We have, by Article 13.21,

$$N = \frac{1}{2\pi i}\int_C \frac{f'(z)}{f(z)}\,dz$$

$$= \frac{1}{2\pi i} \Delta_C \log f(z)$$

$$= \frac{1}{2\pi i} \Delta_C\{\log |f(z)| + i \operatorname{arc} f(z)\}$$

$$= \frac{1}{2\pi i} \{\Delta_C \log |f(z)| + \Delta_C i \operatorname{arc} f(z)\} \qquad \text{by Art. 13.24}$$

$$= \frac{1}{2\pi i} \Delta_C i \operatorname{arc} f(z) \qquad \text{by Art. 13.25}$$

$$= \frac{1}{2\pi} \Delta_C \operatorname{arc} f(z).$$

13.27. ROUCHÉ'S THEOREM.   If $f(z)$ and $g(z)$ are analytic in and on the boundary of a region R bounded by a simple regular closed curve C, and if $|g(z)| < |f(z)|$ on C, then $f(z)$ and $f(z) + g(z)$ have the same number of zeros in R.

Proof: Now, by hypothesis,

$$|f(z)| > |g(z)| \geq 0 \text{ on } C.$$

Therefore $f(z)$ has no zeros on C.

Again,

$$|f(z) + g(z)| \geq |f(z)| - |g(z)| > 0 \text{ on } C.$$

Therefore $f(z) + g(z)$ has no zeros on C.

Now we have

$$f(z) + g(z) = \{f(z) + g(z)\} \frac{f(z)}{f(z)}$$

$$= f(z)\left\{1 + \frac{g(z)}{f(z)}\right\}.$$

Therefore

$$\text{arc } \{f(z) + g(z)\} = \text{arc } f(z) + \text{arc } \left\{1 + \frac{g(z)}{f(z)}\right\},$$

or

$$\Delta_C \text{ arc } \{f(z) + g(z)\} = \Delta_C \text{ arc } f(z) + \Delta_C \text{ arc } \left\{1 + \frac{g(z)}{f(z)}\right\}. \quad (1)$$

Set

$$W = 1 + g(z)/f(z).$$

Then, because $|f(z)| > |g(z)|$ on C,

$$\left|\frac{g(z)}{f(z)}\right| < 1 \text{ on } C.$$

Hence W always lies within the circle of unit radius and center $z = 1$. Therefore, as z describes C, W describes a curve $\bar{C}$ which lies within this circle (see Figure 13.3). That is, W never surrounds the origin. Thus arc W neither increases nor decreases when z describes C. Hence, by Article 13.23,

$$\Delta_C \text{ arc } W = \Delta_C \text{ arc } \left\{1 + \frac{g(z)}{f(z)}\right\} = 0.$$

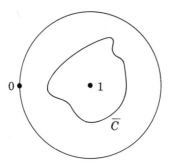

Figure 13.3

Therefore, from (1), in virtue of Article 13.26,

$$N_{f(z)+g(z)} = N_{f(z)}.$$

13.28. FUNDAMENTAL THEOREM OF ALGEBRA. The polynomial

$$P(z) = a_0 z^n + a_1 z^{n-1} + \cdots + a_n, \quad a_0 \neq 0,$$

has exactly n roots.

Proof: Consider the polynomials

$$f \equiv a_0 z^n \quad \text{and} \quad g \equiv a_1 z^{n-1} + \cdots + a_n.$$

Then

$$P = f + g.$$

Now draw a circle C with center at the origin and radius R such that

$$R > \frac{|a_1| + |a_2| + \cdots + |a_n|}{|a_0|}, \, > 1. \tag{1}$$

Then we have, on C,

$$|g| \leq |a_1| R^{n-1} + |a_2| R^{n-2} + \cdots + |a_n|$$
$$< \{|a_1| + |a_2| + \cdots + |a_n|\} R^{n-1} \quad \text{by (1)}$$
$$< |a_0| R^n \quad \text{by (1)}$$
$$= |f|, \text{ on } C.$$

Hence, by Rouché's Theorem, $f + g$ has the same number of zeros within C as has f. Since $z = \infty$ is not a root of $P = f + g$ or of f, we may take R so large as to include within it all the possible zeros of P and f. But f has exactly n zeros. Therefore P also has exactly n zeros.

13.29. THEOREM.   If $\varphi(z)$ and $\psi(z)$ are each analytic at $z = a$, and if $\varphi(a) = \psi(a) = 0$, but $\varphi^{(n)}(a)$ and $\psi^{(n)}(a)$ are not both zero (this being the first instance where at least one of the derivatives is not zero), then

$$\lim_{z \to a} \frac{\varphi(z)}{\psi(z)} = \frac{\varphi^{(n)}(a)}{\psi^{(n)}(a)}.$$

Proof: Writing $\varphi(z)$ and $\psi(z)$ as Taylor's series with remainders, we have

$$\frac{\varphi(z)}{\psi(z)} = \frac{\varphi(a) + \varphi'(a)(z - a) + \cdots + \dfrac{(z - a)^n}{n!} \varphi^{(n)}(a) + R_1(z - a)^{n+1}}{\psi(a) + \psi'(a)(z - a) + \cdots + \dfrac{(z - a)^n}{n!} \psi^{(n)}(a) + R_2(z - a)^{n+1}},$$

where R_1 and R_2 are analytic at $z = a$. Three cases arise:

Case 1. $\varphi^{(n)}(a) = 0, \psi^{(n)}(a) \neq 0$. Here

$$\frac{\varphi(z)}{\psi(z)} = \frac{R_1(z - a)}{\dfrac{\psi^{(n)}(a)}{n!} + R_2(z - a)},$$

whence

$$\lim_{z \to a} \frac{\varphi(z)}{\psi(z)} = 0 = \frac{\varphi^{(n)}(a)}{\psi^{(n)}(a)}.$$

Case 2. $\varphi^{(n)}(a) \neq 0, \psi^{(n)}(a) = 0$. Here

$$\frac{\varphi(z)}{\psi(z)} = \frac{\dfrac{\varphi^{(n)}(a)}{n!} + R_1(z - a)}{R_2(z - a)},$$

whence

$$\lim_{z \to a} \frac{\varphi(z)}{\psi(z)} = \infty = \frac{\varphi^{(n)}(a)}{\psi^{(n)}(a)}.$$

Case 3. $\varphi^{(n)}(a) \neq 0, \psi^{(n)}(a) \neq 0$. Here

$$\frac{\varphi(z)}{\psi(z)} = \frac{\dfrac{\varphi^{(n)}(a)}{n!} + R_1(z - a)}{\dfrac{\psi^{(n)}(a)}{n!} + R_2(z - a)},$$

and

$$\lim_{z \to a} \frac{\varphi(z)}{\psi(z)} = \frac{\varphi^{(n)}(a)}{\psi^{(n)}(a)}.$$

Note: This establishes *L'Hospital's Rule* for analytic complex functions.

13.30. THEOREM. If $f(z)$ is analytic in and on the boundary of a circle Γ, $f(z) \neq 0$ on Γ, and $f(z)$ has only one zero inside Γ at $z = a$, then

$$a = \frac{1}{2\pi i} \int_\Gamma \frac{zf'(z)}{f(z)} \, dz.$$

Proof: Since $f(z)$ has the single zero $z = a$ inside or on Γ, we have

$$f(z) = (z - a)\varphi(z),$$

where $\varphi(z)$ is analytic and nonvanishing inside and on Γ. Therefore

$$\frac{f'(z)}{f(z)} = \frac{(z - a)\varphi'(z) + \varphi(z)}{(z - a)\varphi(z)} = \frac{\varphi'(z)}{\varphi(z)} + \frac{1}{z - a}.$$

and

$$\frac{1}{2\pi i} \int_\Gamma \frac{zf'(z)}{f(z)} \, dz = \frac{1}{2\pi i} \int_\Gamma \frac{z\varphi'(z)}{\varphi(z)} \, dz + \frac{1}{2\pi i} \int_\Gamma \frac{z \, dz}{z - a}$$

$$= 0 + a,$$

by Cauchy's Theorem and Cauchy's integral formula.

Alternative: We see (using the above notation) that

$$\frac{zf'(z)}{f(z)} = \frac{af'(z)}{f(z)} + \frac{f'(z)(z - a)}{f(z)} = \frac{af'(z)}{f(z)} + \frac{f'(z)}{\varphi(z)}.$$

Therefore

$$\frac{1}{2\pi i} \int_\Gamma \frac{zf'(z)}{f(z)} \, dz = \frac{a}{2\pi i} \int_\Gamma \frac{f'(z)}{f(z)} \, dz + \frac{1}{2\pi i} \int_\Gamma \frac{f'(z)}{\varphi(z)} \, dz. \qquad (1)$$

But, since $f'(z)/\varphi(z)$ is analytic and nonvanishing both within and on Γ, the third term in (1) vanishes (by Cauchy's Theorem), and the second term equals a (by Article 13.20). This proves the theorem.

13.31.   PROBLEM.   If $a > e$, show that the equation

$$e^z = az^n$$

has n roots inside the unit circle.

Consider the two functions

$$g(z) = e^z \quad \text{and} \quad f(z) = -az^n.$$

Now

$$|f(z)| = a|z|^n = a \quad \text{on unit circle}$$

and

$$|g(z)| = |e^z| = e^{\cos\theta} \le e < a \quad \text{on unit circle.}$$

Hence

$$|g(z)| < |f(z)| \quad \text{on unit circle.}$$

Moreover, $g(z)$ and $f(z)$ are both analytic inside and on the unit circle. Therefore, by Rouché's Theorem, $f(z)$ and $f(z) + g(z)$ have the same number of zeros inside the unit circle. But $f(z)$ has n zeros there, namely $z = 0$ of order n. Hence

$$g(z) + f(z) = e^z - az^n$$

has n zeros inside the unit circle.

CONTOUR INTEGRATION

13.32.   GENERAL REMARKS.   Cauchy's Residue Theorem can be applied to the evaluation of some definite integrals. The method will be clear after a consideration of the few typical examples discussed below. It should, however, be observed that a definite integral which can be evaluated by Cauchy's method of residues can always be evaluated by other means, though generally not so simply. On the other hand, quite simple definite integrals exist which cannot be evaluated by Cauchy's method, $\int_0^\infty e^{-x^2}dx$ being a case in point.

13.33.   EXAMPLE: *Evaluate* $\int_0^\infty \dfrac{dx}{x^2 + 1}$. Consider the function

$$f(z) = \frac{1}{z^2 + 1} = \frac{1}{(z + i)(z - i)}.$$

This function has a pole of the first order at $z = i$. The residue r_i at $z = i$ is given by

$$\lim_{z \to i} \frac{z - i}{z^2 + 1} = \lim_{z \to i} \frac{1}{z + i} = \frac{1}{2i}.$$

Now consider the closed curve C (see Figure 13.4) composed of the x-axis from $-R$ to $+R$ and the semicircle γ on this segment as diameter and lying above the x-axis. Let us further take $R > 1$. Then $f(z)$ is analytic inside and on the boundary of C except for the pole $z = i$. Hence, by Cauchy's Residue Theorem,

$$\int_C f(z)dz = \frac{2\pi i}{2i} = \pi.$$

Thus we also have

$$\int_C f(z)dz = \int_{-R}^{R} \frac{dx}{x^2 + 1} + \int_{\gamma} \frac{dz}{z^2 + 1} = \pi. \tag{1}$$

Now,

$$\left| \int_{\gamma} \frac{dz}{z^2 + 1} \right| \leq \int_{\gamma} \frac{ds}{|z^2 + 1|} \leq \int_{\gamma} \frac{ds}{R^2 - 1} = \frac{\pi R}{R^2 - 1}, \tag{2}$$

since $|z^2 + 1| \geq |z|^2 - 1 = R^2 - 1 > 0$.

Clearly the extreme left of (2) approaches 0 as $R \to \infty$. Hence we have, from (1), since $1/(x^2 + 1)$ is an even function of x,

$$\lim_{R \to \infty} \left\{ 2 \int_0^R \frac{dx}{x^2 + 1} + \int_{\gamma} \frac{dz}{z^2 + 1} \right\} = 2 \int_0^{\infty} \frac{dx}{x^2 + 1} = \pi.$$

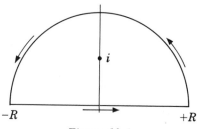

Figure 13.4

Hence

$$\int_0^\infty \frac{dx}{x^2 + 1} = \frac{\pi}{2}. \qquad Ans.$$

Note: We may check this result directly as follows:

$$\int_0^\infty \frac{dx}{x^2 + 1} \doteq \int_0^\infty d(\tan^{-1}x) = \frac{\pi}{2}.$$

13.34. EXAMPLE: *Evaluate* $\int_0^\infty \frac{x^2}{x^4 + 1} dx$. Consider the function

$$f(z) = \frac{z^2}{z^4 + 1} = \frac{z^2}{(z + i\sqrt{i})(z - i\sqrt{i})(z + \sqrt{i})(z - \sqrt{i})}.$$

This function has poles of the first order at the points $z = \sqrt{i}, z = i\sqrt{i}$, the residues at these points being, respectively,

$$r_1 = \lim_{z \to \sqrt{i}} \frac{(z - \sqrt{i})z^2}{z^4 + 1} = \lim_{z \to \sqrt{i}} \frac{z^2}{(z^2 + i)(z + \sqrt{i})} = \frac{1}{4\sqrt{i}}.$$

$$r_2 = \lim_{z \to i\sqrt{i}} \frac{(z - i\sqrt{i})z^2}{z^4 + 1} = \lim_{z \to i\sqrt{i}} \frac{z^2}{(z^2 - i)(z + i\sqrt{i})} = \frac{1}{4i\sqrt{i}}.$$

Now consider the closed curve C (see Figure 13.5) composed of the real axis from $-R$ to $+R$, $(R > 1)$, and the semicircle γ on this segment as diameter and lying above the real axis. Then $f(z)$ is analytic inside and on C except for the poles at $z = \sqrt{i}, z = i\sqrt{i}$. Hence we have

$$\int_C f(z)dz = 2\pi i \left\{ \frac{1}{4\sqrt{i}} + \frac{1}{4i\sqrt{i}} \right\}$$

$$= 2\pi i \left(\frac{i + 1}{4i\sqrt{i}} \right)$$

$$= \frac{\pi(i + 1)}{2\sqrt{i}}$$

$$= \frac{\pi(i + 1)}{\sqrt{2}(i + 1)} \qquad \text{(see note below)}$$

$$= \frac{\pi\sqrt{2}}{2}.$$

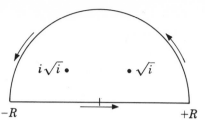

Figure 13.5

Hence we also have

$$\int_C f(z)dz = \int_{-R}^R \frac{x^2dx}{x^4+1} + \int_\gamma \frac{z^2dz}{z^4+1}$$

$$= 2\int_0^R \frac{x^2dx}{x^4+1} + \int_\gamma \frac{z^2dz}{z^4+1}$$

$$= \frac{\pi\sqrt{2}}{2}. \tag{1}$$

Now,

$$\left| \int_\gamma \frac{z^2dz}{z^4+1} \right| \leqq \int_\gamma \frac{|z|^2ds}{|z^4+1|} \leqq \int_\gamma \frac{R^2ds}{R^4-1} = \frac{\pi R^3}{R^4-1}, \tag{2}$$

since

$$|z^4+1| \geqq |z|^4 - 1 = R^4 - 1 > 0.$$

Therefore, because of (2),

$$\lim_{R\to\infty} \left\{ 2\int_0^R \frac{x^2dx}{x^4+1} + \int_\gamma \frac{z^2dz}{z^4+1} \right\} = 2\int_0^\infty \frac{x^2dx}{x^4+1} = \frac{\pi\sqrt{2}}{2}.$$

That is,

$$\int_0^\infty \frac{x^2dx}{x^4+1} = \frac{\pi\sqrt{2}}{4} \qquad Ans.$$

Note: We have

$$i = \cos\frac{\pi}{2} + i\sin\frac{\pi}{2}.$$

Therefore

$$\sqrt{i} = \cos\left(\frac{\pi}{4} + \frac{2k\pi}{2}\right) + i\sin\left(\frac{\pi}{4} + \frac{2k\pi}{2}\right), \quad k = 0, 1$$

$$= \frac{1}{\sqrt{2}} + i\frac{1}{\sqrt{2}}, \quad -\frac{1}{\sqrt{2}} - i\frac{1}{\sqrt{2}}$$

$$= \pm \frac{\sqrt{2}}{2}(1 + i).$$

13.35. EXAMPLE: *Evaluate* $\displaystyle\int_{-\infty}^{\infty} \frac{dx}{x^2 + 2x + 4}$.   Consider   the function

$$f(z) = \frac{1}{z^2 + 2z + 4} = \frac{1}{(z + 1 + i\sqrt{3})(z + 1 - i\sqrt{3})}.$$

Also consider the closed curve C (see Figure 13.6) composed of the x-axis from $-S$ to $+R$ and the semicircle γ on this segment as diameter and lying above the x-axis. Let us take $R > 2$, $S > 2$. The function $f(z)$ is analytic, then, inside and on C except for the first-order pole at $z = -1 + i\sqrt{3}$. The residue at this pole is

$$r = \lim_{z \to -1+i\sqrt{3}} \frac{1}{(z + 1 + i\sqrt{3})} = \frac{1}{2i\sqrt{3}}.$$

Hence

$$\int_C f(z)dz = \frac{2\pi i}{2i\sqrt{3}} = \frac{\pi}{\sqrt{3}}.$$

Hence also

$$\int_C f(z)dz = \int_{-S}^{R} \frac{dx}{x^2 + 2x + 4} + \int_{\gamma} \frac{dz}{z^2 + 2z + 4} = \frac{\pi}{\sqrt{3}}. \qquad (1)$$

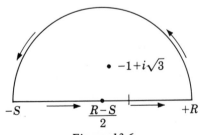

$$\bullet \ -1+i\sqrt{3}$$

$$-S \qquad \frac{R-S}{2} \qquad +R$$

Figure 13.6

Now,

$$\left| \int_\gamma \frac{dz}{z^2 + 2z + 4} \right| \leqq \int_\gamma \frac{ds}{|z^2 + 2z + 4|} \leqq \int_\gamma \frac{ds}{\left(\dfrac{R + S}{2} - \dfrac{|R - S|}{2} - 2 \right)^2}$$

$$= \frac{\pi(R + S)}{2 \left(\dfrac{R + S}{2} - \dfrac{|R - S|}{2} - 2 \right)^2},$$

since

$$|z^2 + 2z + 4| = |z + 1 + i\sqrt{3}| \times |z + 1 - i\sqrt{3}|$$

$$\geqq \{|z| - |1 + i\sqrt{3}|\} \times \{|z| - |1 - i\sqrt{3}|\}$$

$$= \{|z|^2 - 2\}^2 \qquad (\text{since } |1 \pm i\sqrt{3}| = 2)$$

$$\geqq \left\{ \frac{R + S}{2} - \frac{|R - S|}{2} - 2 \right\}^2 > 0.$$

(This follows from the triangle shown in Figure 13.7.) Hence

$$\lim_{\substack{R \to \infty \\ S \to \infty}} \int_\gamma \frac{dz}{z^2 + 2z + 4} = 0 \cdot$$

Therefore, taking the limit of (1) as $R, S \to \infty$, we have

$$\int_{-\infty}^\infty \frac{dx}{x^2 + 2x + 4} = \frac{\pi}{\sqrt{3}} \cdot \qquad Ans.$$

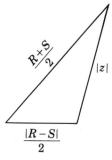

Figure 13.7

Note: We can evaluate this by $\int_{-R}^{R}$ if we prove — as is quite easy — that

$$\int_0^\infty dx/(x^2 + 2x + 4) \quad \text{and} \quad \int_{-\infty}^0 dx/(x^2 + 2x + 4)$$

are convergent.

13.36. **EXAMPLE:**   *Evaluate* $\int_0^\infty \dfrac{\sin x}{x}\, dx$. Consider the function

$$f(z) = e^{iz}/z$$

and the closed curve C shown in Figure 13.8. Take $R > 1$. Then, since there are no singular points inside or on C, we have

$$\int_C f(z)dz = \int_{-R}^{-r}\frac{e^{ix}dx}{x} + \int_r^R \frac{e^{ix}dx}{x} + \int_\gamma \frac{e^{iz}dz}{z} + \int_\Gamma \frac{e^{iz}dz}{z}$$

$$= -\int_r^R \frac{e^{-ix}}{-x}(-dx) + \int_\gamma \frac{e^{iz}dz}{z} + \int_\Gamma \frac{e^{iz}dz}{z}$$

$$= \int_r^R \frac{e^{ix} - e^{-ix}}{x}\, dx + \int_\gamma \frac{e^{iz}dz}{z} + \int_\Gamma \frac{e^{iz}dz}{z}$$

$$= \int_r^R \frac{2i \sin x}{x}\, dx + \int_\gamma \frac{e^{iz}dz}{z} + \int_\Gamma \frac{e^{iz}dz}{z} = 0 \qquad \begin{array}{l}\text{by Art. 10.25,}\\ \text{Vol. I.} \qquad (1)\end{array}$$

Now, on Γ we have $z = Re^{i\theta}$. Hence

$$\left|\int_\Gamma \frac{e^{iz}dz}{z}\right| = \left|\int_0^\pi i\frac{e^{iRe^{i\theta}}}{Re^{i\theta}} Re^{i\theta}d\theta\right|$$

$$\leq \int_0^\pi |e^{iRe^{i\theta}}|\, d\theta$$

$$= \int_0^\pi e^{-R\sin\theta}\, d\theta$$

(since $|e^{iRe^{i\theta}}| = |e^{iR(\cos\theta + i\sin\theta)}| = |e^{iR\cos\theta}|e^{-R\sin\theta}$

$$= |e^{ix}|e^{-R\sin\theta} = |\cos x + i \sin x|e^{-R\sin\theta} = e^{-R\sin\theta})$$

$$= 2\int_0^{\pi/2} e^{-R\sin\theta}\, d\theta$$

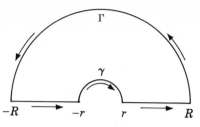

Figure 13.8

(since $e^{-R\sin\theta}$ is symmetrical in the line $x = \pi/2$)

$$< 2\int_0^{\pi/2} e^{-R(2\theta/\pi)}d\theta$$

$$\left(\text{since (see Figure 13.9)} \ \sin\theta \geqq \frac{2\theta}{\pi} \right)$$

$$= \frac{2e^{-(2R\theta/\pi)}}{-\dfrac{2R}{\pi}} \bigg|_0^{\pi/2}$$

$$= \frac{\pi}{R}(1 - e^{-R}). \tag{2}$$

From (2), it follows that

$$\lim_{R\to\infty} \int_\Gamma \frac{e^{iz}dz}{z} = 0.$$

Hence, from (1), taking limit as $R \to \infty$, we have

$$\int_r^\infty \frac{2i \sin x}{x}\,dx + \int_\gamma \frac{e^{iz}dz}{z} = 0. \tag{3}$$

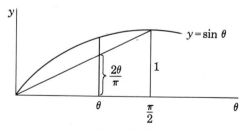

Figure 13.9

Now,

$$\int_\gamma \frac{e^{iz}dz}{z} = \int_\gamma \frac{e^{iz}-1}{z}\,dz + \int_\gamma \frac{dz}{z}. \qquad (4)$$

But

$$\int_\gamma \frac{dz}{z} = \int_\pi^0 \frac{rie^{i\theta}}{re^{i\theta}}\,d\theta = \int_\pi^0 i\,d\theta = -\pi i. \qquad (5)$$

Also, the function

$$F(z) = \frac{e^{iz}-1}{z}$$

has a removable singularity at $z = 0$, for

$$\lim_{z\to 0} \frac{e^{iz}-1}{z} = \lim_{z\to 0} \frac{ie^{iz}}{1} = i.$$

Hence $F(z)$ is bounded in some neighborhood of the origin. That is, we have

$$|F(z)| < M, \quad |z| \le \delta.$$

Therefore, taking $r < \delta$, we have

$$\left| \int_\gamma \frac{e^{iz}-1}{z}\,dz \right| = \left| \int_\gamma F(z)dz \right| \le M\int_\gamma ds = \pi r M,$$

whence it follows that

$$\lim_{r\to 0} \int_\gamma \frac{e^{iz}-1}{z}\,dz = 0. \qquad (6)$$

Then, taking limit as $r \to 0$ in (3), we have, because of (4), (5), and (6),

$$\int_0^\infty \frac{2i\sin x}{x}\,dx - \pi i = 0,$$

whence

$$\int_0^\infty \frac{\sin x}{x}\,dx = \frac{\pi}{2}. \qquad Ans.$$

13.37. EXAMPLE: *Evaluate* $\displaystyle\int_0^\infty \frac{\sin^2 x}{x^2}\,dx$. Consider the function

$$f(z) = \frac{1 - e^{2iz}}{z^2},$$

and also consider the closed curve C composed of the x-axis from $-R$ to $-r$, r to R, and the semicircles γ and Γ above the x-axis and on the segments $-r, r$ and $-R, R$, respectively, as diameters (see Figure 13.10). Then, since there are no singular points inside or on C, we have

$$\int_C f(z)dz = \int_{-R}^{-r} \frac{1 - e^{2ix}}{x^2} dx + \int_r^R \frac{1 - e^{2ix}}{x^2} dx + \int_\gamma f(z)dz + \int_\Gamma f(z)dz$$

$$= \int_r^R \frac{1 - e^{-2ix}}{x^2} dx + \int_r^R \frac{1 - e^{2ix}}{x^2} dx + \int_\gamma f(z)dz + \int_\Gamma f(z)dz$$

$$= \int_r^R \frac{2 - e^{2ix} - e^{-2ix}}{x^2} dx + \int_\gamma f(z)dz + \int_\Gamma f(z)dz$$

$$= \int_r^R \frac{4 \sin^2 x}{x^2} dx + \int_\gamma f(z)dz + \int_\Gamma f(z)dz = 0 \quad \begin{bmatrix} \text{by Art.} \\ \text{10.25,} \\ \text{Vol. I.} \end{bmatrix} \quad (1)$$

Now, on Γ we have $z = Re^{i\theta}$. Hence

$$\left| \int_\Gamma f(z)dz \right| = \left| \int_\Gamma \frac{1 - e^{2iz}}{z^2} dz \right|$$

$$= \left| \int_0^\pi \frac{1 - e^{2iRe^{i\theta}}}{R^2 e^{2i\theta}} Re^{i\theta} d\theta \right|$$

$$\leqq \int_0^\pi \frac{\left| 1 - e^{2iRe^{i\theta}} \right|}{R|e^{i\theta}|} d\theta$$

$$\leqq \int_0^\pi \frac{1 + \left| e^{2iRe^{i\theta}} \right|}{R} d\theta$$

$$= \int_0^\pi \frac{1 + e^{-2R\sin\theta}}{R} d\theta,$$

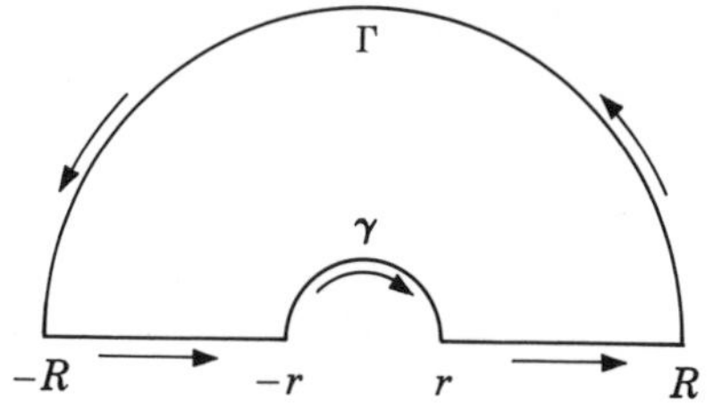

Figure 13.10

$$\text{(since } |e^{2iRe^{i\theta}}| = |e^{2iR(\cos\theta + i\sin\theta)}| = |e^{2iR\cos\theta}|e^{-2R\sin\theta}$$

$$= |e^{ix}|^2 e^{-2R\sin\theta} = e^{-2R\sin\theta})$$

$$= 2 \int_0^{\pi/2} \frac{1 + e^{-2R\sin\theta}}{R} \, d\theta$$

(since the integrand is symmetrical in the line $x = \pi/2$)

$$= 2 \int_0^{\pi/2} \frac{1 + e^{-(4R\theta)/\pi}}{R} \, d\theta$$

(since $\sin\theta \geq 2\theta/\pi, \ 0 \leq \theta \leq \pi/2$ (see Art. 13.36))

$$= \frac{2}{R} \left\{ \theta + \frac{e^{-(4R\theta)/\pi}}{\dfrac{-4R}{\pi}} \right\} \Bigg|_0^{\pi/2}$$

$$= \frac{2}{R} \left\{ \frac{\pi}{2} - \frac{\pi e^{-2R}}{4R} + \frac{\pi}{4R} \right\}. \tag{2}$$

From (2), it follows that

$$\lim_{R \to \infty} \int_\Gamma f(z) dz = 0. \tag{3}$$

Hence, from (1), we have, taking $\lim_{R \to \infty}$,

$$\int_r^\infty \frac{4 \sin^2 x}{x^2} \, dx + \int_\gamma f(z) dz = 0. \tag{4}$$

Now,

$$\int_\gamma \frac{1 - e^{2iz}}{z^2} \, dz = -\int_\gamma \frac{2i \, dz}{z} + \int_\gamma \frac{1 + 2iz - e^{2iz}}{z^2} \, dz. \tag{5}$$

But

$$-\int_\gamma \frac{2i \, dz}{z} = -\int_\pi^0 \frac{2i(ire^{i\theta}) d\theta}{re^{i\theta}} = \int_\pi^0 2 d\theta = -2\pi. \tag{6}$$

Also, the function

$$F(z) = \frac{1 + 2iz - e^{2iz}}{z^2}$$

has a removable singularity at $z = 0$, for

$$\lim_{z \to 0} \frac{1 + 2iz - e^{2iz}}{z^2} = \lim_{z \to 0} \frac{2i - e^{2iz}(2i)}{2z} = \lim_{z \to 0} \frac{-e^{2iz}(2i)^2}{2} = 2.$$

Hence $F(z)$ is bounded in some neighborhood of the origin. That is, we have

$$|F(z)| < M, \quad |z| \leq \delta.$$

Therefore, taking $r < \delta$, we have

$$\left| \int_\gamma \frac{1 + 2iz - e^{2iz}}{z^2} dz \right| = \left| \int_\gamma F(z)dz \right| \leq M \int_\gamma ds = \pi r M,$$

whence it follows that

$$\lim_{r \to 0} \int_\gamma \frac{1 + 2iz - e^{2iz}}{z^2} dz = 0. \qquad (7)$$

Hence in (4), taking $\lim_{r \to \infty}$, we have, by virtue of (5), (6), and (7),

$$\int_0^\infty \frac{4 \sin^2 x}{x^2} dx - 2\pi = 0,$$

whence

$$\int_0^\infty \frac{\sin^2 x}{x^2} dx = \frac{\pi}{2}. \qquad Ans.$$

13.38. EXAMPLE: *Evaluate* $\int_0^\infty \sin x^2 \, dx$ *and* $\int_0^\infty \cos x^2 \, dx$ (Fresnel integrals). Consider the function

$$f(z) = e^{-z^2}$$

and the closed curve C of Figure 13.11. Since $f(z)$ is analytic inside and on C, we have

$$\int_C f(z)dz = 0.$$

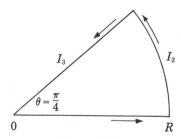

Figure 13.11

Hence

$$\int_0^R e^{-x^2}dx + I_2 + I_3 = 0. \tag{1}$$

Now,

$$I_2 = \int_0^{\pi/4} e^{-R^2e^{2i\theta}}iRe^{i\theta}d\theta, \quad z = Re^{i\theta}.$$

Hence

$$|I_2| \leq R\int_0^{\pi/4} e^{-R^2\cos2\theta}d\theta$$

$$= R\int_0^{\pi/2} e^{-R^2\cos\varphi}\frac{d\varphi}{2}, \quad \varphi = 2\theta,$$

$$= \frac{R}{2}\int_{\pi/2}^0 e^{-R^2\sin t}(-dt), \quad t = \pi/2 - \varphi,$$

$$= \frac{R}{2}\int_0^{\pi/2} e^{-R^2\sin t}dt$$

$$\leqq \frac{R}{2}\int_0^{\pi/2} e^{-R^2\frac{2t}{\pi}}dt \quad \text{see Fig. 13.9}$$

$$= \frac{R}{2}\left[\frac{e^{-\frac{R^2 2t}{\pi}}}{-\frac{2R^2}{\pi}}\right]_0^{\pi/2}$$

$$= \frac{\pi}{4R}(1 - e^{-R^2}).$$

Therefore

$$\lim_{R\to\infty} I_2 = 0. \tag{2}$$

Now,

$$I_3 = \int_R^0 e^{-r^2e^{i(\pi/2)}}e^{i(\pi/4)}dr, \quad z = re^{i(\pi/4)}$$

$$= -\frac{1+i}{\sqrt{2}}\int_0^R (\cos r^2 - i\sin r^2)\,dr, \tag{3}$$

for

$$e^{i(\pi/4)} = \cos\frac{\pi}{4} + i\sin\frac{\pi}{4} = \frac{1+i}{\sqrt{2}},$$

and

$$e^{-r^2e^{i(\pi/2)}} = e^{-r^2(\cos(\pi/2)+i\sin(\pi/2))} = e^{-ir^2} = \cos(-r^2) + i\sin(-r^2)$$

$$= \cos r^2 - i\sin r^2.$$

Now, assuming that

$$\int_0^\infty e^{-x^2}dx = \frac{\sqrt{\pi}}{2},$$ (4)

we have, by (1) and (2),

$$\lim_{R\to\infty}(-I_3) = \frac{\sqrt{\pi}}{2}.$$ (5)

Hence we have

$$\frac{1+i}{\sqrt{2}}\int_0^\infty \cos r^2 - i\sin r^2)dr = \frac{\sqrt{\pi}}{2}.$$ (6)

Equating the real and imaginary parts of the members of (6), we have

$$\frac{1}{\sqrt{2}}\int_0^\infty \cos r^2 dr + \frac{1}{\sqrt{2}}\int_0^\infty \sin r^2 dr = \frac{\sqrt{\pi}}{2},$$

$$\frac{1}{\sqrt{2}}\int_0^\infty \cos r^2 dr - \frac{1}{\sqrt{2}}\int_0^\infty \sin r^2 dr = 0.$$

Hence, adding and subtracting, we find

$$\int_0^\infty \cos r^2 dr = \int_0^\infty \sin r^2 dr = \frac{1}{2}\sqrt{\frac{\pi}{2}}. \qquad Ans.$$

13.39. **EXAMPLE:**   *Evaluate* $\int_0^\infty \dfrac{\cos x}{x^2+k^2}dx$, *(k real, $k \neq 0$).*

Case I: $k > 0$. Consider the function

$$f(z) = \frac{e^{iz}}{z^2+k^2}$$

and the closed curve C in Figure 13.12, $(R > k)$. $f(z)$ has the one singular point $z = ik$ inside or on C. The residue at $z = ik$ is

$$r = \lim_{z\to ik}\frac{e^{iz}}{z+ik} = \frac{e^{-k}}{2ik}.$$

Hence we have

$$\int_C f(z)dz = \frac{\pi e^{-k}}{k}.$$ (1)

Let us denote by I_1 and I_2 the integrals

$$I_1 = \int_{-R}^R \frac{e^{ix}}{x^2+k^2}dx, \quad I_2 = \int_\gamma \frac{e^{iz}}{z^2+k^2}dz.$$

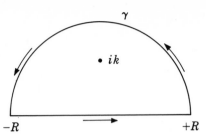

Figure 13.12

Now,

$$I_1 = \int_{-R}^{R} \frac{e^{ix}}{x^2 + k^2}\, dx = -\int_{R}^{0} \frac{e^{-ix}}{x^2 + k^2}\, dx + \int_{0}^{R} \frac{e^{ix}}{x^2 + k^2}\, dx$$

$$= \int_{0}^{R} \frac{e^{ix} + e^{-ix}}{x^2 + k^2}\, dx$$

$$= \int_{0}^{R} \frac{2\cos x}{x^2 + k^2}\, dx, \qquad (2)$$

and

$$I_2 = \int_{\gamma} \frac{e^{iz}}{z^2 + k^2}\, dz = \int_{0}^{\pi} \frac{e^{iRe^{i\theta}}}{R^2 e^{2i\theta} + k^2}\, iRe^{i\theta} d\theta.$$

Hence

$$|I_2| \leqq R \int_{0}^{\pi} \frac{e^{-R\sin\theta}}{R^2 - k^2}\, d\theta$$

$$\text{(since } |e^{iRe^{i\theta}}| = |e^{iR(\cos\theta + i\sin\theta)}| = e^{-R\sin\theta}|e^{iR\cos\theta}| = e^{-R\sin\theta}$$

$$\text{and } |R^2 e^{2i\theta} + k^2| \geqq |R^2 e^{2i\theta}| - k^2 = R^2 - k^2 > 0)$$

$$< R \int_{0}^{\pi} \frac{e^{-2R\theta/\pi}}{R^2 - k^2}\, d\theta \qquad \text{see Fig. 13.9}$$

$$= \frac{R}{R^2 - k^2} \left. \frac{e^{-2R\theta/\pi}}{\dfrac{-2R}{\pi}} \right|_{0}^{\pi}$$

$$= -\frac{\pi}{2(R^2 - k^2)} \{e^{-2R} - 1\},$$

whence

$$\lim_{R\to\infty} I_2 = 0. \tag{3}$$

But, from (1), we have

$$I_1 + I_2 = \pi e^{-k}/k.$$

Hence, taking $\lim_{R\to\infty}$, we have

$$\int_0^\infty \frac{\cos x}{x^2 + k^2}\, dx = \frac{\pi e^{-k}}{2k}. \tag{4}$$

Case II: $k < 0$. The left side of (4) is independent of the sign of k. Therefore the right side must also be made independent of the sign of k. Hence we have, for $k > 0$ or $k < 0$,

$$\int_0^\infty \frac{\cos x}{x^2 + k^2}\, dx = \frac{\pi e^{-|k|}}{2|k|}. \qquad Ans. \tag{5}$$

Case III: $k = 0$. Here the integral diverges.

13.40. **EXAMPLE:** *Evaluate* $\int_0^{2\pi} \dfrac{d\theta}{1 + a^2 - 2a\cos\theta}$, (*a real*,

$a \geq 0$). Consider the function

$$f(z) = \frac{1}{(z - a)\left(z - \dfrac{1}{a}\right)}.$$

Case I: $0 < a < 1$. Denoting the unit circle by C, we notice that the function $f(z)$ has only one singular point, $z = a$, inside or on C. The residue of $f(z)$ at $z = a$ is

$$r = \lim_{z\to a} \frac{1}{z - (1/a)} = \frac{a}{a^2 - 1}.$$

Hence

$$\int_C \frac{dz}{(z - a)\left(z - \dfrac{1}{a}\right)} = \frac{2\pi i a}{a^2 - 1}. \tag{1}$$

But also,

$$\int_C \frac{dz}{(z-a)\left(z-\dfrac{1}{a}\right)} = \int_0^{2\pi} \frac{e^{i\theta}\,id\theta}{(e^{i\theta}-a)\left(e^{ia}-\dfrac{1}{a}\right)}, \quad z = e^{i\theta},$$

$$= \int_0^{2\pi} \frac{e^{i\theta}\,id\theta}{e^{2i\theta} - e^{i\theta}\left(a+\dfrac{1}{a}\right) + 1}$$

$$= \int_0^{2\pi} \frac{id\theta}{e^{i\theta} - \left(a+\dfrac{1}{a}\right) + e^{-i\theta}}$$

$$= \int_0^{2\pi} \frac{id\theta}{(\cos\theta + i\sin\theta) - \left(a+\dfrac{1}{a}\right) + (\cos\theta - i\sin\theta)}$$

$$= \int_0^{2\pi} \frac{ia\,d\theta}{2a\cos\theta - a^2 - 1}$$

$$= -ia \int_0^{2\pi} \frac{d\theta}{1 + a^2 - 2a\cos\theta}.$$

Hence, from (1), we have

$$\int_0^{2\pi} \frac{d\theta}{1 + a^2 - 2a\cos\theta} = \frac{2\pi}{1 - a^2}. \tag{2}$$

Case II: $a > 1$. If $a > 1$, then $f(z)$ has only one singularity, $z = 1/a$, inside or on C. The residue of $f(z)$ at $z = a$ is

$$r = \lim_{z \to 1/a} \frac{1}{z-a} = \frac{a}{1-a^2}.$$

Hence

$$\int_C \frac{dz}{(z-a)\left(z-\dfrac{1}{a}\right)} = \frac{2\pi ia}{1-a^2},$$

and

$$\int_0^{2\pi} \frac{d\theta}{1 + a^2 - 2a\cos\theta} = \frac{2\pi}{a^2 - 1}. \tag{3}$$

The results (2) and (3) may be put into the one formula

$$\int_0^{2\pi} \frac{d\theta}{1 + a^2 - 2a\cos\theta} = \frac{2\pi}{|a^2 - 1|}. \qquad Ans. \qquad (4)$$

Case III: $a = 0$. We note that (4) also holds for this trivial case.

13.41. **EXAMPLE:** *Evaluate* $\displaystyle\int_{C-i\infty}^{C+i\infty} \frac{e^{\omega z}}{z}\, dz$, ($\omega$ *real*, $C > 0$).

Case I: $\omega > 0$. Consider the curve Σ of Figure 13.13, where $G, R, S > 0$. The integrand has the one singularity, $z = 0$, inside or on Σ. The residue at $z = 0$ is

$$r = \lim_{z\to 0} e^{\omega z} = 1.$$

Hence we have

$$\int_{\Sigma} \frac{e^{\omega z}}{z}\, dz = 2\pi i. \qquad (1)$$

Hence we also have

$$\int_{C-iR}^{C+iS} -2\pi i = \int_{C-iR}^{-G-iR} + \int_{-G-iR}^{-G+iS} + \int_{-G+iS}^{C+iS}. \qquad (2)$$

Let us call the integrals in (2) I, I_1, I_2, and I_3, respectively.

For I_1 we have $z = x - iR$. Therefore

$$I_1 = \int_C^{-G} \frac{e^{\omega(x - iR)}}{x - iR}\, dx,$$

and

$$|I_1| \le \int_{-G}^{C} \frac{e^{\omega x}}{R}\, dx = \frac{e^{\omega x}}{\omega R}\bigg|_{-G}^{C} = \frac{e^{\omega C} - e^{-\omega G}}{\omega R} < \frac{e^{\omega C}}{\omega R}. \qquad (3)$$

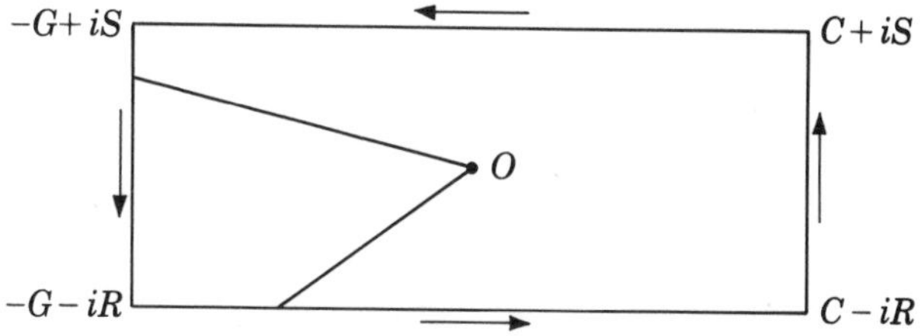

Figure 13.13

For I_3, we have $z = x + iS$. Therefore, similarly to the above, we find

$$|I_3| < \frac{e^{\omega C}}{\omega S} \cdot \qquad (4)$$

For I_2, we have $z = -G + iy$. Therefore

$$I_2 = \int_{-R}^{S} \frac{e^{\omega(-G+iy)}}{-G + iy} i \, dy,$$

and

$$|I_2| \leq \int_{-R}^{S} \frac{e^{-\omega G}}{G} \, dy = \frac{e^{-\omega G}}{G} (S + R). \qquad (5)$$

Hence, from (2), by virtue of (3), (4), and (5),

$$|I - 2\pi i| < \frac{e^{\omega C}}{\omega R} + \frac{e^{\omega C}}{\omega S} + \frac{e^{-\omega G}}{G} (R + S). \qquad (6)$$

Now, since the left side of (6) is independent of G, the above inequality must hold for any G, and hence $G = \infty$. We then have

$$|I - 2\pi i| < \frac{e^{\omega C}}{\omega R} + \frac{e^{\omega C}}{\omega S} \cdot \qquad (7)$$

Now, clearly, the right side of (7) can be made as small as we please by increasing R and S. Hence

$$\lim_{\substack{R \to \infty \\ S \to \infty}} |I - 2\pi i| = 0,$$

or

$$\int_{C-i\infty}^{C+i\infty} \frac{e^{\omega z}}{z} \, dz = 2\pi i. \qquad Ans.$$

Case II: $\omega < 0$. Set $\omega = -u$. Then we have

$$f(z) = e^{-uz}/z, \quad u > 0.$$

Consider the curve Σ of Figure 13.14. As in Case I,

$$\int_{\Sigma} f(z) dz = 2\pi i,$$

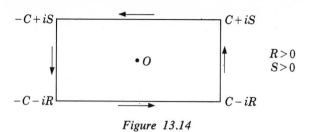

Figure 13.14

and

$$\int_{C-iR}^{C+iS} -2\pi i = \int_{C-iR}^{-C-iR} + \int_{-C-iR}^{-C+iS} + \int_{-C+iS}^{C+iS},$$

or

$$I - 2\pi i = I_1 + I_2 + I_3. \qquad (8)$$

For I_1 we have

$$I_1 = \int_C^{-C} \frac{e^{-u(x-iR)}}{x - iR}\, dx,$$

and

$$|I_1| \leq \int_{-C}^{C} \frac{e^{-ux}}{R}\, dx = \frac{e^{-ux}}{-uR}\bigg|_{-C}^{C} = \frac{e^{-uC} - e^{uC}}{-uR}$$

$$= \frac{e^{uC} - e^{-uC}}{uR} < \frac{e^{uC}}{uR}.$$

Similarly,

$$|I_3| < \frac{e^{uC}}{uS}.$$

Finally

$$I_2 = \int_{-C-iR}^{-C+iS} \frac{e^{-uz}}{z}\, dz = \int_{C+iR}^{C-iS} \frac{e^{uz}}{-z}\, (-dz)$$

$$= -\int_{C-iS}^{C+iR} \frac{e^{uz}}{z}\, dz.$$

Hence, since $u > 0$, we have, by Case I,

$$\lim_{\substack{R \to \infty \\ S \to \infty}} I_2 = -2\pi i.$$

Returning then to (8) and taking limit of both sides as $R \to \infty$ and $S \to \infty$ independently, we find

$$\int_{C-i\infty}^{C+i\infty} \frac{e^{-uz}}{z}\, dz = 0,$$

or

$$\int_{C-i\infty}^{C+i\infty} \frac{e^{\omega z}}{z}\, dz = 0. \qquad Ans.$$

Case III: $\omega = 0$. Here the integral diverges.

13.42. **EXAMPLE:** *Evaluate* $\displaystyle\int_{-\infty}^{\infty} \frac{e^{-zt}dx}{1 + e^{-2\pi x}}$, $(0 < t < 2\pi)$. Consider the function

$$f(z) = \frac{e^{-zt}}{1 + e^{-2\pi z}},$$

and the closed curve C of Figure 13.15. Now, $f(z)$ is analytic inside and on C except for a pole at $z = i/2$ (for $e^{-2\pi(i/2)} = e^{-\pi i} = -1$). The residue at this pole (by L'Hospital's Rule) is

$$r = \lim_{z \to i/2} \frac{z - i/2}{1 + e^{-2\pi z}} e^{-zt} = \lim_{z \to i/2} \frac{e^{-zt}}{-2\pi e^{-2\pi z}}$$

$$= \frac{e^{-it/2}}{-2\pi e^{-(2\pi i)/2}} = \frac{e^{-it/2}}{2\pi} \cdot$$

Hence

$$\int_C f(z)dz = ie^{-it/2}. \qquad (1)$$

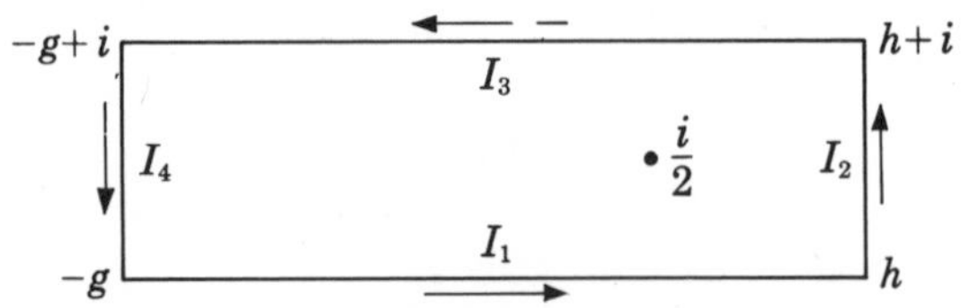

$$h > 0,\ g > 0.$$

Figure 13.15

Now,

$$I_1 = \int_{-g}^{h} \frac{e^{-zt}}{1 + e^{-2\pi z}}\, dx, \quad z = x,$$

$$I_3 = \int_{h}^{-g} \frac{e^{-zt}e^{-it}}{1 + e^{-2\pi x}e^{-2\pi i}}\, dx = e^{-it}I_1, \quad z = x + i.$$

Hence

$$I_1 + I_3 = (1 - e^{-it}) \int_{-g}^{h} \frac{e^{-zt}}{1 + e^{-2\pi x}}\, dx. \tag{2}$$

Now,

$$I_2 = \int_{0}^{1} \frac{e^{-ht}e^{-iyt}}{1 + e^{-2\pi h}e^{-2\pi iy}}\, i\, dy, \quad z = h + iy.$$

Hence

$$|I_2| \leqq \int_{0}^{1} \frac{e^{-ht}dy}{1 - e^{-2\pi h}} = \frac{e^{-ht}}{1 - e^{-2\pi h}} \xrightarrow[h \to \infty]{} 0,$$

since

$$|e^{-iyt}| = \cos(-yt) + i\sin(-yt)| = 1,$$

and

$$|1 + e^{-2\pi h}e^{-2\pi iy}| \geqq 1 - e^{-2\pi h}|e^{-2\pi iy}| = 1 - e^{-2\pi h}, \quad t > 0.$$

Finally,

$$I_4 = -\int_{0}^{1} \frac{e^{gt}e^{-iyt}}{1 + e^{2\pi g}e^{-2\pi iy}}\, i\, dy, \quad z = -g + iy.$$

Hence

$$|I_4| \leqq \int_{0}^{1} \frac{e^{gt}}{e^{2\pi g} - 1}\, dy = \frac{e^{gt}}{e^{2\pi g} - 1} \cdot \frac{e^{-2\pi g}}{e^{-2\pi g}}$$

$$= \frac{e^{-g(2\pi - t)}}{1 - e^{-2\pi g}} \xrightarrow[g \to \infty]{} 0,$$

since $t < 2\pi$.

But, from (1), we have

$$I_1 + I_2 + I_3 + I_4 = ie^{-it/2}.$$

Hence, from (2), taking $\lim_{h\to\infty}$, we have

$$(1 - e^{-it})\int_{-\rho}^{\infty} \frac{e^{-zt}dx}{1 + e^{-2\pi x}} + I_4 = ie^{-it/2}. \tag{3}$$

Again, taking $\lim_{\rho\to\infty}$ in (3), we have

$$(1 - e^{-it})\int_{-\infty}^{\infty} \frac{e^{-zt}dx}{1 + e^{-2\pi x}} = ie^{-it/2},$$

or (by Art. 10.25, Vol. I)

$$\int_{-\infty}^{\infty} \frac{e^{-zt}dx}{1 + e^{-2\pi x}} = \frac{ie^{-it/2}}{1 - e^{-it}} \cdot \frac{e^{it/2}}{e^{it/2}}$$

$$= \frac{i}{e^{it/2} - e^{-it/2}}$$

$$= \frac{1}{2\sin t/2}. \qquad Ans.$$

13.43. THEOREM. If n is a positive integer, then

$$\tfrac{1}{2} + \cos t + \cos 2t + \cdots + \cos nt = \frac{\sin(n + \tfrac{1}{2})t}{2\sin t/2}, \quad 0 < t < 2\pi.$$

Proof (due to Dunham Jackson): Consider the function

$$f(z) = \frac{e^{-zt}}{1 - e^{-2\pi z}}$$

and the closed curve C of Figure 13.16. Now, $f(z)$ is analytic inside and on C except at the first-order poles

$$z = ki, \quad k = 0, \pm 1, \pm 2, \cdots, \pm n.$$

Let us find the residue at the pole $z = ki$. We have

$$r_k = \lim_{z\to ki} \frac{z - ki}{1 - e^{-2\pi z}} \cdot e^{-zt} = \lim_{z\to ki} \frac{e^{-zt}}{2\pi e^{-2\pi z}} \quad \text{by L'Hospital's Rule}$$

$$= \frac{e^{-kit}}{2\pi e^{-2\pi ki}} = \frac{e^{-kit}}{2\pi}.$$

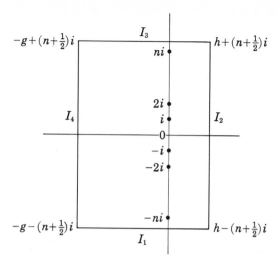

Figure 13.16

Hence

$$\int_C f(z)dz = i \sum_{k=-n}^{n} e^{-kit}$$

$$= i\,[1 + 2\cos t + \cdots + 2\cos nt] \quad \text{by Art. 10.25, Vol. I.}$$
(1)

Now,

$$I_1 = \int_{-g}^{h} \frac{e^{-xt}e^{(n+1/2)it}}{1 - e^{-2\pi x}e^{2\pi(n+1/2)i}}\,dx, \quad z = x - (n + \tfrac{1}{2})i,$$

$$= \int_{-g}^{h} \frac{e^{-xt}e^{(n+1/2)it}}{1 + e^{-2\pi x}}\,dx,$$

since $e^{2\pi(n+1/2)i} = e^{2\pi ni}e^{\pi i} = (+1)(-1) = -1$. Similarly,

$$I_3 = -\int_{-g}^{h} \frac{e^{-xt}e^{-(n+1/2)it}}{1 + e^{-2\pi x}}\,dx, \quad z = x + (n + \tfrac{1}{2})i.$$

Hence

$$I_1 + I_3 = (e^{(n+1/2)it} - e^{-(n+1/2)it})\int_{-g}^{h} \frac{e^{-xt}}{1 + e^{-2\pi x}}\,dx$$

$$= 2i\sin\,(n + \tfrac{1}{2})t \int_{-g}^{h} \frac{e^{-xt}}{1 + e^{-2\pi x}}\,dx.$$
(2)

Also,

$$I_2 = \int_{-(n+1/2)}^{(n+1/2)} \frac{e^{-ht}e^{-iyt}i\,dy}{1 - e^{-2\pi h}e^{-2\pi iy}}, \quad z = h + iy.$$

Hence

$$|I_2| \leqq \int_{-(n+1/2)}^{(n+1/2)} \frac{e^{-ht}}{1 - e^{-2\pi h}}\,dy = \frac{e^{-ht}(2n+1)}{1 - e^{-2\pi h}} \xrightarrow[h\to\infty]{} 0,$$

since $t > 0$. Similarly,

$$|I_4| \leqq \frac{e^{gt}(2n+1)}{e^{2\pi g} - 1} \cdot \frac{e^{-2\pi g}}{e^{-2\pi g}} = \frac{e^{-g(2\pi-t)}(2n+1)}{1 - e^{-2\pi g}} \xrightarrow[g\to\infty]{} 0,$$

since $t < 2\pi$. Hence, as in Article 13.42, we get, by letting $h \to \infty$ and $g \to \infty$,

$$\int_{-\infty}^{\infty} \frac{e^{-xt}dx}{1 + e^{-2\pi x}} = \frac{i[1 + 2\cos t + \cdots + 2\cos nt]}{2i \sin (n + \frac{1}{2})t},$$

or, by virtue of Article 13.42,

$$\tfrac{1}{2} + \cos t + \cdots + \cos nt = \frac{\sin (n + \frac{1}{2})t}{2 \sin t/2}.$$

CHAPTER 14

Infinite Complex Series

We assume the elementary theory of infinite real series.

CONVERGENCE

14.01. DEFINITION.   A *complex sequence* is a sequence whose elements are complex numbers. We write

$$a_1, a_2, \cdots, a_n, \cdots = \{a_n\}.$$

A sequence may be *finite* or *infinite*.

14.02. DEFINITION.   The series of an infinite complex sequence is known as an (*infinite*) *complex series*. Thus, given the sequence $\{a_n\}$, the series of this sequence is $\{S_n\}$, where $S_n = a_1 + \cdots + a_n$. We designate the series by

$$a_1 + a_2 + \cdots + a_n + \cdots \quad \text{or} \quad \sum a_n.$$

14.03. DEFINITIONS.   A complex series

$$a_1 + a_2 + \cdots + a_n + \cdots$$

is *convergent* provided $\lim_{n \to \infty} S_n$ exists. Otherwise the series is *divergent*. If $\lim_{n \to \infty} S_n = S$, then S is defined as the *sum* of the series, and we write

$$S = a_1 + a_2 + \cdots + a_n + \cdots \quad \text{or} \quad S = \sum a_n.$$

14.04. THEOREM.   The complex series $\sum a_n$ converges to S if and only if

$$\sum a_n' \text{ converges to } S',$$

$$\sum a_n'' \text{ converges to } S'',$$

where $a = a' + ia''$, $S = S' + iS''$.

Proof: By Art. 9.07, Vol. I.

14.05.   THEOREM.   If $\sum a_n$ converges, then $\lim\limits_{n \to \infty} a_n = 0$.

Proof: Let $\sum a_n$ converge to S. Then, given $\epsilon > 0$, there exists an m such that

$$|S - S_n| < \epsilon/2, \quad n > m.$$

Also, then,

$$|S - S_{n+1}| < \epsilon/2.$$

Hence

$$|S_{n+1} - S_n| < \epsilon.$$

But

$$S_{n+1} - S_n = a_{n+1},$$

whence

$$|a_{n+1}| < \epsilon.$$

This means that $\lim\limits_{n \to \infty} a_n = 0$.

14.06.   DEFINITION.   We call the series

$$a_{m+1} + a_{m+2} + \cdots$$

a *residual series*, or the *remainder after m terms*, and designate it by $\bar{S}_m$.

14.07.   THEOREM.   For any m the series S and $\bar{S}_m$ converge or diverge simultaneously.

Proof: Suppose series S to be convergent. Then $S = \lim\limits_{n \to \infty} S_n$. Set $n = m + s$. Then

$$S_n = S_m + \bar{S}_{m,s}.$$

Now, as $n \to \infty$, $s \to \infty$. Hence, since S_m is a constant, $\lim\limits_{s \to \infty} \bar{S}_{m,s}$ exists. That is, $\bar{S}_m$ is convergent.

Similarly, if S is divergent then $\bar{S}_m$ is divergent.

14.08.   CAUCHY'S CRITERION.   The series $\sum a_n$ converges if and only if to any $\epsilon > 0$ there corresponds an integer m such that

$$|a_m + a_{m+1} + \cdots + a_{m+p}| < \epsilon, \quad p = 0, 1, 2, \cdots,$$

or, what is the same thing,

$$|S_{m+p} - S_{m-1}| < \epsilon, \quad p = 0, 1, 2, \cdots.$$

Note: We assume this theorem here. There are several ways of establishing it.

(1) We may first prove the theorem for reals, and then, by Article 14.04, show it true for complex series. In proving the theorem for reals, it is the sufficiency part of the condition that presents difficulty.

(2) The theorem may be proved directly for complex series.

14.09. THEOREM. The series $\sum a_n$ converges if and only if to any $\epsilon > 0$ there corresponds an integer m such that

$$|S_{n'} - S_{n''}| < \epsilon, \text{ when } n' > m, n'' > m.$$

Proof: This is an alternative statement of Article 14.08.

14.10. DEFINITION. A complex series $\sum a_n$ *converges absolutely* if $\sum |a_n|$ converges.

14.11. THEOREM. If a complex series converges absolutely, then it converges.

Proof: Let $\sum a_n$ be the series. Then, since $\sum |a_n|$ converges, Cauchy's Criterion claims that for any $\epsilon > 0$ there exists an m such that

$$|a_m| + |a_{m+1}| + \cdots + |a_{m+p}| < \epsilon, \quad p = 0, 1, 2, \cdots.$$

But we have

$$|a_m + a_{m+1} + \cdots + a_{m+p}| \leq |a_m| + |a_{m+1}| + \cdots + |a_{m+p}| < \epsilon.$$

Hence, also by Cauchy's Criterion, $\sum a_n$ converges.

14.12. DEFINITION and NOTATION. If $|a_n| \leq u_n$, then the series $\sum u_n$ is called a *dominant series* of the series $\sum a_n$, and we write

$$\sum a_n \ll \sum u_n.$$

14.13. THEOREM. If a dominant series converges, then the given series converges absolutely.

Proof: Since the dominant series converges, there exists an m such that

$$u_m + u_{m+1} + \cdots + u_{m+p} < \epsilon, \quad p = 0, 1, 2, \cdots.$$

But

$$|a_m| + |a_{m+1}| + \cdots + |a_{m+p}| \leq u_m + u_{m+1} + \cdots + u_{m+p} < \epsilon.$$

Hence $\sum |a_n|$ converges and $\sum a_n$ converges absolutely.

14.14. DEFINITION. A series may converge but not converge absolutely, e.g., $1 - \frac{1}{2} + \frac{1}{3} - \frac{1}{4} + \cdots$. Such a series is said to be *conditionally convergent*.

14.15. THEOREM. $\sum a_n$ converges absolutely if and only if $\sum a_n'$ and $\sum a_n''$ converge absolutely, where $a_n = a_n' + i a_n''$.

(1) Suppose $\sum a_n$ converges absolutely, i.e.,

$$\sum |a_n| = \sum \sqrt{a_n'^2 + a_n''^2}$$

converges. But

$$|a_n'| \leq \sqrt{a_n'^2 + a_n''^2} \quad \text{and} \quad |a_n''| \leq \sqrt{a_n'^2 + a_n''^2}.$$

Hence, by Article 14.13,

$$\sum |a_n'| \quad \text{and} \quad \sum |a_n''|$$

converge. That is, $\sum a_n'$ and $\sum a_n''$ converge absolutely.

(2) Suppose $\sum a_n'$ and $\sum a_n''$ converge absolutely. Set

$$S_n' = |a_1'| + \cdots + |a_n'|,$$
$$S_n'' = |a_1''| + \cdots + |a_n''|.$$

Then

$$\lim_{n \to \infty} (S_n' + S_n'') = \lim_{n \to \infty} S_n' + \lim_{n \to \infty} S_n'',$$

and

$$\sum \{ |a_n'| + |a_n''| \}$$

converges. But

$$|a_n| \leq |a_n'| + |a_n''|.$$

Hence, by Article 14.13, $\sum |a_n|$ converges. That is, $\sum a_n$ converges absolutely.

14.16. THEOREM. The sum of an absolutely convergent complex series is independent of the order of the terms.

Proof: Let $\sum a_n$ be the series and let $a_n = a_n' + a_n''$. Then

$$\sum a_n = \sum (a_n' + ia_n'') = \sum a_n' + i\sum a_n''. \tag{1}$$

By Article 14.15, $\sum a_n'$ and $\sum a_n''$ converge absolutely. But when a series of real terms converges absolutely, its sum is independent of the order of the terms. It follows from (1), then, that the sum of $\sum a_n$ is independent of the order of its terms.

14.17. THEOREM. The sum of a convergent complex series remains unchanged if the terms are grouped in any arbitrary manner.

Proof: Let $\sum a_n$ be a convergent series and let us group the terms into consecutive sets $A_1, A_2, \cdots$, where

$$A_1 = a_1 + \cdots + a_k,$$
$$A_2 = a_{k+1} + \cdots + a_r,$$

$$\cdot \quad \cdot \quad \cdot \quad \cdot \quad \cdot \quad \cdot \quad \cdot \quad \cdot \quad \cdot \quad \cdot$$

We wish to show that $\sum A_n$ converges to the sum of $\sum a_n$. To this end, we set

$$S_n' = A_1 + \cdots + A_n.$$

Then there exists some $m \geq n$ such that

$$S_n' = S_m. \tag{1}$$

As $n \to \infty$, so does $m \to \infty$ (through the values $k, r, \cdots$). Since $\lim S_m = \sum a_n$, it follows from (1) that $\lim S_n' = \lim S_m = \sum a_n$. This proves the theorem.

Note: Articles 14.16 and 14.17 extend the commutative and associative laws of addition to an infinite series provided the series is absolutely convergent. It can be shown that a *real* conditionally convergent series can be made to converge to *any* arbitrarily chosen real number by some arrangement of its terms. A complex conditionally convergent series depends, for its sum, on the arrangement of its terms, but it cannot be made in general to converge to *any* arbitrarily chosen complex number.

POWER SERIES AND THE
CIRCLE OF CONVERGENCE

14.18. THEOREM. If $\sum A_n(z - a)^n$ converges for $z = \xi \neq a$, then it converges absolutely for all z such that $|z - a| < |\xi - a|$.

Proof: Since $\sum A_n(\xi - a)^n$ converges, we have

$$\lim_{n \to \infty} A_n(\xi - a)^n = 0.$$

Hence, given $\epsilon > 0$, there exists an m such that

$$|A_n(\xi - a)^n| < \epsilon, \quad n > m.$$

But there certainly also exists an M such that

$$|A_n(\xi - a)^n| < M, \quad n = 0, 1, \cdots, m.$$

Now take $N = \max(\epsilon, M)$. Then for all n we have

$$|A_n(\xi - a)^n| < N, \tag{A}$$

or

$$|A_n| < N/|\xi - a|^n.$$

Hence

$$\sum A_n(z - a)^n \ll \sum \frac{N|z - a|^n}{|\xi - a|^n}. \tag{1}$$

But $|z - a|/|\xi - a| < 1$, and hence the geometric series on the right of (1) converges. Therefore, by Article 14.13, $\sum A_n(z - a)^n$ converges absolutely.

14.19. THEOREM. If $\sum A_n(z - a)^n$ diverges for $z = \xi \neq a$, then it diverges for all z such that $|z - a| > |\xi - a|$.

Proof: Suppose it does not. Then the series converges for a point z farther from a than is ξ. Then, by Article 14.18, the series converges for all points nearer than z, and hence for ξ. But this contradicts the hypothesis that the series diverges for $z = \xi$. Hence the theorem.

14.20. DEFINITION. If $\sum A_n(z - a)^n$ converges for some $z \neq a$ and diverges for some $z \neq a$, then, clearly, by Articles 14.18 and 14.19, there is a circle C between the two sets of circles of those articles such that for all points inside C the series converges (absolutely) and for all points outside C the series diverges. C is known as the *circle of convergence* for the given power series. Its radius, ρ, is known as the *radius of convergence*. If the series diverges for all $z \neq a$, then $\rho = 0$. If the series converges for all z, then $\rho = \infty$.

14.21. THEOREM.   If in the series $\sum A_n(z - a)^n$,

$$\lim_{n \to \infty} \left| \frac{A_{n+1}}{A_n} \right| = \frac{1}{k}, \quad k \neq 0,$$

then k is the radius of convergence of the given series.

Proof: We have

$$\sum A_n(z - a)^n \ll \sum |A_n||z - a|^n. \tag{1}$$

Now, the series on the right of (1) converges if

$$\lim_{n \to \infty} \frac{|A_{n+1}||z - a|^{n+1}}{|A_n||z - a|^n} = \frac{1}{k}|z - a| < 1,$$

or if

$$|z - a| < k.$$

Hence, by Article 14.13, $\sum A_n(z - a)^n$ converges for all z such that $|z - a| < k$.

Now suppose (see Figure 14.1) $\sum A_n(z - a)^n$ also converges for a point $z = z_2$ such that $|z_2 - a| > k$. Then, by Article 14.18, the series converges absolutely for $z = z_1$ such that

$$k < |z_1 - a| < |z_2 - a|.$$

That is,

$$\sum |A_n||z_1 - a|^n \tag{2}$$

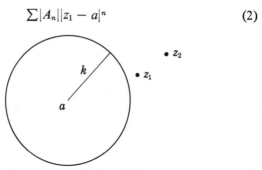

Figure 14.1

converges. But, applying the test-ratio test, we see that

$$\lim_{n\to\infty} \frac{|A_{n+1}||z_1 - a|^{n+1}}{|A_n||z_1 - a|^n} = \frac{1}{k}|z_1 - a| > 1,$$

which means that (2) must diverge. Hence we have a contradiction, and we see that the series must diverge for all z such that $|z - a| > k$. Hence k is the radius of convergence of the series.

Note: The converse is not necessarily true.

14.22. THEOREM. If in the power series $\sum A_n(z - a)^n$

$$\lim_{n\to\infty} \left| \frac{A_{n+1}}{A_n} \right| = 0,$$

then $\rho = \infty$ and the series converges everywhere.

Proof: This theorem is a corollary of Article 14.21.

14.23. THEOREM. If in the power series $\sum A_n(z - a)^n$

$$\lim_{n\to\infty} \left| \frac{A_{n+1}}{A_n} \right| = \infty,$$

then $\rho = 0$ and the series diverges for all $z \neq a$.

Proof: This theorem is a corollary of Article 14.21.

14.24. THEOREM. There exist power series with

$$(1)\ \rho = 0, \quad (2)\ \rho = \infty, \quad (3)\ \rho \neq 0, \infty.$$

Proof: (1) Take $A_n = n!$. Then

$$\lim_{n\to\infty} \left| \frac{A_{n+1}}{A_n} \right| = \lim_{n\to\infty} (n + 1) = \infty, \quad \text{and } \rho = 0.$$

(2) Take $A_n = 1/n!$. Then

$$\lim_{n\to\infty} \left| \frac{A_{n+1}}{A_n} \right| = \lim_{n\to\infty} \frac{1}{n + 1} = 0, \quad \text{and } \rho = \infty.$$

(3) Take $A_n = 1$. Then

$$\lim_{n\to\infty} \left| \frac{A_{n+1}}{A_n} \right| = 1, \quad \text{and } \rho = 1.$$

14.25.   THEOREM.   The three series

$$\sum A_n(z-a)^n, \quad \sum n A_n(z-a)^{n-1}, \quad \sum \frac{A_n}{n+1}(z-a)^{n+1}$$

have the same circle of convergence.

Proof: Let ρ be the radius of convergence of the first series. We shall consider three cases.

Case 1. $0 < \rho < \infty$. Take any point ξ inside the circle of convergence of $\sum A_n(z-a)^n$. Then, as in (A) of Article 14.18, we have an N such that

$$|A_n| < N/|\xi - a|^n$$

for all n. Hence

$$\sum n A_n(z-a)^{n-1} \ll \sum \frac{nN|z-a|^{n-1}}{|\xi - a|^n}. \tag{1}$$

Forming the test-ratio for the right side of (1), we obtain

$$\lim_{n\to\infty} \frac{n+1}{n} \left|\frac{z-a}{\xi-a}\right| = \left|\frac{z-a}{\xi-a}\right| < 1$$

if $|z-a| < |\xi - a|$. Hence the series $\sum n A_n(z-a)^{n-1}$ converges for all $|z-a| < \rho$.

Again, as before,

$$\sum \frac{A_n}{n+1}(z-a)^{n+1} \ll \sum \frac{N}{n+1} \frac{|z-a|^{n+1}}{|\xi - a|^n}. \tag{2}$$

Forming the test-ratio for the right side of (2), we have

$$\lim_{n\to\infty} \frac{n}{n+1} \left|\frac{z-a}{\xi-a}\right| = \left|\frac{z-a}{\xi-a}\right| < 1$$

if $|z-a| < |\xi - a|$. Hence the series

$$\sum \frac{A_n}{n+1}(z-a)^{n+1}$$

converges for all $|z-a| < \rho$.

Now suppose $\sum n A_n(z-a)^{n-1}$ converges for a point z_1 such that $|z_1 - a| > \rho$. Then, by the above proof, the integrated series of this one, namely $\sum A_n(z-a)^n$, converges for $z = z_1$. But this contradicts the hypothesis. Therefore $\sum n A_n (z - a)^{n-1}$ diverges for $|z - a| > \rho$, and this differentiated series of the first has the same circle of convergence as the first.

Again, suppose

$$\sum \frac{A_n}{n + 1} (z - a)^{n+1}$$

converges for a point z_1 such that $|z_1 - a| > \rho$. Then, by the above proof, the differentiated series of this one, namely $\sum A_n (z - a)^n$, converges for z_1. But this contradicts the hypothesis. Therefore

$$\sum \frac{n + 1}{A_n} (z - a)^{n+1}$$

diverges for $|z - a| > \rho$, and this integrated series of the first has the same circle of convergence as the first.

Case 2. $\rho = 0$. Suppose the radius of convergence of $\sum n A_n (z - a)^{n-1}$ is $\rho_1 \neq 0$. Then, by Case 1, we have $\rho = \rho_1$. This proves that $\rho_1 \neq 0$ cannot be. This similarly holds for the integrated series.

Case 3. $\rho = \infty$. As in Case 2.

Note: We have thus shown that any power series may either be differentiated or be integrated term by term, and that the resulting power series will have the same circle of convergence as the given series.

14.26.   THEOREM.   The *real* series $\sum u_n$, $(u_n \geq 0)$, converges or diverges, respectively, according as

$$\sqrt[n]{u_n} \leq l < 1 \quad \text{or} \quad \sqrt[n]{u_n} \geq 1 \quad \text{for all } n.$$

Proof: (1) Suppose $\sqrt[n]{u_n} \leq l < 1$. Since $0 \leq l < 1$, we see that

$$\sum u_n \ll \sum l^n.$$

But the dominant series is a convergent geometric series. Hence $\sum u_n$ converges.

(2) Suppose $\sqrt[n]{u_n} \geq 1$. The series $\sum u_n$ obviously diverges since $\lim_{n \to \infty} u_n \neq 0$ (see Art. 14.05).

14.27.   THEOREM.   The *real* series $\sum u_n$, $(u_n \geq 0)$, converges if $\lim_{n \to \infty} \sqrt[n]{u_n} < 1$ and diverges if $\lim_{n \to \infty} \sqrt[n]{u_n} > 1$.

This theorem is a corollary of Article 14.26, for there exists an m such that, for $n > m$,

$$\sqrt[n]{u_n} \leq l < 1 \quad \text{or} \quad \sqrt[n]{u_n} > 1.$$

14.28. THEOREM. For the power series $\sum A_n(z - a)^n$, if we have

$$\lim_{n \to \infty} \sqrt[n]{|A_n|} = 1/k, \quad k \neq 0,$$

then $\rho = k$.

Proof: We have

$$\sum A_n(z - a)^n \ll \sum |A_n||z - a|^n. \tag{1}$$

But

$$\lim_{n \to \infty} \sqrt[n]{|A_n||z - a|^n} = \lim_{n \to \infty} \sqrt[n]{|A_n|}|z - a|$$

$$= \frac{|z - a|}{k}.$$

Thus the absolute series in (1) converges or diverges (by Art. 14.27) if $|z - a| \lessgtr k$. Hence k is the radius of absolute convergence. But ρ is the radius of absolute convergence (Art. 14.29). Therefore $\rho = k$.

Note: The converse is not necessarily true.

14.29. THEOREM. For a power series the radius of convergence equals the radius of absolute convergence.

Proof: This is essentially proved in Articles 14.18 and 14.19.

14.30. EXERCISES. (a) Find the radius of convergence of $\sum_0^\infty \frac{(2n)!}{(n!)^2} z^n$.

$$\lim_{n \to \infty} \left| \frac{A_{n+1}}{A_n} \right| = \lim_{n \to \infty} \frac{(2n + 2)!}{(n + 1)!(n + 1)!} \cdot \frac{n!n!}{(2n)!}$$

$$= \lim_{n \to \infty} \frac{(2n + 2)(2n + 1)}{(n + 1)(n + 1)}$$

$$= 4.$$

Therefore

$$\rho = \tfrac{1}{4}. \quad Ans.$$

(b) Find the radius of convergence of $\sum_1^\infty \dfrac{n!}{n^n} z^n$.

$$\lim_{n\to\infty} \left| \frac{A_{n+1}}{A_n} \right| = \lim_{n\to\infty} \frac{(n+1)!}{(n+1)^{n+1}} \cdot \frac{n^n}{n!}$$

$$= \lim_{n\to\infty} \frac{(n+1)n^n}{(n+1)^{n+1}}$$

$$= \lim_{n\to\infty} \frac{n^n}{(n+1)^n}$$

$$= \lim_{n\to\infty} \frac{1}{\left(1 + \dfrac{1}{n}\right)^n}$$

$$= 1/e.$$

Therefore

$$\rho = e. \qquad Ans.$$

UPPER AND LOWER LIMITS

14.31. DEFINITIONS. (a) A is a *limit point* of the *real* sequence $\{u_n\}$ if for an arbitrary $\epsilon > 0$ there are infinitely many integers n such that

$$|A - u_n| < \epsilon.$$

(b) $+\infty$ is a *limit point* of the *real* sequence $\{u_n\}$ if for an arbitrary $M > 0$, however large, there are infinitely many integers n such that

$$u_n > M.$$

(c) $-\infty$ is a *limit point* of the *real* sequence $\{u_n\}$ if for an arbitrary $M > 0$, however large, there are infinitely many integers n such that

$$u_n < -M.$$

14.32. DEFINITION. (a) If $+\infty$ is a limit point of the real sequence $\{u_n\}$, then the *upper limit* (or *limit superior*) of $\{u_n\}$, denoted by $\overline{\lim}\, u_n$ (or lim sup u_n), is $+\infty$.

(b) If $+\infty$ is not a limit point of the real sequence $\{u_n\}$, then $\overline{\lim}\, u_n$ is the greatest of the limit points, if there are any finite ones.

(c) If $-\infty$ is the only limit point of $\{u_n\}$, then $\overline{\lim}\, u_n = -\infty$.

14.33. DEFINITION. The *lower limit* (or *limit inferior*) of a real sequence $\{u_n\}$, denoted by $\underline{\lim} u_n$ (or $\lim \inf u_n$), is given by

$$\underline{\lim} u_n = - \overline{\lim} (-u_n).$$

14.34. THEOREM. Every *real* sequence has an upper and a lower limit.

Proof: If $\pm \infty$ are *isolated* from the sequence, then, but for these points, the sequence is bounded and hence (by the Bolzanno-Weierstrass Theorem) has at least one limit point. If $\pm \infty$ is not isolated, then $\pm \infty$ is a limit point.

Case 1. If $+\infty$ is a limit point, then [by (a) of Art. 14.32] $\overline{\lim} u_n = +\infty$.

Case 2. If $-\infty$ is the only limit point, then [by (c) of Article 14.32] $\overline{\lim} u_n = -\infty$.

Case 3. If $+\infty$ is not a limit point and there are finite limit points, then this set of finite limit points is bounded. Moreover it is a closed set. (For let P be a limit point of the set of finite limit points of $\{u_n\}$. Then for any $\epsilon > 0$ we have $|P - u_n| < \epsilon$ for infinitely many integers n. Hence P is also a limit point of $\{u_n\}$.) Thus there is a greatest limit point, say A. Then [by (b) of Article 14.32] $\overline{\lim} u_n = A$.

Thus in all cases $\{u_n\}$ has an upper limit. Similarly, in all cases $\{-u_n\}$ has an upper limit. Therefore (Art. 14.33) in all cases $\{u_n\}$ has a lower limit.

14.35. THEOREM. $\overline{\text{Lim}} \, u_n = \mu$ if and only if for an arbitrary $\epsilon > 0$:

(a) $u_n < \mu + \epsilon$ for all but a finite number of integers n,
(b) $u_n > \mu - \epsilon$ for infinitely many integers n.

Proof: The necessary and sufficient conditions are as follows.

Necessary: Let $\overline{\lim} u_n = \mu$. Suppose part (a) to be not true. Then $[\mu + \epsilon, \infty)$ contains an infinite number of points of $\{u_n\}$. Two cases arise:

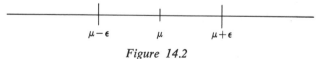

Figure 14.2

(1) ∞ isolated from $\{u_n\}$. Then there exists an $M > 0$ such that (M, ∞) contains no point of $\{u_n\}$. Then $[\mu + \epsilon, M]$ contains infinitely

many points of $\{u_n\}$ and also therefore contains (by the Bolzanno-Weierstrass Theorem) a limit point of $\{u_n\}$.

(2) ∞ not isolated from $\{u_n\}$. Then ∞ is a limit point of $\{u_n\}$.

Thus in either case (1) or (2) there is a limit point to the right of μ. But this is impossible since $\mu = \overline{\lim}\, u_n$. Therefore part (a) is true.

Suppose part (b) to be not true. Then $(\mu - \epsilon, \mu + \epsilon)$ contains only a finite number of points of $\{u_n\}$, and hence μ cannot be a limit point of $\{u_n\}$. This contradiction shows that part (b) is true.

Sufficient: Let μ satisfy parts (a) and (b). By (a) and (b), $(\mu - \epsilon, \mu + \epsilon)$ contains an infinite number of points of $\{u_n\}$ for any $\epsilon > 0$. Hence μ is a limit point of $\{u_n\}$. Suppose ν is a limit point of $\{u_n\}$ lying to the right of μ. Then we may enclose ν in an interval $(\nu - \delta, \nu + \delta)$ not containing μ. This interval must contain an infinite number of points of $\{u_n\}$. Now take ϵ such that $(\mu - \epsilon, \mu + \epsilon)$ and $(\nu - \delta, \nu + \delta)$ do not intersect. Then for this ϵ condition part (a) is contradicted. Therefore there is no limit point ν to the right of μ. That is, $\overline{\lim}\, u_n = \mu$.

14.36. THEOREM. $\overline{\text{Lim}}\, u_n = \infty$ if and only if $u_n > N$ for infinitely many integers n, N being arbitrarily large.

Proof: By (b) of Article 14.31 and (a) of Article 14.32.

14.37. THEOREM. $\overline{\text{Lim}}\, u_n = -\infty$ if and only if $u_n < -N$ for all but a finite number of integers n, N being arbitrarily large.

Proof: By (c) of Article 14.31 and (c) of Article 14.32.

14.38. THEOREM. $\underline{\lim}\, u_n \leq \overline{\lim}\, u_n$.

14.39. THEOREM. It is not necessarily true that

$$\overline{\lim}\, (u_n + v_n) = \overline{\lim}\, u_n + \overline{\lim}\, v_n,$$

$$\overline{\lim}\, (u_n v_n) = \overline{\lim}\, u_n\, \overline{\lim}\, v_n.$$

Proof: Consider

$$
\begin{aligned}
&\{u_n\} = 1, 0, 1, 0, \cdots && \overline{\lim}\, u_n = 1, \\
&\{v_n\} = 0, 1, 0, 1, \cdots && \overline{\lim}\, v_n = 1, \\
&\{u_n + v_n\} = 1, 1, 1, 1, \cdots && \overline{\lim}\, (u_n + v_n) = 1, \\
&\{u_n v_n\} = 0, 0, 0, 0, \cdots && \overline{\lim}\, (u_n v_n) = 0.
\end{aligned}
$$

14.40. THEOREM. If $\overline{\lim}\, u_n = \mu$, then for given $\epsilon > 0$ there exists an n_0 such that

$$u_n < \mu + \epsilon, \quad n > n_0.$$

Proof: By (a) of Article 14.35, $u_n < \mu + \epsilon$ for all but a finite number of integers. Take any n_0 greater than the greatest of these integers and the theorem follows.

14.41. THEOREM. If $u_n \leq v_n$, then $\overline{\lim}\, u_n \leq \overline{\lim}\, v_n$.

Proof: *Case 1.* $\overline{\lim}\, v_n = \infty$. The theorem is obvious.

Case 2. $\overline{\lim}\, v_n = V$. Suppose $U > V$. As shown in Figure 14.3, take

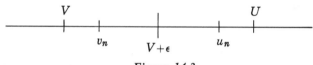

Figure 14.3

$V + \epsilon$ between U and V. Then (Art. 14.40) there exists an n_0 such that

$$v_n < V + \epsilon, \quad n > n_0.$$

Now, since U is a limit point of $\{u_n\}$,

$$|U - u_n| < U - V - \epsilon$$

for infinitely many integers n, and hence for infinitely many integers $n > n_0$. Thus there exists a case where $u_n > v_n$. This contradicts the hypothesis, whence $U \not> V$, and the theorem is proved.

14.42. THEOREM. If $u_n \leq v_n$, then $\underline{\lim}\, u_n \leq \underline{\lim}\, v_n$.

Proof: We have

$$-v_n \leq -u_n.$$

Therefore (Art. 14.41)

$$\overline{\lim}\, (-v_n) \leq \overline{\lim}\, (-u_n),$$

whence

$$\underline{\lim}\, u_n \leq \underline{\lim}\, v_n.$$

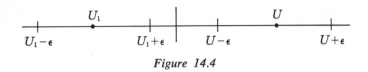

Figure 14.4

14.43. THEOREM. A necessary and sufficient condition that $\lim u_n = U$ is that

$$\overline{\lim}\, u_n = U \quad \text{and} \quad \underline{\lim}\, u_n = U.$$

Proof: *Necessary:* Let $\lim u_n = U$. Then, for given $\epsilon > 0$,

$$U - \epsilon < u_n < U + \epsilon, \quad n > n_0, \text{ say.}$$

Now suppose there is another limit point U_1 (see Figure 14.4). Then we have

$$|U_1 - u_n| < \epsilon$$

for infinitely many integers n, and hence for infinitely many integers $n > n_0$. But this is impossible for $\epsilon < \frac{1}{2}|U - U_1|$. Hence U is the only limit point of $\{u_n\}$, whence

$$\overline{\lim}\, u_n = \underline{\lim}\, u_n.$$

Sufficient: Let $\overline{\lim}\, u_n = \underline{\lim}\, u_n = U$. Since $\overline{\lim}\, u_n = U$, by Article 14.40,

$$u_n < U + \epsilon, \quad n > n_1, \text{ say.}$$

Also, since $\underline{\lim}\, u_n = U = -\overline{\lim}\,(-u_n)$,

$$-u_n < -U + \epsilon, \quad n > n_2, \text{ say,}$$

or

$$u_n < U - \epsilon, \quad n > n_2.$$

Therefore

$$U - \epsilon < u_n < U + \epsilon, \quad n > \max(n_1, n_2),$$

i.e.,

$$\lim u_n = U.$$

14.44. THEOREM. If $u_n \geq 0$ and if $\overline{\lim}\, u_n = 0$, then $\lim u_n = 0$.

Proof: $\underline{\lim}\, u_n \leq \overline{\lim}\, u_n = 0$. Hence, since $u_n \geq 0$, $\underline{\lim}\, u_n = 0$ and $\lim u_n = 0$.

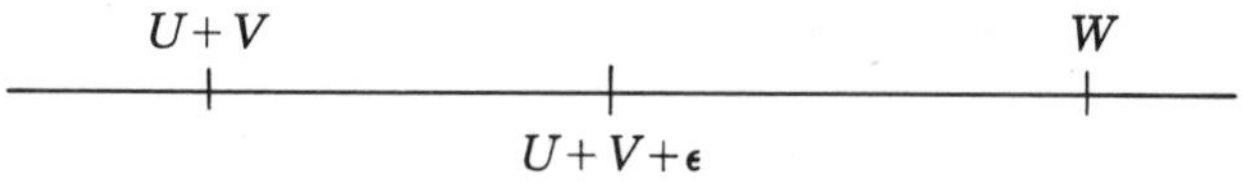

$$U+V \qquad\qquad\qquad\qquad\qquad W$$

$$U+V+\epsilon$$

Figure 14.5

14.45. THEOREM. If $\overline{\lim}\, u_n = U$, $\overline{\lim}\, v_n = V$, then

$$\overline{\lim}\,(u_n + v_n) \leq U + V.$$

Proof: Let $\overline{\lim}\,(u_n + v_n) = W$ and suppose $W > U + V$ (see Figure 14.5). Take $U + V + \epsilon$ between $U + V$ and W. Then we have

$$u_n < U + \epsilon/2, \quad n > n_1,$$

$$v_n < V + \epsilon/2, \quad n > n_2,$$

whence

$$u_n + v_n < U + V + \epsilon, \quad n > n_0, n_0 = \max(n_1, n_2). \qquad (1)$$

But also, since W is a limit point of $\{u_n + v_n\}$,

$$|W - (u_n + v_n)| < W - (U + V + \epsilon) \qquad (2)$$

for infinitely many integers n, and hence for infinitely many integers $n > n_0$.

But (1) and (2) are incompatible (see Figure 14.5). Hence $W \not> U + V$, or

$$\overline{\lim}\,(u_n + v_n) \leq U + V.$$

14.46. THEOREM. If $\overline{\lim}\, u_n = U$, $\lim v_n = V$, then

$$\overline{\lim}\,(u_n + v_n) = U + V.$$

Proof: Since $\lim v_n = V$, we have $\overline{\lim}\, v_n = V$. Hence, by Article 14.45,

$$W = \overline{\lim}\,(u_n + v_n) \leq U + V.$$

Suppose $W < U + V$ (see Figure 14.6). Take $\epsilon < \tfrac{1}{2}(U + V - W)$. Then we have

$$u_n + v_n < W + \epsilon, \quad n > n_1. \qquad (1)$$

$$W \qquad\qquad\qquad\qquad U+V$$

$$W+\epsilon \qquad\qquad U+V-\epsilon$$

Figure 14.6

But, since U is a limit point of $\{u_n\}$,

$$|U - u_n| < \epsilon/2$$

for infinitely many integers n, and hence for infinitely many integers $n > n_1$. Also, since $\lim v_n = V$,

$$|V - v_n| < \epsilon/2$$

for *all* integers $n > n_2$. Hence

$$|(U + V) - (u_n + v_n)| \leq |U - u_n| + |V - v_n| < \epsilon \qquad (2)$$

for infinitely many integers $n > n_0$, where $n_0 = \max(n_1, n_2)$. But, from (1), we have

$$u_n + v_n < W - \epsilon \text{ for all } n > n_0. \qquad (3)$$

Now, (2) and (3) are incompatible (see Figure 14.6). Hence $W \not< U + V$, or

$$\overline{\lim} \, (u_n + v_n) = U + V.$$

14.47.　THEOREM.　If $u_n \geq 0$ and $v_n \geq 0$, $\lim u_n = U$, $\overline{\lim} \, v_n = V$, then $\overline{\lim} \, (u_n v_n) = UV$.

Proof: Case 1.　$U \neq 0, V \neq 0$. Since $\lim u_n = U$, $\overline{\lim} \, v_n = V$, we have, taking $0 < \epsilon < U, V$,

$$U - \epsilon < u_n < U + \epsilon, \quad n > n_1, \qquad (1)$$

and

$$v_n < V + \epsilon, \quad n > n_2, \qquad (2)$$

$$v_n > V - \epsilon \text{ for infinitely many } n > n_2. \qquad (3)$$

Now take $n_0 = \max(n_1, n_2)$ and the relations (1), (2), and (3) hold for $n > n_0$. Hence, multiplying the second inequality of (1) with (2), we have, since all members are positive,

$$u_n v_n < UV + \epsilon(U + V) + \epsilon^2 = UV + \eta_0, \text{ for all } n > n_0,$$

where

$$\eta_0 = \epsilon(U + V) + \epsilon^2.$$

Again, multiplying the first inequality of (1) with (3), we have, since all members are positive,

$$u_n v_n > UV - \epsilon(U + V) + \epsilon^2 = UV - \eta_1, \text{ for infinitely many } n > n_0,$$

where $$\eta_1 = \epsilon(U + V) - \epsilon^2.$$

Hence, since $\eta_0 > \eta_1$, we have

$$u_n v_n < UV + \eta_0, \text{ for all } n > n_0,$$

$$u_n v_n > UV - \eta_0, \text{ for infinitely many } n > n_0.$$

Hence

$$\overline{\lim} \, (u_n v_n) = UV.$$

Case 2. $V = 0$. In this case (Art. 14.44)

$$\lim v_n = \overline{\lim} \, v_n = 0.$$

Hence

$$\lim(u_n v_n) = \lim u_n \lim v_n = UV = 0.$$

Case 3. $U = 0, V \neq 0$. Since $\lim u_n = 0$, we have

$$0 \leqq u_n < \epsilon, \text{ for all } n > n_1. \tag{4}$$

Also, we have

$$v_n < V + \epsilon, \text{ for all } n > n_2, \tag{5}$$

$$v_n > V - \epsilon, \text{ for infinitely many } n > n_2. \tag{6}$$

Now take $n_0 = \max(n_1, n_2)$ and the relations (4), (5), and (6) all hold for $n > n_0$. Proceeding as in Case 1, we find

$$u_n v_n < \epsilon(V + \epsilon) = \eta_1, \text{ for all } n > n_0,$$

$$u_n v_n \geqq 0, \text{ for infinitely many } n > n_0.$$

Hence

$$\overline{\lim} \, (u_n v_n) = 0 = UV.$$

Note: The conclusion of this theorem is not generally true without the condition that $u_n \geq 0$, $v_n \geq 0$. Consider the following sequences:

$$\{u_n\} = -1, -1, -1, -1, \cdots \qquad \lim u_n = -1,$$

$$\{v_n\} = 0, -1, 0, -1, \cdots \qquad \overline{\lim} \, v_n = 0,$$

$$\{u_n v_n\} = 0, 1, 0, 1, \cdots \qquad \overline{\lim} \, (u_n v_n) = 1.$$

The theorem is always true, however, when $u_n \geq 0$ and $v_n \leq 0$.

14.48. **EXERCISE.**   Find $\overline{\lim} \, u_n$ and $\underline{\lim} \, u_n$ if

$$u_n = 1 + (-1)^n + (-1)^n/n, \quad n = 1, 2, \cdots.$$

Writing out the first few terms of the sequence, we have

$$\{u_n\} = -1, 2\tfrac{1}{2}, -\tfrac{1}{3}, 2\tfrac{1}{4}, -\tfrac{1}{5}, 2\tfrac{1}{6}, \cdots.$$

Clearly, then,

$$\underline{\lim} \, u_n = 0 \quad \text{and} \quad \overline{\lim} \, u_n = 2.$$

14.49.   THEOREM.   For the power series $\sum A_n(z - a)^n$ we have $1/\rho = \overline{\lim} \sqrt[n]{|A_n|}$.

Proof: Case 1. $\overline{\lim} \sqrt[n]{|A_n|} = 1/k, \ (k \neq 0, \infty)$. By Article 14.40, we have

$$\sqrt[n]{|A_n|} < \frac{1 + \epsilon}{k}, \text{ for all } n > n_0, \text{ say.}$$

Therefore, for $n > n_0$,

$$|A_n| < \frac{(1 + \epsilon)^n}{k^n},$$

and

$$\sum A_n(z - a)^n \ll \sum \frac{(1 + \epsilon)^n}{k^n} |z - a|^n,$$

a geometric series which converges if

$$(1 + \epsilon)|z - a|/k < 1,$$

or if

$$|z - a| < k/(1 + \epsilon),$$

or if

$$|z - a| < k.$$

Hence $\sum A_n(z - a)^n$ certainly converges for $|z - a| < k$.

Also, by Article 14.35,

$$\sqrt[n]{|A_n|} > (1 - \epsilon)/k,$$

for infinitely many integers n. Hence

$$|A_n||z - a|^n > (1 - \epsilon)^n|z - a|^n/k^n,$$

for infinitely many n. Therefore $\sum |A_n||z - a|^n$ diverges if

$$(1 - \epsilon)^n|z - a|^n/k^n \geq 1,$$

or if

$$|z - a| \geq k/(1 - \epsilon) > k.$$

But since the absolute series diverges for $|z - a| > k$, so does the original series diverge for $|z - a| > k$ (Art. 14.29).

We thus see that $k = \rho$ and the theorem is established.

Case 2. If $\overline{\lim} \sqrt[n]{|A_n|} = 0$, then $\rho = \infty$.

Case 3. If $\overline{\lim} \sqrt[n]{|A_n|} = \infty$, then $\rho = 0$.

14.50. **THEOREM.** If $u_n > 0$, and if

$$\lim_{n \to \infty} \frac{u_{n+1}}{u_n} \quad \text{and} \quad \lim_{n \to \infty} \sqrt[n]{u_n}$$

exist, then these limits are equal.

Proof: Consider the series $\sum u_n z^n$. Then if ρ is the radius of convergence of this series, we have

$$\lim_{n \to \infty} u_{n+1}/u_n = 1/\rho \qquad \text{by Art. 14.21,}$$

$$\lim_{n \to \infty} \sqrt[n]{u_n} = 1/\rho \qquad \text{by Art. 14.28.}$$

Hence we have

$$\lim_{n \to \infty} \frac{u_{n+1}}{u_n} = \lim_{n \to \infty} \sqrt[n]{u_n}.$$

14.51. **THEOREM.** If $u_n > 0$ and if $\lim \sqrt[n]{u_n} = l$, then it does *not* necessarily follow that

$$\lim_{n \to \infty} \frac{u_{n+1}}{u_n} = l.$$

Proof: Consider the sequence

$$\{u_n\} = a, a, a^2, a^2, a^3, a^3, \cdots, \quad a \neq 1, > 0.$$

Then

$$\{\sqrt[n]{u_n}\} = a, a^{1/2}, a^{2/3}, a^{1/2}, a^{3/5}, a^{1/2}, \cdots,$$

and

$$\lim_{n \to \infty} \sqrt[n]{u_n} = a^{1/2}.$$

But

$$\left\{ \frac{u_{n+1}}{u_n} \right\} = 1, a, 1, a, 1, a, \cdots,$$

and

$$\lim_{n \to \infty} \frac{u_{n+1}}{u_n}$$

does not exist.

14.52.   THEOREM.   If $u_n > 0$ and if

$$\lim_{n \to \infty} \frac{u_{n+1}}{u_n} = l \text{ (or } = +\infty),$$

then $\lim \sqrt[n]{u_n} = l$ (or $= +\infty$).

Proof: Case 1. $l = 0$. We have

$$u_{n+1}/u_n < \epsilon, \quad n \geq m, \text{ say.}$$

Thus, in particular, we have

$$\frac{u_{m+1}}{u_m} < \epsilon, \frac{u_{m+2}}{u_{m+1}} < \epsilon, \cdots, \frac{u_{m+p}}{u_{m+p-1}} < \epsilon.$$

Multiplying together these inequalities, we have, since all members are positive,

$$0 < \frac{u_{m+p}}{u_m} < \epsilon^p,$$

or (since $u_m > 0$)

$$0 < u_{m+p} < \epsilon^p u_m,$$

or

$$0 < u_{m+p}^{1/(m+p)} < \epsilon^{p/(m+p)} u_m^{1/(m+p)}.$$

Hence

$$0 \leq \varliminf_{p \to \infty} u_{m+p}^{1/(m+p)} \leq \varlimsup_{p \to \infty} u_{m+p}^{1/(m+p)} \leq \epsilon.$$

Hence

$$\lim_{n \to \infty} u_n^{1/n} = 0 = l.$$

Case 2. $l > 0$. Choose ϵ such that $0 < l - \epsilon$. Then

$$l - \epsilon < \frac{u_{n+1}}{u_n} < l + \epsilon, \quad n \geq m.$$

Hence, in particular,

$$l - \epsilon < \frac{u_{m+1}}{u_m} < l + \epsilon,$$

$$l - \epsilon < \frac{u_{m+2}}{u_{m+1}} < l + \epsilon,$$

$$\cdot \quad \cdot \quad \cdot \quad \cdot \quad \cdot \quad \cdot \quad \cdot \quad \cdot$$

$$l - \epsilon < \frac{u_{m+p}}{u_{m+p-1}} < l + \epsilon.$$

Multiplying together these inequalities, we have, since all members are positive,

$$(l - \epsilon)^p < \frac{u_{m+p}}{u_m} < (l + \epsilon)^p,$$

or

$$(l - \epsilon)^p u_m < u_{m+p} < (l + \epsilon)^p u_m,$$

or

$$(l - \epsilon)^{p/(m+p)} u_m^{1/(m+p)} < u_{m+p}^{1/(m+p)} < (l + \epsilon)^{p/(m+p)} u_m^{1/(m+p)}.$$

Hence

$$(l - \epsilon) \leq \varliminf_{p \to \infty} u_{m+p}^{1/(m+p)} \leq \varlimsup_{p \to \infty} u_{m+p}^{1/(m+p)} \leq (l + \epsilon).$$

Therefore

$$\lim_{n \to \infty} u_n^{1/n} = l.$$

Case 3. $l = \infty$. Here we have

$$N < u_{n+1}/u_n, \quad n > m, N > 0.$$

Hence, in particular, we have

$$N < \frac{u_{m+1}}{u_m}, N < \frac{u_{m+2}}{u_{m+1}}, \cdots, N < \frac{u_{m+p}}{u_{m+p-1}}.$$

Multiplying together these inequalities, we have, since all members are positive,

$$N^p < u_{m+p}/u_m,$$

or

$$N^{p/(m+p)} u_m^{1/(m+p)} < u_{m+p}^{1/(m+p)}.$$

Hence

$$N \leq \varliminf_{p \to \infty} u_{m+p}^{1/(m+p)},$$

and

$$\lim_{n \to \infty} u_n^{1/n} = \infty = l.$$

14.53. *Note:* Article 14.52 may sometimes be used in place of L'Hospital's Rule for evaluating certain exponential indeterminate forms. For example,

$$\lim_{n \to \infty} n^{1/n} = \lim_{n \to \infty} \frac{n + 1}{n} = 1,$$

$$\lim_{n \to \infty} (\log n)^{1/n} = \lim_{n \to \infty} \frac{\log (n + 1)}{\log n} = 1,$$

$$\lim_{n \to \infty} (n!)^{1/n} = \lim_{n \to \infty} \frac{(n + 1)!}{n!} = \lim_{n \to \infty} (n + 1) = \infty.$$

UNIFORM CONVERGENCE OF REAL SERIES

14.54. DEFINITION. Let the series $\sum u_n(x)$ converge to $S(x)$ for every point x in an interval a, b. The series will then be said to *converge uniformly in a, b* provided that to an arbitrary $\epsilon > 0$ there corresponds an integer m *independent of x* in a, b such that, for $n > m$,

$$|S(x) - S_n(x)| < \epsilon \text{ for all } x \text{ in } a, b.$$

14.55. GEOMETRICAL INTERPRETATION OF UNIFORM CONVERGENCE. Suppose $y = S(x)$ to be graphed in the interval a, b (see Figure 14.7). Then, if the series is uniformly convergent in a, b, there exists, for any given $\epsilon > 0$, an m independent of x in a, b such that $y = S_n(x), (n > m)$, lies between the curves $y = S(x) + \epsilon$ and $y = S(x) - \epsilon$.

14.56. THEOREM. If each $u_n(x)$ is continuous in a, b, then it does *not* follow that $S(x)$ is continuous in a, b.

Proof: Consider the series

$$(1 - x) + x(1 - x) + x^2(1 - x) + \cdots$$

in the closed interval $[0, 1]$. Each term of the series is certainly continuous in $[0, 1]$. But

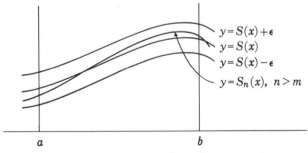

Figure 14.7

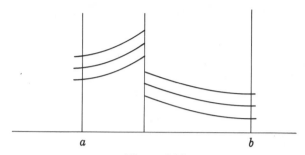

Figure 14.8

$$S(x) = \lim_{n \to \infty} S_n(x) = \lim_{n \to \infty} \frac{(1 - x)(1 - x^{n-1})}{1 - x} = \lim_{n \to \infty} (1 - x^{n-1}) = 1,0$$

according to whether $0 \le x < 1$ or $x = 1$. Hence $S(x)$ is not continuous in $[0, 1]$.

14.57. THEOREM. If each $u_n(x)$ is continuous in a, b but $S(x)$ has a jump discontinuity in a, b, then $\sum u_n(x)$ is not uniformly convergent in a, b.

Proof: Take ϵ less than half the jump (see Figure 14.8). Now $S_n(x)$ is continuous for all n, but no continuous curve $y = S_n(x)$ can be drawn in the band between $y = S(x) + \epsilon$ and $y = S(x) - \epsilon$.

14.58. EXAMPLES. (a) Is $\sin x + \frac{1}{3} \sin 3x + \frac{1}{5} \sin 5x + \cdots$ uniformly convergent in $[-1, 1]$?

Here

$$S(x) = \pi/4, \quad 0 < x < \pi,$$
$$S(x) = -\pi/4, \quad -\pi < x < 0.$$

Hence $S(x)$ has a jump discontinuity at $x = 0$, and (by Art. 14.57) the series is not uniformly convergent in any interval containing the origin.

(b) Let us define a series geometrically such that $y = S_n(x)$ is given as shown in Figure 14.9. Is this series uniformly convergent in $(0, 1)$?

Take any point $x = x_0 > 0$. Then

$$S(x_0) = \lim_{n \to \infty} S_n(x_0) = 0.$$

Thus $S(x) = 0$ in $(0, 1)$. But there exists no m independent of x such that

$$|S_n(x)| < \epsilon, \text{ for all } n > m,$$

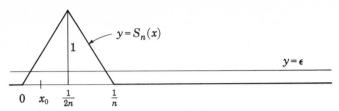

Figure 14.9

for no matter what $\epsilon < 1$ is chosen, there always exists an infinite number of "humps" of $S_n(x)$ above the line $y = \epsilon$. Hence the series does not converge uniformly in $(0, 1)$.

(c) If $S_n(x) = nxe^{-nx^2}$, is the series uniformly convergent in $[0, 1]$? By the ordinary method of differentiation, it is found that the function

$$y = S_n(x) \tag{1}$$

has a maximum of $\sqrt{n/2}\, e^{-1/2}$ at $x = 1/\sqrt{2n}$. Graphing two of the curves (1) for different values of n, we have something like Figure 14.10.

Take any point $x = x_0 \geq 0$. Then we have

$$f(x_0) = \lim_{n \to \infty} S_n(x) = 0.$$

But there exists no m independent of x such that

$$|S_n(x)| < \epsilon, \text{ for all } n > m,$$

for no matter what ϵ is chosen, there always exists an infinite number of "humps" of $S_n(x)$ above the line $y = \epsilon$. Hence the series does not converge uniformly in $[0, 1]$.

The series is uniformly convergent in $[\delta, 1]$, where $0 < \delta < 1$.

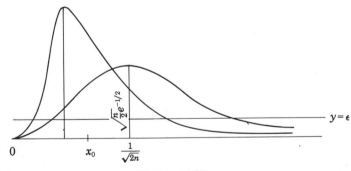

Figure 14.10

14.59. THEOREM. A necessary and sufficient condition for $\sum_0^\infty u_n(x)$ to converge uniformly in a, b is that to an arbitrary $\epsilon > 0$ there correspond an integer m independent of x in a, b such that

$$|u_m(x) + u_{m+1}(x) + \cdots + u_{m+p}(x)| < \epsilon, \quad p = 0, 1, 2, \cdots.$$

Proof: *Necessary:* We are given that

$$|S(x) - S_n(x)| < \epsilon/2, \quad n > n_0, \ n_0 \text{ independent of } x.$$

We wish to prove that

$$|S_{m+p}(x) - S_{m-1}(x)| < \epsilon, \quad p = 0, 1, 2, \cdots.$$

We have

$$|S(x) - S_{m-1}(x)| < \epsilon/2, \quad m \text{ fixed} > n_0 + 1,$$

and

$$|S(x) - S_{m+p}(x)| < \epsilon/2, \quad p = 0, 1, 2, \cdots.$$

Therefore

$$\begin{aligned}
|S_{m+p}(x) - S_{m-1}(x)| &= |S_{m+p}(x) - S(x) + S(x) - S_{m-1}(x)| \\
&\leq |S(x) - S_{m+p}(x)| + |S(x) - S_{m-1}(x)| \\
&< \epsilon, \quad p = 0, 1, 2, \cdots.
\end{aligned}$$

Sufficient: We are given that

$$|S_{m+p}(x) - S_{m-1}(x)| < \epsilon'/2, \quad p = 0, 1, 2, \cdots, m \text{ independent of } x.$$

Hence $S(x) = \lim_{n \to \infty} S_n(x)$ exists (Art. 14.08) for every fixed x and hence for x in general. Take $\epsilon' < \epsilon$. Then

$$|S_{m+p}(x) - S_{m-1}(x)| < \epsilon'/2, \quad m \text{ independent of } x,$$

and

$$|S_{m+q}(x) - S_{m-1}(x)| < \epsilon'/2.$$

Therefore

$$|S_{m+q}(x) - S_{m+p}(x)| < \epsilon'.$$

Now, letting $q \to \infty$, we have

$$|S(x) - S_{m+p}(x)| \leq \epsilon' < \epsilon.$$

Hence the theorem.

14.60. THEOREM.   If each $u_n(x)$ is continuous in a, b and if $S(x)$ is continuous in a, b, then it does *not* necessarily follow that $\sum u_n(x)$ is uniformly convergent in a, b.

Proof: Consider the series

$$(1 - x) + (1 - x)x + (1 - x)x^2 + \cdots, \quad 0 \leq x < 1.$$

Now, certainly, every term of this series is continuous in $[0, 1)$. Also,

$$S(x) = \lim_{n \to \infty} S_n(x) = \lim_{n \to \infty} (1 - x^{n-1}) = 1, \text{ for } 0 \leq x < 1.$$

Hence $S(x)$ is also continuous in $[0, 1)$.

Now suppose the series is uniformly convergent. Then there exists an m independent of x in the interval and such that

$$|S(x) - S_n(x)| = |x^{n-1}| < \tfrac{1}{2}, \text{ for all } n > m.$$

But this is impossible since the value

$$x = \sqrt[m]{\tfrac{1}{2}}$$

will cause the inequality to break down. Hence the series is not uniformly convergent.

14.61. THEOREM.   If $\sum u_n(x)$ converges uniformly in $[a, b]$ to $S(x)$, and if each $u_n(x)$ is continuous in $[a, b]$, then $S(x)$ is continuous in $[a, b]$.

Proof: Since $\sum u_n(x)$ converges uniformly to $f(x)$ in $[a, b]$, then there exists an n_0 such that

$$|S_m(x) - S(x)| < \epsilon/3, \quad m \text{ fixed} > n_0, \text{ for all } x \text{ in } [a, b]. \qquad (1)$$

In particular, the above inequality holds for x_0, x_0 in $[a, b]$. Thus

$$|S_m(x_0) - S(x_0)| < \epsilon/3. \qquad (2)$$

Also, since $u_n(x)$, and hence $S_n(x)$, is continuous at x_0,

$$|S_m(x) - S_m(x_0)| < \epsilon/3, \text{ when } |x - x_0| < \delta. \qquad (3)$$

From inequalities (1), (2), and (3), we obtain

$$|S(x) - S(x_0)| < \epsilon, \quad |x - x_0| < \delta.$$

Hence

$$\lim_{x \to x_0} S(x) = S(x_0),$$

and $S(x)$ is continuous at x_0, any point of $[a, b]$.

14.62 THEOREM. If the sum of a series of functions, each continuous in $[a, b]$, is discontinuous in $[a, b_1]$, then the series is not uniformly convergent in $[a, b]$.

This is an immediate corollary to Article 14.61. The converse of this theorem is not true (see Art. 14.60). Also in connection with this theorem, see the special case of Article 14.57.

14.63. THEOREM. If $u_n(x)$ is continuous in $[a, b]$ for each n, then it does *not* follow that

$$\int_a^b S(x)dx = \sum \int_a^b u_n(x)dx.$$

Proof: Consider the series

$$u_n(x) = (n + 1)xe^{-(n+1)x^2} - nxe^{-nx^2}. \qquad (1)$$

Here $u_n(x)$ is continuous in $[0, 1]$ for each n. Moreover [see Art. 14.58, Example (c)],

$$S(x) = 0.$$

Now,

$$S_n(x) = nxe^{-nx^2}.$$

Hence

$$\begin{aligned}
\sum_1^\infty \int_0^1 u_n(x)dx &= \lim_{n\to\infty} \int_0^1 \sum_1^n u_n(x)dx \\
&= \lim_{n\to\infty} \int_0^1 nxe^{-nx^2}dx \\
&= \lim_{n\to\infty} \left. -\frac{e^{-nx^2}}{2}\right|_0^1 \\
&= \lim_{n\to\infty} \tfrac{1}{2}(1 - e^{-n}) \\
&= \tfrac{1}{2}.
\end{aligned}$$

But

$$\int_0^1 S(x)dx = 0.$$

Note: This theorem is to be expected, for, if it were not true, then

$$\int_a^b S(x)dx = \lim_{n\to\infty} \int_a^b S_n(x)dx$$

$$= \lim_{n \to \infty} \lim_{m \to \infty} \sum_{1}^{m} S_n(x_k) \Delta x_k. \tag{1}$$

But

$$\int_a^b S(x)dx = \lim_{m \to \infty} \sum_{1}^{m} S(x_k) \Delta x_k$$

$$= \lim_{m \to \infty} \lim_{n \to \infty} \sum_{1}^{m} S_n(x_k) \Delta x_k. \tag{2}$$

Now we know that in general the two iterated limits (1) and (2) are not equal.

14.64.   THEOREM.   If $u_n(x)$ is continuous in $[a, b]$ and if $\sum u_n(x)$ converges uniformly in $[a, b]$ to $S(x)$, then $\sum \int_a^b u_n(x)dx$ converges to $\int_a^b S(x)dx$.

Proof: By Article 14.61, $S(x)$ is continuous in $[a, b]$. Hence

$$\int_a^b S(x)dx$$

exists. Now let ϵ be any given positive number and form $\epsilon/(b - a)$. Then, since $\sum u_n(x)$ converges uniformly in $[a, b]$ to $S(x)$, there exists an m independent of x such that

$$|S(x) - S_n(x)| < \epsilon/(b - a), \quad n > m, x \text{ in } [a, b].$$

Hence

$$\left| \int_a^b S(x)dx - \int_a^b S_n(x)dx \right| \leq \int_a^b |S(x) - S_n(x)|dx$$

$$< \frac{\epsilon}{b - a} b - a$$

$$= \epsilon, \quad n > m,$$

and $\sum \int_a^b u_n(x)dx$ converges to $\int_a^b S(x)dx$.

14.65.   THEOREM.   If $S(x) = \sum u_n(x)$, then it does *not* follow that $S'(x) = \sum u_n'(x)$.

Proof: We have [see Art. 14.58, Example (a)]

$$\frac{\pi}{4} = \sin x + \frac{\sin 3x}{3} + \frac{\sin 5x}{5} + \cdots, \quad 0 < x < \pi.$$

Now, differentiating the series, we find

$$\cos x + \cos 3x + \cos 5x + \cdots \neq 0, \text{ for } x = \pi/4.$$

Note: This theorem is to be expected, for, if it were not true, then

$$S'(x) = \lim_{n \to \infty} S'_n(x)$$

$$= \lim_{n \to \infty} \lim_{\Delta x \to 0} \frac{\Delta S_n(x)}{\Delta x}. \tag{1}$$

But

$$S'(x) = \lim_{\Delta x \to 0} \frac{\Delta S(x)}{\Delta x}$$

$$= \lim_{\Delta x \to 0} \lim_{n \to \infty} \frac{\Delta S_n(x)}{\Delta x}. \tag{2}$$

We know that in general the two iterated limits (1) and (2) are not equal.

14.66. THEOREM. If $\sum u_n(x)$ converges uniformly in $[a, b]$, then it does *not* follow that $\sum u'_n(x)$ converges uniformly in $[a, b]$.

Proof: $\sum \sin nx/n^2$ converges uniformly in $-\infty < x < \infty$ [see Art. 14.74(a)]. But $\sum \cos nx/n$ does not converge at $x = 0$.

14.67. THEOREM. If $u_n(x)$ is of class C^1 in $[a, b]$, and if $\sum u'_n(x)$ converges uniformly in $[a, b]$, and if $\sum u_n(x)$ converges to $S(x)$ in $[a, b]$, then $S(x)$ is of class C^1 in $[a, b]$ and $S'(x) = \sum u'_n(x)$ in $[a, b]$.

Proof: Let

$$\varphi(x) = \sum u'_n(x), \quad x \text{ in } [a, b].$$

Applying Article 14.64, we have

$$\int_a^x \varphi(x)dx = \sum \int_a^x u'_n(x)dx$$

$$= \sum \{u_n(x) - u_n(a)\}, \quad x \text{ in } [a, b]. \tag{1}$$

But, by hypothesis,

$$S(a) = \sum u_n(a). \tag{2}$$

Hence, adding (1) and (2), we have

$$\int_a^x \varphi(x)dx + S(a) = \sum u_n(x) = S(x).$$

Differentiating, we have

$$\varphi(x) = S'(x).$$

14.68.   THEOREM.   If $u_n(x)$ is of class C^1 in $[a, b]$, and if $\sum u_n'(x)$ converges uniformly in $[a, b]$ to $S'(x)$, then it does *not* follow that $\sum u_n(x)$ converges to $S(x)$ in $[a, b]$.

Proof: Consider the series

$$\sum (1 + x^n/n!).$$

This series diverges for $x = 0$, for then every term is 1. But the derived series

$$\sum x^{n-1}/(n - 1)!$$

converges uniformly for $|x| < \delta$ [see Art. 14.74(b)]. Moreover, $1 + x^n/n!$ is of class C^1 in any neighborhood of the origin.

Note: Thus we have shown that the third condition of Article 14.67 is necessary to that theorem.

14.69.   THEOREM.   If $\sum u_n(x)$ converges uniformly to $S(x)$ in $[a, b]$, and if $\varphi(x)$ is continuous in $[a, b]$, then the series $\sum u_n(x)\varphi(x)$ converges uniformly in $[a, b]$.

Proof: Since $\varphi(x)$ is continuous in the closed interval $[a, b]$, there exists an M such that

$$|\varphi(x)| < M, \quad x \text{ in } [a, b]. \tag{1}$$

Now let ϵ be an arbitrary positive number. Then, since $\sum u_n(x)$ converges uniformly to $S(x)$ in $[a, b]$, there exists an m independent of x such that, for all x in $[a, b]$,

$$|S(x) - S_n(x)| < \epsilon/M, \quad n > m. \tag{2}$$

Multiplying together inequalities (1) and (2), we have, since all members are positive,

$$\begin{aligned} |\varphi(x)||S(x) - S_n(x)| &= |S(x)\varphi(x) - S_n(x)\varphi(x)| \\ &< \epsilon, \quad n > m, x \text{ in } [a, b]. \end{aligned}$$

Hence $\sum u_n(x)\varphi(x)$ converges uniformly in $[a, b]$.

14.70.   THEOREM.   If $\sum u_n(x)$ converges uniformly in $(0, 1]$ to $S(x)$, and if $u_n(x)$ is continuous in $[0, 1]$ for all n, then $\lim\limits_{x \to 0+} S(x)$ exists.

Proof: Since $\sum u_n(x)$ converges uniformly in $(0, 1]$ to $S(x)$, there exists an n_0 independent of x such that, for all x in $(0, 1]$,

$$|S_m(x) - S(x)| < \epsilon/4, \quad m > n_0.$$

Take $m > n_0$ fixed, and let x' and x'' be two points in $(0, 1]$. Then we have

$$|S_m(x') - S(x')| < \epsilon/4, \qquad (1)$$

$$|S_m(x'') - S(x'')| < \epsilon/4. \qquad (2)$$

Also, since $u_n(x)$ is continuous in $[0, 1]$ for all n, so is $S_n(x)$ continuous in $[0, 1]$ for all n. Hence there exists a δ such that

$$|S_m(0) - S_m(x')| < \epsilon/4, \quad 0 < x' < \delta \leq 1, \qquad (3)$$

$$|S_m(0) - S_m(x'')| < \epsilon/4, \quad 0 < x'' < \delta \leq 1. \qquad (4)$$

From inequalities (1), (2), (3), and (4) we get

$$|S(x'') - S(x')| < \epsilon, \quad 0 < x', x'' < \delta \leq 1.$$

That is,

$$\lim_{\substack{x' \to 0+ \\ x'' \to 0+}} \{S(x'') - S(x')\} = 0.$$

Hence $\lim_{x \to 0+} S(x)$ exists.

14.71. WEIERSTRASS M-TEST. If $M_k, M_{k+1}, \ldots$ exist such that

$$\sum_k^\infty u_n(x) \ll \sum_k^\infty M_n \text{ in } a, b,$$

and if $\sum_k^\infty M_n$ converges, then $\sum u_n(x)$ converges uniformly in a, b.

Proof: Let ϵ be any given positive number. Take m such that

$$|M_m + \cdots + M_{m+p}| < \epsilon, \quad p = 0, 1, 2, \ldots.$$

This can always be done since $\sum M_n$ converges. Certainly the m is independent of x. Hence

$$|u_m(x) + \cdots + u_{m+p}(x)| \leq |u_m(x)| + \cdots + |u_{m+p}(x)|$$
$$\leq |M_m + \cdots + M_{m+p}|$$
$$< \epsilon, \quad p = 0, 1, 2, \cdots, \qquad x \text{ in } a, b.$$

Hence, by Article 14.59, $\sum u_n(x)$ converges uniformly in a, b.

14.72. THEOREM. Any series which converges uniformly by the Weierstrass M-Test also converges absolutely.

Proof: See Article 14.13.

14.73.   THEOREM.   Uniform convergence does not necessitate absolute convergence, nor does absolute convergence necessitate uniform convergence.

Proof: (1) $\sum (-1)^n x^{2n+1}/(2n + 1)$ converges uniformly in $[0, 1]$ [see Art. 14.74(f)] but does not converge absolutely throughout $[0, 1]$, for, setting $x = 1$, we see that $1 + \frac{1}{3} + \frac{1}{5} + \frac{1}{7} + \cdots$ diverges.

(2) $\sum (1 - x)x^n$ converges absolutely in $[0, 1]$ but does not converge uniformly there (see the proof of Art. 14.60).

14.74.   APPLICATIONS OF THE WEIERSTRASS M-TEST.

(a) Show that $\sum \sin nx/n^2$ converges uniformly in $-\infty < x < \infty$.

For

$$\sum \sin nx/n^2 \ll \sum 1/n^2, \quad -\infty < x < \infty,$$

and $\sum 1/n^2$ converges.

(b) Show that $\sum x^n/n!$ converges uniformly in $-\delta \le x \le \delta$.

For

$$\sum x^n/n! \ll \sum \delta^n/n!, \quad -\delta \le x \le \delta,$$

and $\sum \delta^n/n! = e^\delta$.

(c) Is $\sum_0^\infty x^n/n!$ uniformly convergent in $-\infty < x < \infty$?

The series is *not* uniformly convergent in $-\infty < x < \infty$. Suppose it is. Then there exists an m independent of x in the interval such that, for any given $\epsilon > 0$,

$$\left| \frac{x^m}{m!} + \frac{x^{m+1}}{(m + 1)!} + \cdots + \frac{x^{m+p}}{(m + p)!} \right| < \epsilon, \qquad (1)$$

for $p = 0, 1, 2, \cdots$. Now take

$$x > (\epsilon m!)^{1/m}.$$

Then

$$\frac{x^m}{m!} > \epsilon,$$

and (1) fails for this x and $p = 0$. Hence the series does *not* converge uniformly in $-\infty < x < \infty$.

(d) Is $\sum\limits_{1}^{\infty} 2x/(n^2 - x^2)$ uniformly convergent in

$$(1) \quad -\tfrac{1}{2} < x < \tfrac{1}{2},$$
$$(2) \quad -1 < x < 1?$$

(1) Consider the interval $-\delta \leq x \leq \delta$, $(\delta < 1)$. Then in this interval

$$\sum_{1}^{\infty} 2x/(n^2 - x^2) \ll \sum_{1}^{\infty} 2\delta/(n^2 - \delta^2).$$

But the dominant series is convergent since $n^2 - \delta^2$ is an integral expression in n whose degree exceeds that of the numerator by more than 1. Hence, by the Weierstrass M-Test, $\sum\limits_{1}^{\infty} 2x/(n^2 - x^2)$ converges uniformly in $-\delta \leq x \leq \delta$, $(\delta < 1)$, and hence certainly for $-\tfrac{1}{2} < x < \tfrac{1}{2}$.

(2) The series is also uniformly convergent in $-1 < x < 1$. For we have

$$\sum_{1}^{\infty} \frac{2x}{n^2 - x^2} = \frac{2x}{1 - x^2} + \sum_{2}^{\infty} \frac{2x}{n^2 - x^2}.$$

Now,

$$\sum_{2}^{\infty} \frac{2x}{n^2 - x^2} \ll \sum_{2}^{\infty} \frac{2}{n^2 - 1}, \quad -1 < x < 1.$$

But the dominant series converges. Hence the original series converges uniformly (Art. 14.71).

(e) Discuss the uniform convergence of $\sum\limits_{0}^{\infty} x^2/(1 + x^2)^n$.

Consider x such that $0 < e \leq x^2 \leq \delta$. For such x's we have

$$\sum_{0}^{\infty} x^2/(1 + x^2)^n \ll \sum_{0}^{\infty} \delta/(1 + e)^n.$$

But the dominant series, being a geometric series with ratio <1, is convergent. Hence, by the Weierstrass M-Test, the given series converges uniformly for $e \leq x^2 \leq \delta$.

The series also converges uniformly for $0 < e \leq x^2 < \infty$. For let us take $e = 2$, say, and consider $2 \leq x^2 < \infty$. We have

$$\sum \frac{x^2}{(1 + x^2)^n} \ll \sum \frac{x^2}{x^{2n}} = \sum \frac{1}{x^{2n-2}} \ll \sum \frac{1}{2^{2n-2}},$$

which gives a Weierstrass M-series. Also, by the first part, we have uniform convergence for $0 < e \leq x^2 \leq 2$, and so we have uniform convergence for $0 < e \leq x^2 < \infty$.

However, the series is *not* uniformly convergent for $0 < x^2 \leq \delta$. For, since the series is a geometric one, we have

$$S_n(x) = \frac{x^2\left[1 - \dfrac{1}{(1+x^2)^n}\right]}{1 - \dfrac{1}{1+x^2}} = \frac{(1+x^2)^n - 1}{(1+x^2)^{n-1}}.$$

and

$$S(x) = \lim_{n \to \infty} S_n(x) = 1 + x^2.$$

Now suppose the series is uniformly convergent for $0 < x^2 \leq \delta$. Then there exists an m independent of x for $0 < x^2 \leq \delta$ and such that

$$|S(x) - S_n(x)| = \left|1 + x^2 - \frac{(1+x^2)^n - 1}{(1+x^2)^{n-1}}\right|$$

$$= \left|\frac{1}{(1+x^2)^{n-1}}\right|$$

$$< \tfrac{1}{2}, \text{ for } n > m, 0 < x^2 \leq \delta.$$

But this last inequality is not true for all admitted x, for, no matter what m is, we can find an x sufficiently close to 0 such that

$$\left|\frac{1}{(1+x^2)^{n-1}}\right| > \tfrac{1}{2}.$$

Thus the series is *not* uniformly convergent for $0 < x^2 \leq \delta$.

(f) Show that

$$\sum_0^\infty (-1)^n \frac{x^{2n+1}}{2n + 1}$$

converges uniformly in $0 \leq x \leq 1$.

For any point in the interval we have

$$\lim_{n \to \infty} (-1)^n \frac{x^{2n+1}}{2n + 1} = 0.$$

Moreover,

$$\frac{x^{2n+3}}{2n + 3} < \frac{x^{2n+1}}{2n + 1}$$

for all points in the interval. Hence the series is an alternating convergent series in the interval. Suppose, then, that the series converges to $S(x)$ in $0 \leq x \leq 1$. Hence, since the error made by breaking off a convergent alternating series at any term does not exceed numerically the value of the first of the terms discarded, we have

$$|S(x) - S_n(x)| \leq |u_{n+1}(x)|$$

$$= \left| \frac{x^{2n+3}}{2n+3} \right|$$

$$\leq \left| \frac{1}{2n+3} \right|, \quad 0 \leq x \leq 1.$$

But, given any $\epsilon > 0$, we may certainly choose an m independent of x in the interval such that $1/(2n+3) < \epsilon$ for all $n > m$. Thus we have

$$|S(x) - S_n(x)| < \epsilon, \quad \text{all } n > m, 0 \leq x \leq 1.$$

Hence the series is uniformly convergent in this interval.

Note: Since changing x to $-x$ only multiplies the series by -1, we have that the series converges uniformly in $-1 \leq x \leq 1$.

We may readily show by a Weierstrass M-Test that the series is uniformly convergent in $-1 \leq x \leq 1$. For in this interval

$$\sum_0^\infty (-1)^n \frac{x^{2n+1}}{2n+1} \ll \sum_0^\infty \frac{1}{2n+1},$$

and this dominant series is convergent.

(g) Show that

$$\log \left(\frac{1}{1-x_0} \right) = \sum_1^\infty \frac{x_0^n}{n}, \quad |x_0| < 1.$$

For

$$\sum x^n \ll \sum |x_0|^n, \quad |x| \leq |x_0| < 1.$$

Hence, by the Weierstrass M-Test, $\sum x^n$ converges uniformly to $1/(1-x)$ for $|x| \leq |x_0|$. Then, by Article 14.64 (integrating from 0 to x_0), we have

$$\log \left(\frac{1}{1-x_0} \right) = \sum_0^\infty \frac{x_0^{n+1}}{n+1} = \sum_1^\infty \frac{x_0^n}{n}, \quad |x_0| < 1.$$

UNIFORM CONVERGENCE OF COMPLEX SERIES

14.75. DEFINITION. The series $\sum u_n(x, y)$ *converges uniformly* to $S(x, y)$ in a region R if to an arbitrary $\epsilon > 0$ there corresponds an integer m *independent of* (x, y) *in R* such that, for all $n > m$,

$$|S(x, y) - S_n(x, y)| < \epsilon, \text{ for all } (x, y) \text{ in } R.$$

14.76. DEFINITION. The complex series $\sum u_n(z)$ *converges uniformly* to $S(z)$ in a region R if to an arbitrary $\epsilon > 0$ there corresponds an integer m *independent of z in R* such that, for all $n > m$,

$$|S(z) - S_n(z)| < \epsilon, \text{ for all } z \text{ in } R.$$

14.77. DEFINITION. The complex series $\sum u_n(z)$ *converges uniformly* to $S(z)$ along a curve C if to an arbitrary $\epsilon > 0$ there corresponds an integer m *independent of z on C* such that, for all $n > m$,

$$|S(z) - S_n(z)| < \epsilon, \text{ for all } z \text{ on } C.$$

14.78. THEOREM. A necessary and sufficient condition for $\sum u_n(z)$ to converge uniformly in R (or on C) is that to an arbitrary $\epsilon > 0$ there correspond an integer m independent of z in R (or on C) such that

$$|u_m(z) + \cdots + u_{m+p}(z)| < \epsilon, \quad p = 0, 1, 2, \cdots.$$

Proof: The proof is analogous to that of Article 14.59.

14.79. THEOREM. If $\sum u_n(z)$ converges uniformly to $S(z)$ in R (or on C), and if $u_n(z)$ is continuous in R (or on C), then $S(z)$ is continuous in R (or on C).

Proof: The proof is analogous to that of Article 14.61.

14.80. THEOREM. If $u_n(z)$ is continuous on a regular curve C, and if $\sum u_n(z)$ converges uniformly on C to $S(z)$, then $\sum \int_C u_n(z)dz$ converges to $\int_C S(z)dz$.

Proof: The proof is analogous to that of Article 14.64.

14.81. THEOREM (WEIERSTRASS M-TEST). If $M_k, M_{k+1}, \cdots$ exist such that

$$\sum_k^\infty u_n(z) \ll \sum_h^\infty M_n \text{ in } R \text{ (or on } C),$$

and if $\sum_k^\infty M_n$ converges, then $\sum u_n(z)$ converges uniformly and absolutely in R (or on C).

Proof: The proof is analogous to that of Article 14.71.

14.82. THEOREM. If $u_n(z)$ is analytic in a simply connected domain D, and if $\sum u_n(z)$ converges uniformly to $S(z)$ in every closed circular region contained in D, then $S(z)$ is analytic in D.

Proof: As shown in Figure 14.11, let γ be any circle in D and let C be any regular closed curve in γ. By Article 14.79, $S(z)$ is continuous in γ. Then, by Article 14.80,

$$\int_C S(z)dz = \sum \int_C u_n(z)dz. \tag{1}$$

But, by Cauchy's Theorem (Art. 11.10, Vol. I), the right member of (1) is zero. Hence

$$\int_C S(z)dz = 0.$$

Hence, by Morera's Theorem (Art. 11.34, Vol. I), $S(z)$ is analytic in γ, and hence at its center z_0. But z_0 is any point of D. Hence the theorem.

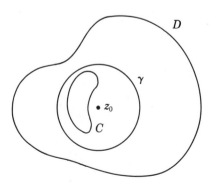

Figure 14.11

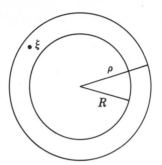

Figure 14.12

14.83. THEOREM. If $\sum a_n z^n$ has a radius of convergence $\rho > 0$ (or $= \infty$), then $\sum a_n z^n$ converges uniformly in $|z| \leq R$, $R < \rho$ (or $R < \infty$).

Proof: As shown in Figure 14.12, take ξ any point between the circles $|z| = \rho$ and $|z| = R$. Then, by (A) of Article 14.18,

$$|a_n| < N/|\xi|^n, \text{ for all } n.$$

Hence

$$\sum a_n z^n \ll \sum \frac{N}{|\xi|^n} R^n, \quad |z| \leq R.$$

But the dominant series converges (since it is geometric with common ratio $R/|\xi| < 1$). Hence, by the Weierstrass M-Test, $\sum a_n z^n$ converges uniformly for $|z| \leq R$.

Note: This theorem is not necessarily true for $|z| < \rho$. For consider the series

$$\frac{1}{1-z} = \sum z^n, \quad |z| < 1. \tag{1}$$

Here $\rho = 1$. Now, if the theorem is true for $|z| < \rho = 1$, then there exists an m such that, for $\epsilon > 0$,

$$\left| \frac{1}{1-z} - \frac{1-z^n}{1-z} \right| = \frac{|z|^n}{|1-z|} < \epsilon, \quad \text{for all } n > m \text{ and all } |z| < 1.$$

But this is not true, since, for any n, $|z|^n/|1 - z|$ may be made as large as we choose by taking $|z|$ sufficiently near to 1. Hence the series (1) does not converge uniformly in the open circular region $|z| < \rho = 1$.

14.84. THEOREM.   If $\sum a_n z^n$ converges absolutely at a single point z_0 on its circle of convergence, then it converges absolutely and uniformly on its circle of convergence.

Proof: We have $|z_0| = \rho$. Hence we have, for $|z| = \rho$,

$$\sum a_n a^n \ll \sum |a_n| |z_0|^n = \sum |a_n| \rho^n, \quad |z| = \rho.$$

But the dominant series converges. Hence $\sum a_n z^n$, by the Weierstrass M-Test, converges absolutely and uniformly on the circle of convergence.

14.85. THEOREM.   The sum of a convergent power series is an analytic function inside the circle of convergence.

Proof: $a_n z^n$ is analytic inside the circle of convergence and, by Article 14.83, $\sum a_n z^n$ converges uniformly inside and on every circle lying within the open circle of convergence. Hence the conditions of Article 14.82 hold, and $\sum a_n z^n$ is analytic inside the circle of convergence.

14.86. THEOREM.   If $\sum a_n z^n$ has a radius of convergence ρ, and converges to $S(z)$, then

$$\int_{\substack{0 \\ C}}^{z} S(z)dz = \sum \frac{a_n z^{n+1}}{n+1}, \quad |z| < \rho,$$

where C is any regular curve inside the circle $|z| < \rho$.

Proof: $a_n z^n$ is certainly continuous on C, and, by Article 14.83, $\sum a_n z^n$ converges uniformly on C to $S(z)$. Hence the conditions of Article 14.80 hold, and

$$\sum \int_{\substack{0 \\ C}}^{z} a_n z^n dz = \sum \frac{a_n z^{n+1}}{n+1}$$

converges to $\int_{\substack{0 \\ C}}^{z} S(z)dz$ for $|z| < \rho$.

14.87. THEOREM.   If $u_n(z)$ is analytic in a domain D for all n, and if $\sum u_n(z)$ converges uniformly to $f(z)$ in every closed circular region R inside D, then

$$f^{(k)}(z) = \sum u_n^{(k)}(z) \text{ in } D, \quad k = 0, 1, 2, \cdots.$$

Proof: As shown in Figure 14.13, let z_0 be any fixed point in D. Draw circle γ in D with z_0 as center. Consider the series $\sum u_n(t)$, where

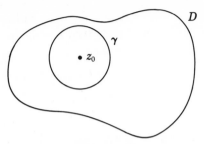

Figure 14.13

t is on γ. Then, by the hypothesis, $\sum u_n(t)$ converges uniformly to $f(t)$ on γ. Hence

$$\frac{k!}{2\pi i}\frac{f(t)}{(t-z_0)^{k+1}} = \sum \frac{k!}{2\pi i}\frac{u_n(t)}{(t-z_0)^{k+1}}, \tag{1}$$

and the convergence is uniform (for $1/(t-z_0)^{k+1}$ is continuous along the closed path γ; hence we may apply a theorem analogous to Article 14.69). Therefore, integrating in the positive sense about γ, we have [by Cauchy's integral formula (Art. 11.26, Vol. I)]

$$f^{(k)}(z_0) = \sum u_n^{(k)}(z_0).$$

Note: This proves that $f(z)$ is analytic in D.

14.88. THEOREM. If $f(z) = \sum_{0}^{\infty} a_n z^n$ has a radius of convergence ρ, then $f'(z) = \sum_{0}^{\infty} a_n n z^{n-1}$ has a radius of convergence ρ.

Proof: By Articles 14.86 and 14.87.

14.89. THEOREM. Every convergent power series is the Taylor's series of some analytic function.

Proof: Let

$$f(z) = \sum_{0}^{\infty} a_n(z-a)^n.$$

Then, by Article 14.88,

$$f^{(k)}(z) = \sum_{k}^{\infty} a_n n(n-1)\cdots(n-k+1)(z-a)^{n-k} = a_k k! + P,$$

where P contains the factor $(z-a)$. Hence

$$f^{(k)}(a) = a_k k!,$$

or

$$a_k = f^{(k)}(a)/k!.$$

Hence

$$f(z) = \sum_0^\infty a_n(z - a)^n = \sum_0^\infty \frac{f^{(n)}(a)}{n!}(z - a)^n,$$

the Taylor's series of $f(z)$ at $z = a$.

ABEL'S THEOREM

14.90. ABEL'S LEMMA. If $a_0, a_1, \cdots, a_n$ are *complex* numbers such that $|S_k| < M$, $(k = 0, 1, 2, \cdots, n$, and $S_k = a_0 + a_1 + \cdots + a_k)$, and if $b_0, b_1, \cdots, b_n$ are *real* numbers such that $b_0 \leq b_1 \leq \cdots \leq b_n \leq 0$, then

$$|a_0b_0 + a_1b_1 + \cdots + a_nb_n| < Mb_0.$$

Proof: We have

$$a_0 = S_0, \quad a_k = S_k - S_{k-1}, \quad k = 1, 2, 3, \cdots, n.$$

Therefore

$$|a_0b_0 + a_1b_1 + a_2b_2 + \cdots + a_{n-1}b_{n-1} + a_nb_n|$$
$$= |S_0b_0 + (S_1 - S_0)b_1 + (S_2 - S_1)b_2 + \cdots$$
$$\quad + (S_{n-1} - S_{n-2})b_{n-1} + (S_n - S_{n-1})b_n|$$
$$= |S_0(b_0 - b_1) + S_1(b_1 - b_2) + \cdots + S_{n-1}(b_{n-1} - b_n) + S_nb_n|$$
$$\leqq |S_0|(b_0 - b_1) + |S_1|(b_1 - b_2) + \cdots + |S_{n-1}|(b_{n-1} - b_n) + |S_n|b_n$$
$$< M(b_0 - b_1 + b_1 - b_2 + \cdots + b_{n-1} - b_n + b_n)$$
$$= Mb_0.$$

14.91. ABEL'S THEOREM. If $f(z) = \sum a_nz^n$ has a radius of convergence $\rho > 0$, and if $\sum a_nz_0{}^n$, where $|z_0| = \rho$, converges to S, then $\lim_{z \to z_0} f(z) = S$ if the approach is along the radius through z_0.

Proof: Consider the transformation $w = z/z_0$. Let $z = r \operatorname{cis} \theta$. Then for any point z on the radius through z_0 we have

$$w = \frac{r \operatorname{cis} \theta}{r_0 \operatorname{cis} \theta} = \frac{r}{r_0},$$

whence w lies on the positive real axis. Moreover, we see that $z = 0$ goes into $w = 0$, and $z = z_0$ into $w = 1$. Hence (see Figure 14.14),

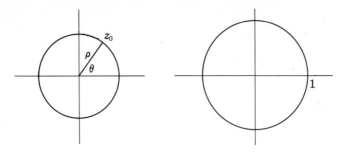

Figure 14.14

under our transformation, the circle of convergence goes into the unit circle, the radius in question falling on the positive x-axis. Our problem is therefore reduced to

> *Given:* $f(z) = \sum a_n z^n$, $\rho = 1$, $S = \sum a_n$.
>
> *Prove:* $\lim\limits_{x \to 1-} f(x) = S$.

Let $\epsilon > 0$ be given. Then, since $\sum a_n$ converges, there exists an m such that

$$|a_m + \cdots + a_{m+p}| < \epsilon, \quad p = 0, 1, 2, \cdots.$$

Letting p take on the specific values $0, 1, 2, \cdots$, we get

$$|a_m| < \epsilon$$
$$|a_m + a_{m+1}| < \epsilon$$
$$\cdots \cdots \cdots \cdots$$
$$|a_m + \cdots + a_{m+p}| < \epsilon.$$

Also, since $0 \leq x \leq 1$,

$$x^m \geq x^{m+1} \geq \cdots \geq x^{m+p} \geq 0.$$

Hence, applying Abel's Lemma (Art. 14.90), we have

$$|a_m x^m + a_{m+1} x^{m+1} + \cdots + a_{m+p} x^{m+p}| < x^m \epsilon \leq \epsilon,$$

for x in $[0, 1]$. Hence (by Art. 14.59) $\sum a_n x^n$ converges uniformly in $[0, 1]$ to $f(x)$. But each $a_n x^n$ is continuous in $[0, 1]$. Thus $f(x)$ is also continuous in $[0, 1]$ (by Art. 14.61). Hence

$$\lim_{x \to 1-} f(x) = f(1) = \sum a_n = S.$$

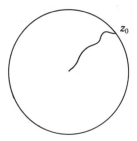

Figure 14.15

Note: There is a generalization of this theorem, due to O. Stolz, which states that the approach to the point on the circumference may be along any curve which is not tangent to the circumference (see Figure 14.15).

14.92. APPLICATIONS OF ABEL'S THEOREM. (a) We know that

$$\ln(1 + x) = x - \frac{x^2}{2} + \frac{x^3}{3} - \cdots, \quad |x| < 1.$$

Setting $x = 1$, we have $1 - \frac{1}{2} + \frac{1}{3} - \cdots$, an alternating series whose terms numerically decrease and approach the limit 0. Hence this series converges. Therefore, by Abel's Theorem,

$$\ln 2 = \lim_{x \to 1-} \ln(1 + x) = 1 - \tfrac{1}{2} + \tfrac{1}{3} - \cdots.$$

(b) We know that

$$\tan^{-1}x = x - \frac{x^3}{3} + \frac{x^5}{5} - \cdots, \quad |x| < 1.$$

Setting $x = 1$, we have

$$1 - \tfrac{1}{3} + \tfrac{1}{5} - \cdots,$$

which converges. Hence, by Abel's Theorem,

$$\pi/4 = \tan^{-1}1 = \lim_{x \to 1-} \tan^{-1}x = 1 - \tfrac{1}{3} + \tfrac{1}{5} - \cdots.$$

(c) *The converse of Abel's Theorem is not necessarily true.* For consider

$$f(x) = 1/(1 + x) = 1 - x + x^2 - \cdots, \quad |x| < 1.$$

Here $\lim\limits_{x\to 1-} f(x) = \tfrac{1}{2}$. But putting $x = 1$ in the series, we get

$$1 - 1 + 1 - 1 + \cdots,$$

a divergent series.

14.93. TAUBER'S THEOREM (A LIMITED CONVERSE OF ABEL'S THEOREM). If $a_n \geq 0$, $(n = 0, 1, 2, \cdots)$, and if $f(x) = \sum\limits_{0}^{\infty} a_n x^n$ for $|x| < 1$, and if $\lim\limits_{x\to 1-} f(x) = S$, then $\sum a_n$ converges to S.

Proof: We are given

$$f(x) = \lim\limits_{n\to\infty} \sum\limits_{0}^{n} a_n x^n, \quad |x| < 1.$$

Therefore, since the series is an increasing one,

$$\sum\limits_{0}^{m} a_n x^n \leq f(x), \quad 0 \leq x < 1.$$

Taking the limit as $x \to 1-$, we then have

$$\sum\limits_{0}^{m} a_n \leq S.$$

Hence $\sum a_n$, being a positive series, must converge to a limit less than or equal to S. By Abel's Theorem, the limit is actually S.

Note: There is a generalization of this theorem, due to Hardy and Littlewood, which states the theorem to be true when

$$-\frac{K}{n} \leq a_n, \quad n = 0, 1, 2, \cdots, K \text{ fixed.}$$

DOUBLE SERIES

14.94. DEFINITIONS. The infinite array

$$
\begin{array}{llll}
a_{00} + & a_{01} + & a_{02} + & \cdots \\
+\, a_{10} + & a_{11} + & a_{12} + & \cdots \\
+\, a_{20} + & a_{21} + & a_{22} + & \cdots \\
+\, \cdot\ \cdot & \cdot\ \cdot & \cdot\ \cdot & \cdot\ \cdot
\end{array}
$$

is known as a *double series* and is denoted by

$$\sum\limits_{m=0}^{\infty} \sum\limits_{n=0}^{\infty} a_{mn}.$$

The series

$$a_{00} + a_{01} + a_{10} + a_{02} + a_{11} + a_{20} + \cdots,$$

indicated by the arrows above, is known as the *diagonal series* of the double series.

a_{mn} NONNEGATIVE

14.95. DEFINITION.   The double series $\sum \sum a_{mn}, (a_{mn} \geqq 0)$, *converges* if one (and hence every) simple series made up of all the terms of the double series converges. The sum of this simple series is defined as the *sum* of the double series.

Note: The "and hence every" is justified by the fact that if a simple series of nonnegative numbers converges, then the series formed by any rearrangement of it also converges to the same limit. In fact, any absolutely convergent series has a sum independent of the order of its terms.

14.96. THEOREM.   If $\sum \sum a_{mn}, (a_{mn} \geq 0)$, converges to S, then

$$S = \sum_{m=0}^{\infty} \sum_{n=0}^{\infty} a_{mn} = \sum_{n=0}^{\infty} \sum_{m=0}^{\infty} a_{mn}.$$

Proof: (1) Let the diagonal series of the double series be denoted by

$$a_0 + a_1 + a_2 + \cdots = S. \tag{1}$$

Now consider the kth row of the double series, and let

$$S_n = a_{k0} + a_{k1} + \cdots + a_{kn}.$$

Then certainly

$$S_n \leq S, \text{ for all } n,$$

since every term of the kth row is contained in the simple series (1). Hence the kth row, being a series of nonnegative terms, must converge to some $A_k \leq S$.

(2) Now form the sum

$$(a_{00} + a_{01} + \cdots + a_{0n}) + (a_{10} + a_{11} + \cdots + a_{1n})$$
$$+ \cdots + (a_{k0} + a_{k1} + \cdots + a_{kn}) \leq S.$$

Let $n \to \infty$. Then, by part (1),

$$A_0 + A_1 + \cdots + A_k \leq S, \text{ for all } k.$$

Hence, this being a series of nonnegative terms, we certainly have

$$\sum_0^{\infty} A_n = S_N \leq S.$$

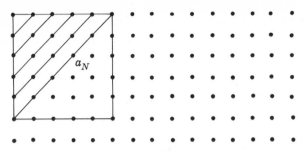

Figure 14.16

(3) Let us be given any $\epsilon > 0$. Then we may choose an N such that

$$S - \epsilon < a_0 + a_1 + \cdots + a_N. \qquad (2)$$

Let us mark these terms in the double series and then complete the diagonal on which a_N is found (see Figure 14.16), and consider the square array having this last diagonal as a diagonal. Let this square have $k + 1$ columns and $k + 1$ rows. Then, since $a_{mn} \geq 0$ and because of (2), we have

$$S - \epsilon < (a_{00} + a_{01} + \cdots + a_{0k}) + (a_{10} + a_{11} + \cdots + a_{1k}) + \cdots$$
$$+ (a_{k0} + a_{k1} + \cdots + a_{kk}) + (\quad) + \cdots.$$

Now let $k \to \infty$. Then, by parts (1) and (2), we have

$$S - \epsilon < S_N.$$

But $\epsilon > 0$ was arbitrary. Therefore $S_N = S$. That is,

$$\sum_{m=0}^{\infty} \sum_{n=0}^{\infty} a_{mn} = S.$$

(4) By reversing the rows and columns and proceeding exactly as above, we may show that

$$\sum_{n=0}^{\infty} \sum_{m=0}^{\infty} a_{mn} = S.$$

Hence the theorem.

14.97.   THEOREM.   If $a_{mn} \geq 0$ and if $\displaystyle\sum_{m=0}^{\infty} \sum_{n=0}^{\infty} a_{mn}$ converges, then the double series converges and we may (by Art. 14.96) interchange the order of summation.

Proof: By hypothesis, we have

$$A_k = \sum_{n=0}^{\infty} a_{kn}, \quad S = \sum_{k=0}^{\infty} A_k.$$

Now let the diagonal series of the double series be

$$a_0 + a_1 + a_2 + \cdots.$$

Suppose

$$a_0 + a_1 + a_2 + \cdots + a_N \tag{1}$$

involves $k + 1$ rows and $k + 1$ columns. Then

$$a_0 + a_1 + \cdots + a_N \le (a_{00} + \cdots + a_{0k}) + \cdots + (a_{k0} + \cdots + a_{kk})$$
$$\le A_0 + A_1 + \cdots + A_k$$
$$\le S.$$

Hence the sum of the diagonal series is less than or equal to S. But it cannot be less than S, for it contains all the terms whose sum is S. Hence the sum of the diagonal series is S, and the theorem is proved.

Note: This is known as the *iterated sum* test.

14.98. THEOREM.   If each row and each column of a double series converge, then it does *not* follow that the double series converges.

Proof: Consider

$$1 + 0 + 0 + 0 + \cdots$$
$$+ 0 + 1 + 0 + 0 + \cdots$$
$$+ 0 + 0 + 1 + 0 + \cdots$$
$$\cdot \ \cdot \ \cdot \ \cdot \ \cdot \ \cdot \ \cdot \ \cdot \ \cdot \ \cdot,$$

a_{mn} COMPLEX

14.99. DEFINITION.   If $|a_{mn}| \le b_{mn}$, then $\sum \sum b_{mn}$ is said to *dominate* $\sum \sum a_{mn}$, and we write

$$\sum \sum a_{mn} \ll \sum \sum b_{mn}.$$

14.100. DEFINITION. $\sum \sum a_{mn}$ *converges absolutely* if $\sum \sum |a_{mn}|$ converges.

14.101. THEOREM.   If $\sum \sum a_{mn}$ converges absolutely, then all simple series of $\sum \sum a_{mn}$ converge to the same sum S.

Proof: Let $\sum a_n$ be any simple series of $\sum \sum a_{mn}$. Since $\sum \sum |a_{mn}|$ converges, so does $\sum |a_n|$. Thus $\sum a_n$ converges, to S, say. Let $\sum b_n$ be any other simple series of $\sum \sum a_{mn}$. Then $\sum b_n$ is merely a rearrangement of $\sum a_n$, which is absolutely convergent. Thus $\sum b_n$ also converges to S. Hence the theorem.

14.102. DEFINITION. The sum S of Article 14.101 is defined as the *sum* of $\sum \sum a_{mn}$.

14.103. THEOREM. If $\sum \sum a_{mn} \ll \sum \sum b_{mn}$ and if $\sum \sum b_{mn}$ converges, then $\sum \sum a_{mn}$ converges.

Proof: Take any simple series $\sum a_n$ of $\sum \sum a_{mn}$. Then $\sum a_n \ll \sum b_n$. But $\sum b_n$ converges. Therefore $\sum |a_n|$ converges. Thus $\sum \sum |a_{mn}|$ converges. Hence (Art. 14.102) $\sum \sum a_{mn}$ converges.

Note: This is known as the *comparison* test.

14.104. THEOREM. If $\sum \sum a_{mn}$ converges absolutely, then

$$\sum \sum a_{mn} = \sum_{m=0}^{\infty} \sum_{n=0}^{\infty} a_{mn} = \sum_{n=0}^{\infty} \sum_{m=0}^{\infty} a_{mn}.$$

Proof: We have

$$a_{mn} = |a_{mn}| - \{|a_{mn}| - a_{mn}\}. \tag{1}$$

Also,

$$\sum \sum \{|a_{mn}| - a_{mn}\} \ll \sum \sum 2|a_{mn}|.$$

But the dominant series converges, by hypothesis. Hence (Art. 14.103) $\sum \sum \{|a_{mn}| - a_{mn}\}$ converges. Let $\sum a_n$ be any simple series of $\sum \sum a_{mn}$. Now

$$a_n = |a_n| - \{|a_n| - a_n\},$$

whence

$$S = \sum a_n = \sum |a_n| - \sum \{|a_n| - a_n\}. \tag{2}$$

Hence, from (2), writing the convergent series on the right of (2) in iterated form (which may be done since the nonnegative double series $\sum \sum |a_{mn}|$ and $\sum \sum \{|a_{mn}| - a_{mn}\}$ converge), we have

$$\sum \sum a_{mn} = \sum_{m=0}^{\infty} \sum_{n=0}^{\infty} |a_{mn}| - \sum_{m=0}^{\infty} \sum_{n=0}^{\infty} \{|a_{mn}| - a_{mn}\}$$

$$\sum_{m=0}^{\infty} \left[\sum_{n=0}^{\infty} |a_{mn}| - \sum_{n=0}^{\infty} \{|a_{mn}| - a_{mn}\} \right] \tag{3}$$

$$= \sum_{m=0}^{\infty} \sum_{n=0}^{\infty} a_{mn}.$$

Similarly, we may show that

$$\sum \sum a_{mn} = \sum_{n=0}^{\infty} \sum_{m=0}^{\infty} a_{mn}.$$

Hence the theorem.

Note: In (3) we have used the fact that the limit of a sum is the sum of the limits.

14.105. NOTES. (a) The absolute convergence of the rows and the absolute convergence of the sums of the rows are *not* sufficient to insure absolute convergence of the double series.
Consider

$$
\begin{array}{ll}
0 & 1 - 1 + 0 + 0 + \cdots \\
0 & 1 - 1 + 0 + 0 + \cdots \\
0 & 1 - 1 + 0 + 0 + \cdots
\end{array}
$$

$$\cdots \cdots \cdots \cdots \cdots .$$

(b) The absolute convergence of the rows and of the columns is *not* sufficient to insure absolute convergence of the double series.
Consider

$$
\begin{array}{l}
0 + 1 + 0 + 0 + 0 + \cdots \\
-1 + 0 + 1 + 0 + 0 + \cdots \\
0 - 1 + 0 + 1 + 0 + \cdots \\
0 + 0 - 1 + 0 + 1 + \cdots
\end{array}
$$

$$\cdots \cdots \cdots \cdots \cdots \cdots$$

14.106. THEOREM. The complex series $\sum \sum a_{mn}$ converges absolutely if and only if

$$\sum \sum a'_{mn} \quad \text{and} \quad \sum \sum a''_{mn},$$

where $a_{mn} = a'_{mn} + i a''_{mn}$, converge absolutely, and $\sum \sum a_{mn} = A = A' + iA''$, where

$$\sum \sum a'_{mn} = A' \quad \text{and} \quad \sum \sum a''_{mn} = A''.$$

MULTIPLICATION OF SERIES

14.107.   THEOREM.   If $A = \sum_0^\infty a_n$ and $B = \sum_0^\infty b_n$, the series converging absolutely, then

$$AB = \quad a_0b_0 + a_0b_1 + a_0b_2 + \cdots$$
$$+ a_1b_0 + a_1b_1 + a_1b_2 + \cdots$$
$$\cdot \ \cdot \ \cdot \ \cdot \ \cdot \ \cdot \ \cdot \ \cdot \ \cdot \ \cdot \ \cdot \qquad (1)$$
$$+ a_nb_0 + a_nb_1 + a_nb_2 + \cdots$$
$$\cdot \ \cdot \ \cdot \ \cdot \ \cdot \ \cdot \ \cdot \ \cdot \ \cdot \ \cdot \ \cdot.$$

Proof: First of all, the double series (1) converges absolutely, for

$$|a_nb_0| + |a_nb_1| + |a_nb_2| + \cdots \to |a_n|K, \qquad (2)$$

where

$$K = |b_0| + |b_1| + |b_2| + \cdots,$$

which exists by hypothesis. Hence, summing these sums (2), we have

$$\sum |a_n|K = KL,$$

where

$$L = |a_0| + |a_1| + |a_2| + \cdots,$$

which exists by hypothesis. Thus the absolute double series of (1) converges, by Article 14.97. The series (1) itself, then, converges absolutely.

Hence (Art. 14.104) the double series (1) is equal to its sum by rows, or to

$$\sum_{k=0}^\infty \sum_{n=0}^\infty a_kb_n = \sum_{k=0}^\infty a_kB = AB.$$

Note: Thus two absolutely convergent complex series may be multiplied as if the series were infinite polynomials, for writing (1) out by its diagonal series, we have

$$AB = a_0b_0 + (a_0b_1 + a_1b_0) + (a_0b_2 + a_1b_1 + a_2b_0) + \cdots$$
$$+ (a_0b_n + a_1b_{n-1} + \cdots + a_nb_0) + \cdots. \qquad (3)$$

14.108.   DEFINITION.   If we are given two finite sequences $\{A_n\}$ and $\{B_n\}$, then

$$A_0B_n + A_1B_{n-1} + A_2B_{n-2} + \cdots + A_nB_0$$

is known as the *faltung* of $\{A_n\}$ and $\{B_n\}$.

14.109. THEOREM. If

$$f(z) = \sum_{}^{\infty} A_n z^n, \quad |z| < \rho,$$

$$\varphi(z) = \sum_{}^{\infty} B_n z^n, \quad |z| < \rho,$$

then

$$f(z)\varphi(z) = \sum_{}^{\infty} C_n z^n, \quad |z| < \rho,$$

where C_n is the faltung of $\{A_n\}$ and $\{B_n\}$.

Proof: This theorem is an immediate corollary to (3) of Article 14.107 (see Art. 14.18).

14.110. THEOREM. If

$$\sum A_n \text{ converges to } A,$$
$$\sum B_n \text{ converges to } B,$$
$$\sum C_n \text{ converges to } C,$$

where C_n is the faltung of $\{A_n\}$ and $\{B_n\}$, then

$$C = AB.$$

Proof: Set up the power series

$$f(z) = \sum A_n z^n.$$

This series then converges absolutely for $|z| < 1$. Similarly,

$$\varphi(z) = \sum B_n z^n \quad \text{and} \quad \psi(z) = \sum C_n z^n$$

converge absolutely for $|z| < 1$. Hence, by Article 14.109,

$$f(z)\varphi(z) = \varphi(z), \quad |z| < 1. \tag{1}$$

Now, applying Abel's Theorem (Art. 14.91), we have

$$\lim_{x \to 1-} f(x) = A, \quad \lim_{x \to 1-} \varphi(x) = B, \quad \lim_{x \to 1-} \psi(x) = C.$$

Hence, by (1),

$$\lim_{x \to 1-} \{f(x)\varphi(x)\} = \lim_{x \to 1-} \varphi(x),$$

or

$$AB = C.$$

CHAPTER 15

Analytic Continuation

GENERAL

15.01. DEFINITION. Given $f_1(z)$ analytic in a domain D_1, $f_2(z)$ analytic in a domain D_2, D_1 and D_2 having a common part $D_1D_2 \neq 0$, D_2 and containing a neighborhood N in which $f_1 \equiv f_2$. Then f_2 is called an *analytic continuation* of f_1.* (See Figure 15.1.)

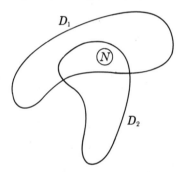

Figure 15.1

Note: By virtue of Article 11.52, Vol. I, $f_1 \equiv f_2$ in any simply connected portion of D_1D_2 which contains neighborhood N.

15.02. THEOREM. If f is analytic in D, and if f_1, f_2 are analytic continuations of f, both analytic in a domain D_3 which overlaps D, then $f_1 \equiv f_2$ in D_3. (See Figure 15.2.)

Proof: By definition,

$$f_1 \equiv f \text{ in } DD_1,$$
$$f_2 \equiv f \text{ in } DD_2.$$

* It is more common today to write $D_1 \cap D_2$ for D_1D_2, and to denote the null set by $\varnothing$ instead of by 0.

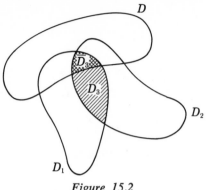

Figure 15.2

Hence

$$f_1 \equiv f_2 \text{ in } (DD_1)(DD_2) = \bar{D}_3.$$

Therefore, by Article 11.52, Vol. I,

$$f_1 \equiv f_2 \text{ in } D_3.$$

Note: This, of course, does not include the domain R in, say, Figure 15.3. That is, R is not a part of D_3.

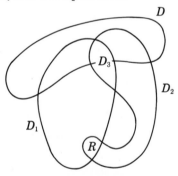

Figure 15.3

STANDARD METHOD OF CONTINUATION

15.03. PRELIMINARY.   By Article 11.48, Vol. I, any function $f(z)$ analytic at $z = a$ can be represented in some circle $|z - a| < r$ by its Taylor's expansion about $z = a$. Conversely, by Articles 14.85 and 14.89, any convergent power series is the Taylor series of some function analytic in the circle of convergence.

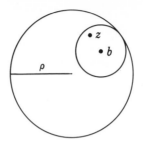

Figure 15.4

15.04. THEOREM. If $f(z) = \sum\limits_{0}^{\infty} A_n z^n$ for $|z| < \rho, (\rho > 0)$, and if $0 < |b| < \rho$, then

$$f(z) = \sum_{0}^{\infty} B_n(z - b)^n \text{ for } |z - b| < \rho - |b|,$$

and

$$B_k = \sum_{k}^{\infty} \binom{n}{k} A_n b^{n-k}.$$

Proof: As shown in Figure 15.4, take any point z inside the circle $|z - b| < \rho - |b|$, and set $h = z - b$. Then $|h| = |z - b|$. Now, by hypothesis,

$$f(z) = f(b + h) = \sum A_n(b + h)^n.$$

Writing this out as a double series, we have

$$A_0$$

$$A_1 \binom{1}{0} b + A_1 \binom{1}{1} h$$

$$A_2 \binom{2}{0} b^2 + A_2 \binom{2}{1} bh + A_2 \binom{2}{2} h^2 \qquad (1)$$

$$\cdot \quad \cdot \quad \cdot \quad \cdot \quad \cdot \quad \cdot \quad \cdot \quad \cdot \quad \cdot \quad \cdot \quad \cdot \quad \cdot$$

$$A_n \binom{n}{0} b^n + A_n \binom{n}{1} b^{n-1}h + \cdots + A_n \binom{n}{n} h^n$$

$$\cdot \quad \cdot \quad \cdot \quad \cdot \quad \cdot \quad \cdot \quad \cdot \quad \cdot \quad \cdot \quad \cdot \quad \cdot \quad \cdot$$

Let us sum the columns of this double series, calling the coefficient of h^k, B_k. Then

$$B_0 = \sum_0^\infty A_n \binom{n}{0} b^n$$

$$B_1 = \sum_1^\infty A_n \binom{n}{1} b^{n-1} \tag{2}$$

$$\cdot \quad \cdot \quad \cdot \quad \cdot \quad \cdot \quad \cdot \quad \cdot$$

$$B_k = \sum_k^\infty A_n \binom{n}{k} b^{n-k}.$$

Then, summing these sums, we have

$$f(b + h) = \sum_0^\infty B_n h^n = \sum_0^\infty B_n (z - b)^n,$$

providing that the double series (1) converges absolutely, for a double series can be summed by columns if it is absolutely convergent. Applying a test for absolute convergence, we have

$$|A_0|$$
$$|A_1|(|b| + |h|)$$
$$\cdot \quad \cdot \quad \cdot \quad \cdot \quad \cdot \quad \cdot$$
$$|A_n|(|b| + |h|)^n$$
$$\cdot \quad \cdot \quad \cdot \quad \cdot \quad \cdot$$

for the sums of the rows when absolute values are inserted. Summing *these* sums, we have

$$\sum |A_n|(|b| + |h|)^n,$$

which certainly converges when $|b| + |h| < \rho$, inasmuch as $\sum A_n z^n$ converges when $|z| < \rho$. Hence the proof is complete.

Note: $\binom{n}{k} = \dfrac{n!}{k!(n-k)!}, \binom{n}{0} = 1.$

15.05. DEFINITION. An *element* of an analytic function is any convergent power series which represents it in some circle of convergence.

Notes: (1) Thus, since

$$\frac{1}{1 - z} = 1 + z + z^2 + \cdots, \tag{1}$$

and also

$$\frac{1}{1 - z} = \frac{1}{1 - a} + \frac{z - a}{(1 - a)^2} + \frac{(z - a)^2}{(1 - a)^3} + \cdots, \tag{2}$$

either of the series (1) and (2) is an *element* of $1/(1 - z)$. [(1) is the Taylor's series about $z = 0$, and (2) the Taylor's series about $z = a$.]

(2) By Article 15.04, every analytic function has infinitely many elements.

(3) Weierstrass defined a function $f(z)$ to be analytic at $z = a$ if and only if

$$f(z) = \sum_0^\infty A_n(z - a)^n \text{ for } |z - a| < \rho, \quad \rho > 0.$$

15.06. DEFINITION. A *monogenic* analytic function is the aggregate of all values obtained from an element by analytic continuation.

15.07. DEFINITIONS. If a function f_0 may be continued from a point z_0 to a point z_1 by a finite number of successive elements the centers of whose circles of convergence lie along a curve C connecting z_0 to z_1, then f_0 is said to be *continued to z_1 along the curve C* (see Figure 15.5). In particular, if C is a straight line joining z_0 to z_1, then f_0 is said to be *continued radially to z_1*.

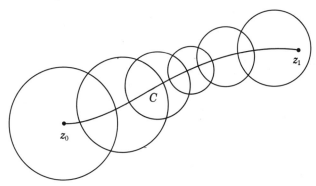

Figure 15.5

15.08. DEFINITION. The method of continuation by power series is known as the *standard method of continuation*.

15.09. THEOREM. If a function can be continued along a curve C from z_0 to z_1, then $\rho(z)$, where $\rho(z)$ is the radius of convergence as z moves along C, is a continuous function of z.

Proof: Take z and $z + h$ (see Figure 15.6), any two neighboring points on C, and let ρ and ρ' be the radii of convergence at these two

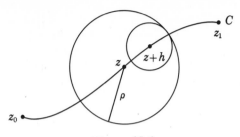

Figure 15.6

points, respectively. Further, suppose h so small that $|h| < \rho$. Then, by Article 15.04,

$$\rho' \geq \rho - |h|. \tag{1}$$

Two cases present themselves. Either

$$(a) \quad |h| < \rho' \quad \text{or} \quad (b) \quad |h| \geq \rho'.$$

Case (a). If $|h| < \rho'$, then (Art. 15.04)

$$\rho \geq \rho' - |h|. \tag{2}$$

Case (b). If $|h| \geq \rho'$, then

$$\rho' - |h| \leq 0,$$

and certainly

$$\rho \geq \rho' - |h|.$$

Thus relation (2) holds in either case. Therefore we always have, by (1) and (2),

$$- |h| \leq \rho' - \rho \leq |h|.$$

Hence, as $|h| \to 0$, $\rho' \to \rho$, and ρ is continuous at z.

15.10.   THEOREM.   The standard method of continuation is effective if any method is.

Proof: Suppose that $f(z)$ has been continued by some method from z_0 to z_1. Then there exists some domain D including z_1 and overlapping the circle of convergence at z_0 in which $f(z)$ is analytic. As shown in Figure 15.7, draw a broken line C connecting z_0 to z_1 and such that no part of C is exterior to both D and the circle of convergence at z_0. Take z as any point on C and consider $\rho(z)$. Then $\rho(z) > 0$ and, as in Article 15.09, continuous at z. Therefore, being positive and continuous along

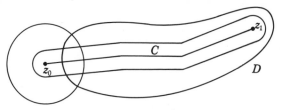

Figure 15.7

the curve C with end points z_0 and z_1, $\rho(z)$ has a positive lower bound for z on C. Hence a $\delta > 0$ exists such that

$$\rho(z) > \delta \text{ on } C.$$

Mark off segments of length $\delta/2$ (or less) along C from z_0 to z_1. Then the circles of convergence at these points (and there is a finite number of them) will continue $f(z)$ from z_0 to z_1.

15.11. DEFINITION. Starting with a given function element $f(z)$ defined so as to be single-valued and analytic throughout a neighborhood of a point z_0, we regard the totality of functional values defined by all possible analytic continuations of $f(z)$ as constituting the *monogenic analytic function F(z)*.

Note: This definition is due to Weierstrass.

SINGULARITIES

15.12. THEOREM. If $f(z) = \sum a_n z^n$ for $|z| < \rho$, then $z = \rho$ is a singularity of $f(z)$ if and only if the circle of convergence for the point $z = \rho/2$ has a radius of convergence $r = \rho/2$.

Proof: If $r > \rho/2$, then $f(z)$ would be continued analytically over $z = \rho$.

15.13. LEMMA. If $a_n \geq 0$, $f(x) = \sum a_n x^n$ for $|x| < 1$, and if $\sum a_n \to \infty$, then $\lim_{x \to 1-} f(x) = \infty$.

Proof: Suppose

$$\lim_{x \to 1-} f(x) = A.$$

Then, by Tauber's Theorem (Art. 14.93),

$$\sum a_n = A.$$

This proves the theorem

Example: Consider

$$f(x) = \frac{1}{1-x} = 1 + x + x^2 + \cdots = \sum_0^\infty x^n.$$

Here $a_n = 1 > 0$, $f(x) = \sum x^n$ for $|x| < 1$, and $\sum a_n \to \infty$. Hence

$$\lim_{x \to 1-} f(x) = \infty,$$

as is obvious from $f(x) = 1/(1-x)$.

15.14.   THEOREM.   There exist power series which diverge everywhere on their circles of convergence.

Proof: Consider the series (due to Weierstrass)

$$f(z) = \sum_0^\infty z^{n!}.$$

Here $\rho = 1$ (Art. 14.49). As shown in Figure 15.8, let us select a point

$$z_0 = e^{2\pi i p/q}, \quad p \text{ and } q \text{ integers},$$

on the circle of convergence. Take z as any point on the radius through z_0. Then

$$z = re^{2\pi i p/q},$$

where r is the distance from the origin to z. Taking $r < 1$, we have

$$f(z) = \sum_0^\infty (re^{2\pi i p/q})^{n!}$$

$$= 2re^{2\pi i p/q} + \cdots + r^{q!}e^{\,2\pi i p(q-1)!} + \cdots$$

$$= 2re^{2\pi i p/q} + \cdots + r^{q!} + r^{(q+1)!} + \cdots$$

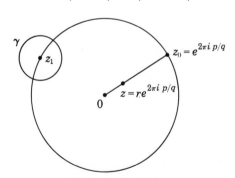

Figure 15.8

because the exponent $p(q - 1)!$ is an integer. Thus the series clearly diverges when $r = 1$. Hence, by Article 5.13, Vol. I,

$$\lim_{\substack{z \to z_0 \\ \text{radially}}} f(z) = \infty. \tag{1}$$

But such points z_0 are everywhere dense on the circle of convergence. Hence (1) must hold for all points on the circle. For suppose it does not hold at the point z_1. Then, since z_1 is not an isolated point of convergence for the series, there exists a circle γ with center z_1 such that, for all points on the circle of convergence and interior to γ, the series converges. But this is impossible since points z_0 are everywhere dense on the circle of convergence. Hence the theorem.

15.15. DEFINITION. A curve of singular points is called a *cut*.

Thus $|z| = 1$ is a cut for $f(z) = \sum_{0}^{\infty} z^{n!}$.

Other examples are:

$$f(z) = \sum z^{2^n} \text{ has } |z| = 1 \text{ as a cut,}$$
$$f(z) = \sum (\tfrac{1}{2})^n z^{n^2} \text{ has } |z| = 1 \text{ as a cut.}$$

15.16. THEOREM (DUE TO FABRY). If $f(z) = \sum a_n z^{\lambda_n}$, ($\lambda_n$ an integer), has $\rho = 1$, and if

$$\lim_{n \to \infty} \frac{\lambda_n}{n} = \infty,$$

then $|z| = 1$ is a cut.

We will not prove this theorem here. The examples in Articles 5.14 and 5.15, Vol. I come under this theorem.

15.17. EXAMPLES. (a) The element $\sum_{1}^{\infty} (-1)^{n-1} z^n / n$ may be continued to a wider domain by means of the series

$$\log 2 - \sum_{1}^{\infty} (1 - z)^n / n 2^n.$$

By Maclaurin's series, we have

$$\log (1 + z) = \sum_{1}^{\infty} (-1)^{n-1} z^n / n, \tag{1}$$

for that branch of $\log (1 + z)$ for which

$$\log(1 + z) = \log|1 + z| + i \arc(1 + z), \quad -\pi < \arc(1 + z) \leq \pi,$$

the series converging (by the test-ratio test) inside the circle $|z| = 1$ (see Figure 15.9).

Also, by Taylor's series, we have, for the same branch,

$$\log(1 + z) = \log 2 + \frac{z - 1}{2} - \frac{(z - 1)^2}{2 \cdot 2^2} + \frac{(z - 1)^3}{3 \cdot 2^3} - \cdots$$

$$= \log 2 + \sum_1^\infty (-1)^{n-1} \frac{(z - 1)^n}{n2^n}$$

$$= \log 2 + \sum_1^\infty \frac{(1 - z)^n}{n2^n}. \tag{2}$$

By the test-ratio test, since

$$\lim_{n \to \infty} \frac{n2^n}{(n + 1)2^{n+1}} = \lim_{n \to \infty} \frac{n}{2(n + 1)} = \frac{1}{2},$$

the series (2) converges inside the circle $|z - 1| = 2$. Thus, since $|z - 1| < 2$ overlaps $|z| < 1$, the element (1) may be continued to the wider domain $|z - 1| < 2$ by means of the series (2).

(b) The power series $\sum_1^\infty z^n/n$ and $i\pi + \sum_1^\infty (2 - z)^n/n$ have no common region of convergence but are analytic continuations of the same function.

By Maclaurin's series, we have, for a certain branch of $\log\left(\dfrac{1}{1 - z}\right)$,

$$\log\left(\frac{1}{1 - z}\right) = z + \frac{z^2}{2} + \frac{z^3}{3} + \cdots = \sum_1^\infty z^n/n, \tag{1}$$

the series converging (by the test-ratio test) in the circle (see Figure 15.10)

$$|z| < 1. \tag{2}$$

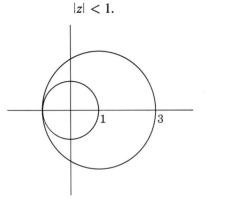

Figure 15.9

Also, by Taylor's series and for the same branch, expanding about the point $z = 2$,

$$\log\left(\frac{1}{1-z}\right) = \log(-1) + (z-2) - \frac{(z-2)^2}{2} + \frac{(z-2)^3}{3} - \cdots$$

$$= \pi i - \sum_{1}^{\infty} (-1)^{n-1} \frac{(z-2)^n}{n}$$

$$= \pi i - \sum_{1}^{\infty} \frac{(2-z)^n}{n}, \tag{3}$$

the series converging (by the test-ratio test) in the circle

$$|z - 2| < 1. \tag{4}$$

Again, by Taylor's series and for the same branch, expanding about the point $z = i$,

$$\log\left(\frac{1}{1-z}\right) = \log\left(\frac{1}{1-i}\right) + \frac{(z-i)}{(1-i)} + \frac{(z-i)^2}{2(1-i)^2} + \frac{(z-i)^3}{3(1-i)^3} + \cdots$$

$$= \log\left(\frac{1}{1-i}\right) + \sum_{1}^{\infty} \frac{(z-i)^n}{n(1-i)^n}, \tag{5}$$

the series converging (by the test-ratio test) in the circle

$$|z - i| < \sqrt{2}. \tag{6}$$

The series (1) and (3), although they have no common region of convergence, are both analytic continuations of the same element (5).

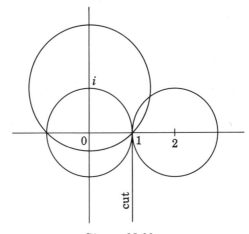

Figure 15.10

CHAPTER 16

Laurent Series

THE SERIES

16.01. DEFINITION.   A two-way series of the form

$$\sum_{-\infty}^{\infty} a_n(z - a)^n \tag{1}$$

is known as a *Laurent series*. We may write (1) as

$$\sum_{0}^{\infty} a_n(z - a)^n + \sum_{1}^{\infty} \frac{a_{-n}}{(z - a)^n}. \tag{2}$$

The *sum* of the Laurent series (1) is defined as the sum of the sums of the two series in (2).

16.02. THEOREM.   If a Laurent series converges, then it converges in an annular region of the form

$$r < |z - a| < R.$$

Proof: By (2) of Article 16.01.

16.03. THEOREM.   If $f(z)$ is analytic in the annular region $r < |z - a| < R$, then

$$f(z) = \sum_{-\infty}^{\infty} a_n(z - a)^n, \quad r < |z - a| < R,$$

where

$$a_n = \frac{1}{2\pi i} \int_{\gamma} \frac{f(t)}{(t - a)^{n+1}} \, dt,$$

γ being any circle

$$|z - a| = g, \quad -r < g < R.$$

  Proof: No generality is lost by taking a at the origin. Let us then do so. Take z_0 inside the annular region. We can then construct circles γ_1

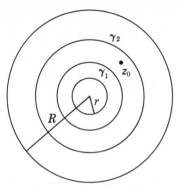

Figure 16.1

and γ_2 inside and outside z_0, respectively, and also lying within the annular region. Applying Cauchy's integral formula (Art. 11.26, Vol. I), we have

$$f(z_0) = \frac{1}{2\pi i} \int_{\gamma_2} \frac{f(t)}{t - z_0}\, dt + \frac{1}{2\pi i} \int_{\gamma_1} \frac{f(t)}{t - z_0}\, dt. \qquad (1)$$

Now we have

$$\frac{1}{t - z_0} = \frac{1}{t} + \frac{z_0}{t^2} + \frac{z_0^2}{t^3} + \cdots$$

$$= \sum_{0}^{\infty} \frac{z_0^n}{t^{n+1}}, \text{ for } \left|\frac{z_0}{t}\right| < 1. \qquad (2)$$

Now for t on γ_2 we have, where R_2 is the radius of γ_2,

$$\sum_{0}^{\infty} \frac{z_0^n}{t^{n+1}} \ll \sum_{0}^{\infty} \frac{|z_0|^n}{R_2^{n+1}}.$$

But this dominant series converges since $|z_0| < R_2$. Hence, by the Weierstrass M-Test,

$$\sum_{0}^{\infty} z_0^n / t^{n+1}$$

converges uniformly for t on γ_2. Hence, since $f(t)$ is analytic on γ_2,

$$\sum_{0}^{\infty} \frac{f(t) z_0^n}{t^{n+1}}$$

converges uniformly for t on γ_2 to $f(t)/(t - z_0)$ (as in Art. 14.69).

Moreover, $f(t)z_0^n/t^{n+1}$ is continuous on γ_2. Hence the requirements of Article 14.80 are satisfied, and we have

$$\frac{1}{2\pi i}\int_{\gamma_2}\frac{f(t)}{t-z_0}\,dt = \sum_0^\infty \frac{z_0^n}{2\pi i}\int_{\gamma_2}\frac{f(t)}{t^{n+1}}\,dt. \qquad (3)$$

Similarly, consider the series

$$\frac{1}{t-z_0} = -\frac{1}{z_0-t} = -\frac{1}{z_0} - \frac{t}{z_0^2} - \frac{t^2}{z_0^3} - \cdots$$

$$= -\sum_0^\infty t^n/z_0^{n+1}, \text{ for } \left|\frac{t}{z_0}\right| < 1. \qquad (4)$$

Now for t on γ_1 we have, where R_1 is the radius of γ_1,

$$\sum_0^\infty t^n/z_0^{n+1} \ll \sum_0^\infty R_1^n/|z_0|^{n+1}.$$

But this dominant series converges, since $R_1 < |z_0|$. Hence, by the Weierstrass M-Test,

$$\sum_0^\infty t^n/z_0^{n+1}$$

converges uniformly for t on γ_1. Hence, since $f(t)$ is analytic on γ_1,

$$\sum_0^\infty f(t)t^n/z_0^{n+1}$$

converges uniformly for t on γ_1 to $-f(t)/(t-z_0)$. Moreover, $f(t)t^n/z_0^{n+1}$ is continuous on γ_1. Hence the requirements of Article 14.80 are satisfied, and we have

$$\frac{1}{2\pi i}\int_{\gamma_1}\frac{f(t)}{t-z_0}\,dt = -\sum_0^\infty \frac{1}{2\pi i z_0^{n+1}}\int_{\gamma_1} f(t)t^n dt. \qquad (5)$$

Substituting (3) and (5) in (1), we have

$$f(z_0) = \sum_0^\infty \frac{z_0^n}{2\pi i}\int_{\gamma_2}\frac{f(t)}{t^{n+1}}\,dt + \sum_0^\infty \frac{1}{2\pi i z_0^{n+1}}\int_{\gamma_1} f(t)t^n dt$$

$$= \sum_0^\infty a_n z_0^n + \sum_1^\infty a_n z_0^{-n},$$

where

$$a_n = \frac{1}{2\pi i}\int_\gamma \frac{f(t)}{t^{n+1}}\,dt,$$

where γ is any concentric circle of the annular region. (We may replace γ_1 and γ_2 each by γ, by Article 11.22, Vol. I).

Example: Consider the function

$$f(z) = \frac{1}{z^2 - 3z + 2} = \frac{1}{z - 2} - \frac{1}{z - 1}.$$

We have (see Figure 16.2)

$$\frac{1}{z - 1} = -(1 + z + z^2 + \cdots), \text{ for } |z| < 1, \tag{1}$$

$$\frac{1}{z - 2} = -\left(\frac{1}{2} + \frac{z}{2^2} + \frac{z^2}{2^3} + \cdots\right), \text{ for } |z| < 2, \tag{2}$$

$$\frac{1}{z - 1} = \frac{1}{z} + \frac{1}{z^2} + \frac{1}{z^3} + \cdots, \text{ for } |z| > 1, \tag{3}$$

$$\frac{1}{z - 2} = \frac{1}{z} + \frac{2}{z^2} + \frac{2^2}{z^3} + \cdots, \text{ for } |z| > 2. \tag{4}$$

Case 1. $|z| < 1$. By (1) and (2),

$$f(z) = \sum_0^\infty \left(1 - \frac{1}{2^{n+1}}\right) z^n.$$

Case 2. $1 < |z| < 2$. By (2) and (3),

$$f(z) = \cdots - \frac{1}{z^2} - \frac{1}{z} - \frac{1}{2} - \frac{z}{2^2} - \frac{z^2}{2^3} - \cdots.$$

Case 3. $|z| > 2$. By (3) and (4),

$$f(z) = \sum_0^\infty \frac{(2^n - 1)}{z^{n+1}}.$$

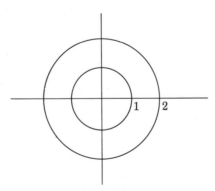

Figure 16.2

16.04. THEOREM. Every Laurent series may be written as a Fourier series.

Proof: Let

$$f(z) = \sum_{-\infty}^{\infty} A_n z^n$$

be any Laurent series. Then, setting

$$z = re^{i\theta},$$

we have

$$f(re^{i\theta}) = \sum_{-\infty}^{\infty} A_n r^n e^{ni\theta},$$

where, by Article 16.03,

$$A_n r^n = \frac{r^n}{2\pi i} \int_0^{2\pi} \frac{f(re^{i\theta})}{r^{n+1} e^{i(n+1)\theta}} re^{i\theta} i \, d\theta$$

$$= \frac{1}{2\pi} \int_0^{2\pi} \frac{f(re^{i\theta})}{e^{ni\theta}} \, d\theta.$$

Thus

$$f(re^{i\theta}) = \sum_{-\infty}^{\infty} a_n e^{ni\theta}, \tag{1}$$

where

$$a_n = \frac{1}{2\pi} \int_0^{2\pi} f(re^{i\theta}) e^{-ni\theta} d\theta. \tag{2}$$

Or from (1) we have

$$f(re^{i\theta}) = \sum_{-\infty}^{\infty} a_n (\cos n\theta + i \sin n\theta)$$

$$= a_0 + \sum_1^{\infty} \{(a_n + a_{-n}) \cos n\theta + i(a_n - a_{-n}) \sin n\theta\}. \tag{3}$$

But from (2) we have

$$a_n + a_{-n} = \frac{1}{2\pi} \int_0^{2\pi} f(re^{i\theta})(e^{-ni\theta} + e^{ni\theta}) d\theta$$

$$= \frac{1}{\pi} \int_0^{2\pi} f(re^{i\theta}) \cos n\theta \, d\theta. \tag{4}$$

$$i(a_n - a_{-n}) = \frac{i}{2\pi} \int_0^{2\pi} f(re^{i\theta})(e^{-ni\theta} - e^{ni\theta}) d\theta$$

$$= \frac{1}{\pi} \int_0^{2\pi} f(re^{i\theta}) \sin n\theta \, d\theta. \tag{5}$$

$$a_0 = \frac{1}{2\pi} \int_0^{2\pi} f(re^{i\theta}) d\theta. \tag{6}$$

Substituting (4), (5), and (6) in (3), we find

$$f(re^{i\theta}) = \frac{\alpha_0}{2} + \sum_1^\infty \{\alpha_n \cos n\theta + \beta_n \sin n\theta\}, \tag{7}$$

where

$$\alpha_n = \frac{1}{\pi} \int_0^{2\pi} F(\theta) \cos n\theta \, d\theta, \quad n = 1, 2, \cdots,$$

$$\beta_n = \frac{1}{\pi} \int_0^{2\pi} F(\theta) \sin n\theta \, d\theta, \quad n = 1, 2, \cdots,$$

$$\alpha_0 = \frac{1}{\pi} \int_0^{2\pi} F(\theta) \, d\theta,$$

$$F(\theta) = f(re^{i\theta}).$$

Hence (7) is a Fourier series, and the theorem is proved.

SINGULARITIES

16.05. EXAMINATION OF SINGULARITIES BY MEANS OF THE LAURENT EXPANSION.   Let $z = a$ be an isolated singularity of $f(z)$. Then $f(z)$ is analytic in some region about $z = a$. Thus a Laurent expansion exists about $z = a$, and we have (Art. 16.03)

$$f(z) = \sum_{-\infty}^\infty A_n(z - a)^n, \quad 0 < |z - a| \leq \delta, \text{ say.}$$

Now suppose the following. (a) $A_n = 0, (n = -1, -2, -3, \cdots)$. Then

$$f(z) = \sum_0^\infty A_n(z - a)^n$$

and the singularity $z = a$ is *removable*, for we may define $f(a) = A_0$, and then $f(z)$ will be analytic at $z = a$.

(b) $A_n = 0, [n = -(m + 1), - (m + 2), \cdots, \text{ but } A_{-m} \neq 0]$. Then

$$f(z) = \frac{A_{-m}}{(z - a)^m} + \cdots + \frac{A_{-1}}{z - a} + A_0 + A_1(z - a) + \cdots$$

$$= \frac{1}{(z-a)^m} \{A_{-m} + A_{-m+1}(z-a) + \cdots\}$$

$$= \frac{1}{(z-a)^m} \varphi(z), \text{ say.}$$

Notice that

$$\varphi(a) = A_{-m} \neq 0,$$

$\varphi(z)$ is analytic at $z = a$.

Hence in this case $z = a$ is a *pole of order m* (see Arts. 12.12 and 12.16). Also notice that (alternative of Art. 11.24, Vol. I)

$$\frac{1}{2\pi i}\int_C f(z)dz = A_{-1}, \quad C: |z-a| = \delta.$$

Thus A_{-1} is the *residue* of $f(z)$ at $z = a$.

(c) $A_n \neq 0$ for infinitely many negative n's. Then $z = a$ is an *essential singularity*. For $z = a$ must be a pole, a removable singularity, or an essential singularity. By elimination, we see that it is the last.

Now suppose $z = \infty$ is an isolated singularity. Then there exists a circle of radius R such that $f(z)$ is analytic, except at infinity, in the exterior of this circle. Thus there exists a Laurent series

$$f(z) = \sum_{-\infty}^{\infty} A_n z^n, \quad R < |z| < \infty.$$

Now suppose the following.

(d) $A_n = 0$, $(n = 1, 2, 3, \cdots)$. Then $f(z)$ has a *removable singularity* at $z = \infty$, for we may define $f(\infty) = A_0$ and then $f(z)$ will be analytic at $z = \infty$.

(e) $A_n = 0$, $(n = m + 1, m + 2, \cdots$, but $A_m \neq 0)$. Then $f(z)$ has a *pole of order m* at $z = \infty$. The proof is similar to that in part (b). Here the *residue* is $-A_{-1}$.

(f) $A_n \neq 0$ for infinitely many positive n's. Then $z = \infty$ is, by elimination, an *essential singularity*.

16.06. THEOREM. If $\begin{cases} a \\ \infty \end{cases}$ is an isolated singularity of $f(z)$, then

$$f(z) = \sum_{-\infty}^{\infty} A_n(z-a)^n, \quad 0 < |z-a| < \delta,$$

$$f(z) = \sum_{-\infty}^{\infty} A_n z^n, \quad R < |z| < \infty.$$

Proof: See Article 16.05.

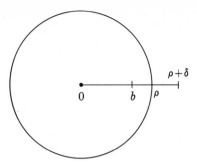

Figure 16.3

16.07.   THEOREM.   If $a_n \geq 0$ and if $\overline{\lim} \sqrt[n]{a_n} = 1/\rho \neq 0$, then $z = \rho$ is a singularity of

$$f(z) = \sum_0^\infty a_n z^n.$$

Proof: Suppose $f(z)$ is analytic at $z = \rho$. Take b between 0 and ρ (see Figure 16.3). Then

$$f(z) = \sum_{k=0}^\infty \frac{f^{(k)}(b)(z - b)^k}{k!}, \qquad (1)$$

the circle of convergence including within its interior the point $z = \rho$, and hence also some point $\rho + \delta$, $(\delta > 0)$. Therefore

$$f(\rho + \delta) = \sum_{k=0}^\infty \frac{f^{(k)}(b)(\rho + \delta - b)^k}{k!} \qquad (2)$$

$$= \sum_{k=0}^\infty \sum_{n=k}^\infty \binom{n}{k} a_n b^{n-k}(\rho + \delta - b)^k, \qquad (3)$$

since

$$\frac{f^{(k)}(b)}{k!} = \sum_{n=k}^\infty \binom{n}{k} a_n b^{n-k} \qquad \text{by Art. 15.04.} \qquad (4)$$

Now, every term in (3) is positive or zero. Consider the double series formed by (3). The sum of the kth row is (4), and the sum of these rows is (2). Hence (by Art. 14.97) the double series converges. (This is where the fact that $a_n \geq 0$ comes in.) Hence we may change the order of summation, obtaining

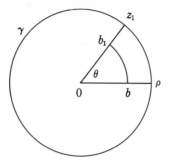

Figure 16.4

$$f(\rho + \delta) = \sum_{n=0}^{\infty} a_n \sum_{k=0}^{\infty} \binom{n}{k} b^{n-k}(\rho + \delta - b)^k$$

$$= \sum_{n=0}^{\infty} a_n(\rho + \delta)^n, \tag{5}$$

for (by the binomial theorem)

$$\sum_{k=0}^{n} \binom{n}{k} b^{n-k}(\rho + \delta - b)^k = \{(\rho + \delta - b) + b\}^n.$$

$$= (\rho + \delta)^n.$$

But (5) is a contradiction of the hypothesis which says that the power series

$$f(z) = \sum_{0}^{\infty} a_n z^n$$

diverges outside the circle $|z| = \rho$.

Alternative (due to Pringsheim): As shown in Figure 16.4, take b on the real axis between 0 and ρ, and expand $f(z)$ about b, giving

$$f(z) = \sum_{0}^{\infty} \frac{f^{(k)}(b)(z - b)^k}{k!}. \tag{1}$$

Calling ρ_b the radius of convergence of this series, we have

$$\overline{\lim} \sqrt[k]{\frac{|f^{(k)}(b)|}{k!}} = 1/\rho_b, \quad \rho_b \geq \rho - b. \tag{2}$$

Now, there is at least one singular point

$$z_1 = \rho e^{i\theta}$$

on the circle of convergence γ of $f(z)$. Take

$$b_1 = be^{i\theta}.$$

Then, expanding $f(z)$ about b_1, we have

$$f(z) = \sum_{k=0}^{\infty} \frac{f^{(k)}(be^{i\theta})(z - be^{i\theta})^k}{k!}. \tag{3}$$

Since z_1 is a singular point, we know that the radius of convergence of (3) is $\rho - b$. Hence

$$\overline{\lim} \ \sqrt[k]{\frac{|f^{(k)}(be^{i\theta})|}{k!}} = \frac{1}{\rho - b}.$$

But we have

$$\frac{f^{(k)}(be^{i\theta})}{k!} = \sum_{n=k}^{\infty} a_n \binom{n}{k} (be^{i\theta})^{n-k}.$$
$$\text{(by Art. 15.04)}$$

Hence

$$\left| \frac{f^{(k)}(be^{i\theta})}{k!} \right| \leq \sum_{n=k}^{\infty} a_n \binom{n}{k} b^{n-k} \tag{4}$$

$$= \frac{f^{(k)}(b)}{k!}. \tag{5}$$

[It is in (4) that the fact that $a_n \geq 0$ enters.] Therefore, from (5),

$$\overline{\lim} \ \sqrt[k]{\left| \frac{f^{(k)}(be^{i\theta})}{k!} \right|} \leq \overline{\lim} \ \sqrt[k]{\frac{|f^{(k)}(b)|}{k!}},$$

or

$$1/(\rho - b) \leq 1/\rho_b,$$

whence

$$\rho_b \leq \rho - b,$$

or, because of (2),

$$\rho_b = \rho - b,$$

and ρ is a singular point of $f(z)$, because all other points on the circle $|z - b| = \rho_b$ are nonsingular points of $f(z)$.

16.08. THEOREM (DUE TO FABRY).   If in the power series $f(z) = \sum a_n z^n$, $\lim\limits_{n \to \infty} a_n/a_{n+1}$ exists and is equal to η, then $z = \eta$ is a singular point of the function $f(z)$.

We shall not prove this theorem. Note that it is an extension of Article 16.07.

Examples: (a) $1/(1 - z) = \sum\limits_{0}^{\infty} z^n$. Here $\lim\limits_{n \to \infty} a_n/a_{n+1} = 1$. Hence $z = 1$ is a singular point of $1/(1 - z)$, as we obviously see.

(b) $\log(i - z) = \log i - \sum\limits_{1}^{\infty} \dfrac{1}{n}\left(\dfrac{z}{i}\right)^n$ (we restrict ourselves to a particular branch of the log function). Here

$$\lim_{n \to \infty} a_n/a_{n+1} = \lim_{n \to \infty} \frac{(n + 1)i^{n+1}}{ni^n} = i.$$

Hence $z = i$ is a singular point of $\log(i - z)$, as we obviously see.

(c) $\dfrac{1}{1 - z} + \log(1 + z) = \sum\limits_{0}^{\infty}\left(1 + \dfrac{(-1)^n}{n}\right) z^n$, $(|z| < 1)$. Here there are two singular points, $z = \pm 1$. However, Fabry's Theorem yields only one of them. Thus

$$\lim_{n \to \infty} \frac{\{n + (-1)^n\}(n + 1)}{\{(n + 1) + (-1)^{n+1}\}n} = 1.$$

BRANCH POINTS

16.09. THEOREM.   If $f(z)$ has a branch point at $z = a$ about which m branches of the function are cyclically permuted (branch point of order $m - 1$), then each branch can be represented in the form

$$f(z) = \sum_{-\infty}^{\infty} A_n(z - a)^{n/m},$$

for $z \neq a$ but sufficiently near to a.

Proof: Set $(z - a) = u^m$. This transformation maps the neighborhood of $z = a$ into a neighborhood of 0 in the u-plane (see Figure 16.5), and in this neighborhood the mapping is single-valued. Thus

$$f(a + u^m) \tag{1}$$

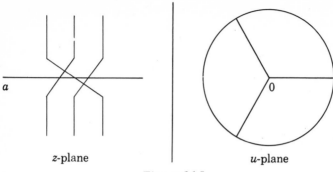

z-plane   u-plane

Figure 16.5

is a single-valued function of u in a neighborhood of $u = 0$. Moreover, (1), being an analytic function of an analytic function, is itself analytic in a *deleted* neighborhood of $u = 0$. Hence there exists a Laurent development, and we have

$$f(a + u^m) = \sum_{-\infty}^{\infty} A_n u^n, \quad 0 < |u| < \delta.$$

Transforming back to the z-plane, we have

$$f(z) = \sum_{-\infty}^{\infty} A_n (z - a)^{n/m}. \tag{2}$$

Note: A branch point is certainly a singularity, but not, by our definition, an isolated singularity. For $f(z)$ is not single-valued, and hence certainly not analytic, in any neighborhood of the point. Even if the function is made single-valued by using sheets, it still is not analytic on a cut.

16.10. DEFINITION.   We extend the definitions of pole and zero (with orders) to branch points by means of the coefficients A_n in (2) of Article 16.09, following the classification given in Article 16.05.

Thus if in (2) of Article 16.09

$$A_n = 0, \quad n = \cdots, 0, 1, 2, \cdots, m - 1, \quad A_m \neq 0,$$

then $f(z)$ has a zero of order m at the branch point $z = a$, etc.

16.11. THEOREM.   If $f(z)$ has a branch point at $z = \infty$ of order $m - 1$, then each branch of $f(z)$ can be represented in the form

$$f(z) = \sum_{-\infty}^{\infty} a_n z^{n/m},$$

for $z \neq \infty$ but sufficiently near to $z = \infty$.

Proof: Consider $f(1/z)$. This has a branch point at $z = 0$. Therefore, by Article 16.09,

$$f(1/z) = \sum_{-\infty}^{\infty} A_n z^{n/m},$$

or

$$f(z) = \sum_{-\infty}^{\infty} A_n z^{-n/m}$$

$$= \sum_{-\infty}^{\infty} a_n z^{n/m},$$

where $a_n = A_{-n}$.

16.12.   EXAMPLES.   (a) $z^{3/2}$ has a branch point at $z = 0$ and at $z = \infty$. The former is a zero of the third order and the latter a pole of the third order: For

$$z^{3/2} = \cdots + 0 + 0 \cdot z^{1/2} + 0 \cdot z + z^{3/2} + 0 + \cdots,$$

whence

$$A_n = 0, \quad n = \cdots, 0, 1, 2, \quad A_3 \neq 0.$$

Hence $z = 0$ is a zero of the third order, etc.

(b) $z^{-3/2}$ has a zero of the third order at $z = \infty$ and a pole of the third order at $z = 0$.

PRINCIPAL PARTS

16.13.   DEFINITION. $f(z)$ is *entire* if it is analytic in the unextended plane.

16.14.   AGREEMENT. $f(z)$ is *meromorphic* in a domain D if it is analytic there except possibly for poles (see Article 12.27). When we say $f(z)$ is meromorphic, without specifying any domain, we shall mean that it is meromorphic in the *unextended* plane.

Notes: (1) We have the following classification:

$$\text{meromorphic} \supset \text{entire}.$$

(2) If $f(z)$ is entire, then

$$f(z) = \sum_{0}^{\infty} f^{(n)}(0) z^n / n!, \text{ for all } z \neq \infty.$$

16.15. DEFINITION.   If $f(z)$ has a Laurent expansion about $z = a$,

$$f(z) = \sum_{-\infty}^{\infty} a_n(z - a)^n, \quad 0 < |z - a| < \delta,$$

then

$$\sum_{-\infty}^{-1} a_n(z - a)^n$$

is called the *principal part* of $f(z)$ at $z = a$. We shall designate it by P_a.

Note: This definition is a generalization of that given for the principal part of a pole (Article 12.17).

16.16. THEOREM.   If $f(z)$ is rational with poles a_k, ∞, then

$$f(z) = \sum_{k=1}^{n} P_{a_k} + P_{\infty} + C,$$

for every $z \neq a_k$, ∞.

Proof: This is (2) of Article 12.30. Thus we can construct, to within an additive constant, a rational function with prescribed poles and principal parts at these poles.

16.17. THEOREM.   The principal part of a function $f(z)$ at $z = a$ is analytic in the extended plane, except perhaps at $z = a$.

Proof: By hypothesis, $f(z)$ has a Laurent expansion at $z = a$. That is,

$$f(z) = \sum_{-\infty}^{\infty} a_n(z - a)^n = \sum_{-\infty}^{-1} + \sum_{0}^{\infty}. \tag{1}$$

Now, $\sum_{-\infty}^{\infty}$ converges except at a in some circle γ with center at a. Hence $\sum_{-\infty}^{-1}$ and $\sum_{0}^{\infty}$ likewise converge in γ, except perhaps at a. But $\sum_{-\infty}^{-1}$ also converges outside γ.

16.18. THEOREM.   If $f(z)$ is analytic in the *extended* plane, except perhaps for singularities at the points $a_1, a_2, \cdots, a_n$, ∞ with principal parts $P_{a_1}, P_{a_2}, \cdots, P_{a_n}, P_{\infty}$, then

$$f(z) = \sum_{k=1}^{n} P_{a_k} + P_{\infty} + C, \text{ for } z \neq a_k, \infty,$$

where C is an arbitrary constant.

Proof: Consider the function

$$F(z) = f(z) - P_{a_1} - P_{a_2} - \cdots - P_{a_n} - P_\infty.$$

(1) Take $z \neq a_1, \cdots, a_n, \infty$. Then $f(z)$ is analytic, and, by Article 16.17, each P is analytic. Hence $F(z)$ is analytic at $z \neq a_k, \infty$.

(2) Now take $z = a_k$. By Article 16.17, each P except P_{a_k} is analytic at $z = a_k$. Also, $f(z)$ has a Laurent expansion at a_k, namely

$$f(z) = P_{a_k} + Q_{a_k},$$

where Q_{a_k} is analytic at a_k. Therefore

$$f(z) - P_{a_k}$$

is analytic at a_k. Hence if we define

$$F(a_k) = Q_{a_k} - P_{a_1}(a_k) - \cdots - P_\infty(a_k),$$

then we have $F(z)$ analytic at $z = a_k$. Thus $z = a_k$ is a removable singularity of $F(z)$.

(3) Similarly, $z = \infty$ is a removable singularity of $F(z)$.

Thus, removing the singularities a_k and ∞, we have $F(z)$ analytic in the entire extended plane, and hence, by Lionville's Theorem,

$$F(z) = C, \text{ a constant}.$$

This proves the theorem.

Note: This theorem is a generalization of Article 16.16.

16.19. THEOREM. There exist infinitely many functions analytic in the extended plane, except for a finite number of prescribed singularities with prescribed principal parts. Any two differ by a constant.

Proof: This theorem is a corollary to Article 16.18.

16.20. THEOREM. If $F(z)$ is a function analytic in the *unextended* plane, except for *isolated* singularities at the points $a_0, a_1, a_2, \cdots$ with principal parts $P_{a_0}, P_{a_1}, P_{a_2}, \cdots$, then the most general function with these properties is

$$F(z) + E(z),$$

where $E(z)$ is entire.

Proof: Let $f(z)$ be any other function satisfying the prescribed conditions. Consider the function

$$H(z) \equiv f(z) - F(z).$$

Take $z \neq a_k$. Then both $f(z)$ and $F(z)$, and hence also $H(z)$, are analytic at z. Now take $z = a_k$, and expand both $f(z)$ and $F(z)$ by a Laurent expansion about $z = a_k$. This may be done by the hypothesis that $F(z)$ and $f(z)$ are both analytic except at the points $a_0, a_1, \cdots$. Furthermore, by hypothesis, the principal parts of $F(z)$ and $f(z)$ at $z = a_k$ are the same. Therefore, combining the Laurent expansions, we have

$$f(z) - F(z) = \sum_0^\infty A_n(z - a_k)^n,$$

which is analytic at $z = a_k$. Hence $H(z)$ has a removable singularity at $z = a_k$. Thus $H(z)$ can be made analytic in the unextended plane. That is, $H(z)$ is entire, and our theorem is proved.

16.21. THE MITTAG-LEFFLER THEOREM.   If $f(z)$ is analytic in the *unextended* plane, except perhaps for *isolated* singularities at the points $a_0, a_1, a_2, \cdots$ with principal parts $P_{a_0}, P_{a_1}, P_{a_2}, \cdots$, then

$$f(z) = \sum_{k=0}^\infty [P_{a_k} - G_k(z)] + E(z), \tag{1}$$

where $G_k(z)$ are suitable polynomials and $E(z)$ is entire.

Proof: (1) Let us suppose the points $a_0, a_1, a_2, \cdots$ ordered in the following fashion:

$$a_0 = 0 < |a_1| \leq |a_2| \leq |a_3| \leq \cdots, \quad a_j \neq a_k.$$

If $a_0 = 0$ is not one of the singular points, then $P_{a_0} = 0$. Thus the points are arranged according to their distances from the origin. If several are at the same distance, then we take these in their counterclockwise order about the origin, starting on the positive real axis.

(2) Let us choose $G_0 = 0$.

(3) Since the points a_k are isolated, $P_{a_k}, (k \neq 0)$, is analytic at the origin. P_{a_k} may therefore be expanded in a power series about the origin thus:

$$P_{a_k}\left(\frac{1}{z - a_k}\right) = b_{k0} + b_{k1}z + b_{k2}z^2 + \cdots,$$

the series converging for $|z| < |a_k|$. The series is therefore uniformly convergent for $|z| \leq \frac{1}{2}|a_k|$ (Art. 14.83). Hence, by the definition of uniform convergence, for $\epsilon = \frac{1}{2}^k$ there exists an n_k independent of z in $|z| \leq \frac{1}{2}|a_k|$ such that

$$|P_{a_k} - b_{k0} - b_{k1}z - \cdots - b_{kn_k}z^{n_k}| < \frac{1}{2}^k, \quad |z| \leq \frac{1}{2}|a_k|.$$

We define

$$G_k(z) \equiv b_{k0} + b_{k1}z + \cdots + b_{kn_k}z^{n_k}.$$

Thus we have

$$|P_{a_k} - G_k| < \tfrac{1}{2}^k, \quad |z| \leq \tfrac{1}{2}|a_k|.$$

(4) Now draw *any* circle with center at the origin and radius R. Also draw the circle $|z| = 2R$ (see Figure 16.6). Suppose a_{N+1} to be the first point *outside* the larger circle.

(5) Calling

$$F(z) \equiv \sum_{k=0}^{\infty} [P_{a_k} - G_k],$$

let us set

$$F_1(z) \equiv \sum_{k=0}^{N} [P_{a_k} - G_k],$$

$$F_2(z) \equiv \sum_{k=N+1}^{\infty} [P_{a_k} - G_k].$$

(6) Now, certainly, each term of $F_2(z)$ is analytic in $|z| \leq R$. Also, we have shown that

$$|P_{a_{N+l}} - G_{N+l}| < \tfrac{1}{2}^{N+l}, \text{ for } |z| \leq \tfrac{1}{2}|a_{N+l}|,$$

and hence for $|z| \leq R < \tfrac{1}{2}|a_{N+l}|$. Hence

$$\sum_{k=N+1}^{\infty} [P_{a_k} - G_k] \ll \sum_{k=N+1}^{\infty} \tfrac{1}{2}^k, \quad |z| \leq R.$$

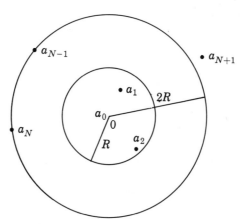

Figure 16.6

Thus, applying the Weierstrass M-Test, we find that the series $F_2(z)$ converges uniformly in $|z| \leq R$. Therefore $F_2(z)$ is certainly analytic in $|z| \leq R$ (Art. 14.82).

(7) Now, $F_1(z)$ has the same singularities with the same principal parts as has $f(z)$ inside the circle $|z| < R$. Thus $F_1(z)$ is analytic in $|z| < R$, except for the points a_k in $|z| < R$.

(8) Therefore $F(z) = F_1(z) + F_2(z)$ is analytic inside $|z| < R$, except for the points a_k in this circle. But R may be chosen arbitrarily large. Hence $F(z)$ is analytic in the unextended plane, except for the set of singular points $a_0, a_1, a_2, \cdots$. Applying Article 16.20, we then have

$$f(z) = F(z) + E(z),$$

which proves the theorem.

Note: In the above proof we may employ in place of the series $\sum \frac{1}{2}^k$ any convergent series $\sum p_k$ of positive terms. Our G's will depend on our choice for this series.

16.22. **PROBLEM.** Construct an $f(z)$ analytic except for singularities at the points $a_0 = 0, a_1, a_2, \cdots$, where $\sum_1^\infty 1/|a_k|$ converges.

Let us construct a function which has poles of the first order at the points a_k and principal parts $1/(z - a_k)$. Now, for $|z| \leq \frac{1}{2}|a_k|$ we have

$$\left| \frac{1}{z - a_k} \right| \leq \frac{1}{|a_k| - |z|} \qquad \text{by Art. 1.30, Vol. I}$$

$$\leq \frac{2}{|a_k|} \qquad \text{since } |z| \leq \tfrac{1}{2}|a_k|.$$

Selecting $p_k = 2/|a_k|$ (see note, Art. 16.21), we find that in the Mittag-Leffler Theorem we may take $G_k = 0$ for $k = 0, 1, 2, \cdots$, whence we may take

$$f(z) = \sum_0^\infty 1/(z - a_k).$$

Example: A function with first-order poles at the points $z = 1, 4, 9, 16, \cdots$ and with residues $= 1$ at these poles is

$$f(z) = \sum_1^\infty 1/(z - n^2).$$

16.23.   PROBLEM.   Construct an $f(z)$ analytic except for singu-
larities at the points $a_0 = 0, a_1, a_2, \cdots$, where $\sum_1^\infty 1/|a_k|^2$ converges.

Let us construct a function which has poles of the first order at
the points a_k and principal parts $1/(z - a_k)$. Now, for $k \neq 0$ and
$|z| \leq \min(\frac{1}{2}|a_k|, R)$, where R is arbitrarily chosen,

$$\left| \frac{1}{z - a_k} + \frac{1}{a_k} \right| = \left| \frac{z}{a_k(z - a_k)} \right|$$

$$\leq \frac{R}{|a_k|^2 - |a_k||z|} \qquad \text{by Art. 1.30, Vol. I}$$

$$\leq \frac{2R}{|a_k|^2}.$$

Selecting $p_k = 2R/|a_k|^2$ (see note, Art. 16.21), we find that in the
Mittag-Leffler Theorem we may take

$$G_0 = 0, \quad G_k = -1/a_k, \ (k = 1, 2, \cdots),$$

whence we may take

$$f(z) = \frac{1}{z} + \sum_1^\infty \frac{z}{a_k(z - a_k)}.$$

Example: A function with first-order poles at the points $z = 1, 2, 3, 4, \cdots$ and with residues equal to 1 at these poles is

$$f(z) = \sum_1^\infty z/n(z - n).$$

16.24.   THEOREM.   If $\sum_1^\infty 1/|a_k|^{\lambda+1}$ converges, then

$$f(z) \equiv \frac{1}{z} + \sum_1^\infty \left[\frac{1}{z - a_k} + \frac{1}{a_k} + \frac{z}{a_k^2} + \cdots + \frac{z^{\lambda-1}}{a_k^\lambda} \right]$$

is a function having first-order poles at $a_0 = 0, a_1, a_2, \cdots$ and having
residues equal to 1 at these poles.

This is a generalization of Articles 16.22 and 16.23.

Note: If $a_k = \log k$, then $\sum_1^\infty 1/(\log k)^\lambda$ diverges for all λ. Hence the
above theorem cannot be applied in this case and we must fall back upon
the Mittag-Leffler Theorem for the determination of the G's.

16.25. MORE COMPLETE STATEMENT OF THE MITTAG-LEFFLER THEOREM. If $f(z)$ is analytic in the unextended plane, except perhaps for isolated singularities at the points $a_0 = 0, a_1, a_2, \cdots$ with principal parts $P_{a_0}, P_{a_1}, P_{a_2}, \cdots$, then

$$f(z) = \sum_0^\infty [P_{a_k} - G_k(z)] + E(z),$$

where, if

$$P_{a_k} = \sum_{i=0}^\infty b_{ki}z^i, \quad k \neq 0,$$

and if $\sum p_k$, is a convergent series of positive terms, $G_k(z)$ for $k \neq 0$ is determined as

$$G_k = \sum_{i=0}^l b_{ki}z^i$$

such that

$$|P_{a_k} - G_k| < p_k, \quad |z| \leq \min(\tfrac{1}{2}|a_k|, R),$$

for any arbitrarily chosen R, and where $G_0 = 0$, and $E(z)$ is entire.

16.26. EXERCISE. Follow through the proof of the Mittag-Leffler Theorem for the function

$$f(z) = \frac{1}{e^{2iz} - 1}, \tag{1}$$

determining the polynomials $G_k(z)$ explicitly.

Clearly, $f(z)$ is analytic everywhere in the unextended plane except for the first-order poles

$$z = n\pi, \quad n = 0, \pm 1, \pm 2, \cdots.$$

Since

$$\varphi(n\pi) \equiv \lim_{z \to n\pi} \frac{z - n\pi}{e^{2iz} - 1} = \lim_{z \to n\pi} \frac{1}{2ie^{2iz}} = \frac{1}{2i},$$

we see that the principal part $P_{n\pi}$ at the pole $z = n\pi$ is (for $n \neq 0$)

$$P_{n\pi} = \frac{\varphi(n\pi)}{z - n\pi}$$

$$= \frac{1}{2i(z - n\pi)} \tag{2}$$

$$= \frac{i}{2n\pi}\left[1 + \frac{z}{n\pi} + \frac{z^2}{(n\pi)^2} + \cdots\right], \quad |z| < |n|\pi. \tag{3}$$

Also,

$$P_0 = \frac{1}{2iz}.$$ (4)

Let us order the poles in the following manner:

$$k: \quad 0 \quad 1 \quad 2 \quad 3 \quad \cdots$$
$$\text{Poles:} \quad 0 \quad -\pi \quad \pi \quad -2\pi \quad \cdots.$$

Then the kth pole is

$$z = \frac{k}{2}\pi \ (k \text{ even}), \quad z = -\left(\frac{k+1}{2}\right)\pi \ (k \text{ odd}).$$

Let us consider separately the two cases k even and k odd.

(a) k even ($\neq 0$). Then, from (3),

$$P_{a_k} = P_{(k/2)\pi} = \frac{i}{k\pi}\left[1 + \left(\frac{2z}{k\pi}\right) + \left(\frac{2z}{k\pi}\right)^2 + \cdots\right], \quad |z| < \frac{k\pi}{2}.$$

Therefore, in the circle $|z| < k\pi/4$,

$$\left|P_{a_k} - \frac{i}{k\pi}\left[1 + \left(\frac{2z}{k\pi}\right) + \cdots + \left(\frac{2z}{k\pi}\right)^k\right]\right|$$

$$= \left|\frac{i}{k\pi}\left[\left(\frac{2z}{k\pi}\right)^{k+1} + \left(\frac{2z}{k\pi}\right)^{k+2} + \cdots\right]\right|$$

$$\leq \left|\frac{i}{k\pi}\left[\frac{1}{2^{k+1}} + \frac{1}{2^{k+2}} + \cdots\right]\right|$$

$$\leq \left|\frac{i}{k\pi}\left[\frac{1}{2^k}\right]\right| \quad \text{(summing the infinite geometric progression)}$$

$$< \frac{1}{2^k}.$$ (5)

(b) k odd. From (3) we have

$$P_{a_k} = P_{-\left(\frac{k+1}{2}\right)\pi} = -\frac{i}{(k+1)\pi}\left[1 - \left\{\frac{2z}{(k+1)\pi}\right\} + \left\{\frac{2z}{(k+1)\pi}\right\}^2 - \cdots\right]$$

$$|z| < \frac{k+1}{2}\pi.$$

Therefore, in the circle $|z| < \dfrac{k+1}{4}\pi$,

$$
\left| P_{a_k} + \frac{i}{(k+1)\pi}\left[1 - \left\{ \frac{2z}{(k+1)\pi} \right\} + \cdots - \left\{ \frac{2z}{(k+1)\pi} \right\}^k \right] \right|
$$

$$
= \left| \frac{i}{(k+1)\pi}\left[\left\{ \frac{2z}{(k+1)\pi} \right\}^{k+1} - \left\{ \frac{2z}{(k+1)\pi} \right\}^{k+2} + \cdots \right] \right|
$$

$$
\leq \left| \frac{1}{(k+1)\pi}\left[\frac{1}{2^{k+1}} + \frac{1}{2^{k+2}} + \cdots \right] \right|
$$

$$
\leq \left| \frac{1}{(k+1)\pi}\left[\frac{1}{2^k} \right] \right|
$$

$$
< \frac{1}{2^k}. \tag{6}
$$

Therefore, by (5) and (6), we may take

$$
G_{a_k} = \frac{i}{k\pi}\left[1 + \left(\frac{2z}{k\pi}\right) + \cdots + \left(\frac{2z}{k\pi}\right)^k \right], \quad k \text{ even, } k \neq 0,
$$

$$
G_{a_k} = -\frac{i}{(k+1)\pi}\left[1 - \left\{ \frac{2z}{(k+1)\pi} \right\} + \cdots - \left\{ \frac{2z}{(k+1)\pi} \right\}^k \right], \, k \text{ odd,}
$$

$$
G_0 = 0.
$$

Or, writing these in terms of n, we have

$$
G_{n\pi} = \frac{i}{2n\pi}\left[1 + \frac{z}{n\pi} + \cdots + \left(\frac{z}{n\pi}\right)^{2n} \right], \quad n \text{ positive,}
$$

$$
G_{n\pi} = \frac{i}{2n\pi}\left[1 + \frac{z}{n\pi} + \cdots + \left(\frac{z}{n\pi}\right)^{-(2n+1)} \right], \quad n \text{ negative,}
$$

$$
G_{n\pi} = 0, \quad n = 0.
$$

Although these polynomials for G_{a_k} are not necessarily the "shortest" ones, they probably are as neat as any others.

    The proof of the Mittag-Leffler Theorem may now be followed through for the function (1), the polynomials G_{a_k} being those given above.

SOME PARTIAL FRACTION DEVELOPMENTS

16.27. **THEOREM.** $\cot z = \dfrac{1}{z} + \displaystyle\sum_{-\infty}^{\infty}{}' \left(\dfrac{1}{z - n\pi} + \dfrac{1}{n\pi} \right)$, $(z \neq n\pi)$,

where the prime on the $\sum$ indicates omission of the 0th term.

Proof: Now, $\cot z = \cos z / \sin z$ has singularities only at

$$z = n\pi, \quad n = 0, \pm 1, \pm 2, \cdots.$$

These singularities are poles of the first order. Moreover, since (by L'Hospital's Rule)

$$\lim_{z \to n\pi} (z - n\pi) \frac{\cos z}{\sin z} = 1,$$

we have the principal parts at the poles given by

$$1/(z - n\pi). \tag{1}$$

Further,

$$\sum 1/|n\pi| \text{ diverges}$$

but

$$\sum 1/(n\pi)^2 \text{ converges.}$$

Hence, by Article 16.24,

$$f(z) \equiv \frac{1}{z} + \sum_{-\infty}^{\infty}{}' \left(\frac{1}{z - n\pi} + \frac{1}{n\pi} \right)$$

is a function having first-order poles at $z = n\pi$, $(n = 0, \pm 1, \pm 2, \cdots)$, and with residues equal to 1 at these poles. Therefore $\cot z$ is either this function $f(z)$ or $f(z) + E(z)$, where $E(z)$ is some entire function. As a matter of fact,

$$\cot z = f(z).$$

To show that this is so, let us consider the function

$$F(z) = \cot z - \frac{1}{z}, \quad z \neq n\pi, n = 0, \pm 1, \cdots),$$

$$F(0) = 0.$$

Then, since

$$\lim_{z \to 0} \left\{ \cot z - \frac{1}{z} \right\} = \lim_{z \to 0} \frac{z \cos z - \sin z}{z \sin z} = 0, \qquad \text{by L'Hospital's Rule,}$$

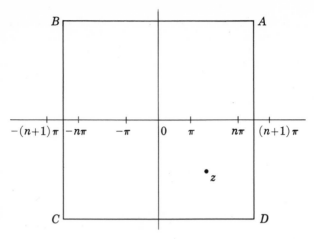

Figure 16.7

$F(z)$ is analytic at $z = 0$. As shown in Figure 16.7, we construct the square $ABCD$, where

$$A: \{(n + \tfrac{1}{2})\pi, (n + \tfrac{1}{2})\pi\},$$
$$B: \{-(n + \tfrac{1}{2})\pi, (n + \tfrac{1}{2})\pi\},$$
$$C: \{-(n + \tfrac{1}{2})\pi, -(n + \tfrac{1}{2})\pi\},$$
$$D: \{(n + \tfrac{1}{2})\pi, -(n + \tfrac{1}{2})\pi\}.$$
$$(2)$$

We call the boundary of this square C_n, and let $z \neq k\pi$ be any point inside the square. We consider the integral

$$\frac{1}{2\pi i}\int_{C_n} \frac{F(t)}{t - z}\, dt. \qquad (3)$$

Let us calculate the residue of $F(t)/(t - z)$ at the point t.
   (a) $t = z \neq k\pi$:

$$\lim_{t \to z} \frac{(t - z)F(t)}{t - z} = F(z). \qquad (4)$$

(b) $t = k\pi$:

$$\lim_{t \to k\pi} \frac{(t - k\pi)F(t)}{t - z} = \lim_{t \to k\pi} \{(t - k\pi)F(t)\}/(k\pi - z)$$

$$= \frac{1}{k\pi - z} \quad \text{by (1).} \qquad (5)$$

Hence, by Article 13.05, we have, since $t = z, k\pi$ are the only singularities of $F(t)/(t - z)$,

$$\frac{1}{2\pi i} \int_{C_n} \frac{F(t)}{t - z}\, dt = F(z) - \sum_{-n}^{n}{}' \frac{1}{z - k\pi}. \tag{6}$$

Now,

$$\frac{F(t)}{t - z} \equiv \frac{F(t)}{t} + \frac{zF(t)}{t(t - z)}, \tag{7}$$

whence (6) becomes

$$\frac{1}{2\pi i} \int_{C_n} \frac{F(t)dt}{t - z} + \frac{z}{2\pi i} \int_{C_n} \frac{F(t)dt}{t(t - z)} = F(z) - \sum_{-n}^{n}{}' \frac{1}{z - k\pi}. \tag{8}$$

Similarly, calculating the residue at t of $F(t)/t$, we have $t = k\pi$, $(k \neq 0)$:

$$\lim_{t \to k\pi} \frac{(t - k\pi)F(t)}{t} = \lim_{t \to k\pi} (t - k\pi)F(t)/k\pi$$

$$= \frac{1}{k\pi} \qquad \text{by (1)}, \tag{9}$$

and $t = 0$:

$$\lim_{t \to 0} \frac{tF(t)}{t} = F(0) = 0. \tag{10}$$

Therefore, by Article 13.05, we have

$$\frac{1}{2\pi i} \int_{C_n} \frac{F(t)}{t}\, dt = \sum_{-n}^{n}{}' 1/k\pi. \tag{11}$$

Substituting (11) in (8), we have

$$F(z) = \sum_{-n}^{n}{}' \left[\frac{1}{z - k\pi} + \frac{1}{k\pi} \right] + R_n, \tag{12}$$

where

$$R_n = \frac{z}{2\pi i} \int_{C_n} \frac{F(t)dt}{t(t - z)}. \tag{13}$$

Now let us show that $F(t)$ is bounded on C_n. With this end in mind, we note that:

(i) $\qquad\qquad$ $1/z$ is bounded for z on C_n, $\qquad\qquad$ (14)

(ii) $\qquad\qquad$ letting $z = x + iy$, then

$$\cos z = \cos (x + iy) = \frac{e^{i(x+iy)} + e^{-i(x+iy)}}{2}$$

$$= \frac{e^{ix-y} + e^{-ix+y}}{2},$$

$$\overline{\cos z} = \frac{e^{-ix-y} + e^{ix+y}}{2}.$$

Hence

$$|\cos^2 z| = \cos z \,\overline{\cos z}$$

$$= \frac{e^{-2y} + e^{2y} + e^{2ix} + e^{-2ix}}{4}$$

$$= \frac{e^{-2y} + e^{2y} + 2\cos 2x}{4}. \qquad (15)$$

Again,

$$\sin z = \frac{e^{i(x+iy)} - e^{-i(x+iy)}}{2i}$$

$$= \frac{e^{ix-y} - e^{-ix+y}}{2i},$$

$$\overline{\sin z} = \frac{e^{-ix-y} - e^{ix+y}}{-2i}.$$

Hence

$$|\sin^2 z| = \sin z \,\overline{\sin z}$$

$$= \frac{e^{-2y} + e^{2y} - 2\cos 2x}{4}. \qquad (16)$$

From (15) and (16) we have

$$|\cot^2 z| = \frac{e^{-2y} + e^{2y} + 2\cos 2x}{e^{-2y} + e^{2y} - 2\cos 2x}. \qquad (17)$$

Now on the side DA of the square we have

$$|\cot^2 z|\Big|_{z=(n+1/2)\pi+iy} = \frac{e^{2y} + e^{-2y} + 2\cos (2n+1)\pi}{e^{2y} + e^{-2y} - 2\cos (2n+1)\pi}$$

$$= \frac{e^{2y} + e^{-2y} - 2}{e^{2y} + e^{-2y} + 2} < 1. \qquad (18)$$

Similarly, on the side BC of the square we have $|\cot^2 z| < 1$.

Now, on the side AB we have

$$|\cot^2 z|\Big|_{x+(n+1/2)\pi i} = \frac{e^{(2n+1)\pi} + e^{-(2n+1)\pi} + 2\cos 2x}{e^{(2n+1)\pi} + e^{-(2n+1)\pi} - 2\cos 2x}$$

$$\leq \frac{e^{(2n+1)\pi} + e^{-(2n+1)\pi} + 2}{e^{(2n+1)\pi} + e^{-(2n+1)\pi} - 2}$$

$$= \frac{\{e^{(n+1/2)\pi} + e^{-(n+1/2)\pi}\}^2}{\{e^{(n+1/2)\pi} - e^{-(n+1/2)\pi}\}^2}$$

$$= \frac{\{1 + e^{-(2n+1)\pi}\}^2}{\{1 - e^{-(2n+1)\pi}\}^2}$$

$$\xrightarrow[n\to\infty]{} 1. \tag{19}$$

Therefore we must have $|\cot^2 z| < 2$ for z on C_n and n sufficiently large, say $n > n_0$. Thus $|\cot^2 z|$ is bounded on C_n. Therefore

$$|F(z)| \leq |\cot z| + |1/z|\Big|_{z \text{ on } C_n}$$

or

$$|F(z)| < N, \text{ say,} \tag{20}$$

for z on C_n and n sufficiently large, say $n > n_1$.

Now, from (13)

$$|R_n| \leq \frac{|z|N8l_n}{2\pi(l_n - |z|)}, \tag{21}$$

where

$$l_n \equiv (n + \tfrac{1}{2})\pi.$$

Since

$$|t - z| \geq |t| - |z| \geq l_n - |z|,$$

and since, for sufficiently large n,

$$l_n - |z| > 0,$$

it follows from (21) that

$$\lim_{n\to\infty} R_n = 0. \tag{22}$$

Therefore from (12) we have

$$\cot z = \frac{1}{z} + \sum_{-\infty}^{\infty}{}' \left(\frac{1}{z - n\pi} + \frac{1}{n\pi}\right). \tag{23}$$

16.28.   THEOREM. $\cot z = \dfrac{1}{z} + \displaystyle\sum_1^\infty \dfrac{2z}{z^2 - n^2\pi^2}$, $(z \neq n\pi)$.

Proof: $\cot z = \dfrac{1}{z} + \displaystyle\sum_{-\infty}^{\infty}{}' \left(\dfrac{1}{z - n\pi} + \dfrac{1}{n\pi} \right)$

$$= \dfrac{1}{z} + \sum_1^\infty \left(\dfrac{1}{z - n\pi} + \dfrac{1}{n\pi} + \dfrac{1}{z + n\pi} - \dfrac{1}{n\pi} \right)$$

$$= \dfrac{1}{z} + \sum_1^\infty \dfrac{2z}{z^2 - n^2\pi^2} \cdot$$

16.29.   THEOREM.

$$\tan z = \sum_{-\infty}^{\infty}{}' \left[\dfrac{1}{(n + \tfrac{1}{2})\pi - z} - \dfrac{1}{n\pi} \right] + \dfrac{1}{\dfrac{\pi}{2} - z}$$

$$= 2z \sum_0^\infty 1/[(n + \tfrac{1}{2})^2\pi^2 - z^2], \quad z \neq (n + \tfrac{1}{2})\pi.$$

Proof: We first establish a simple trigonometric identity. We have

$$\cot 2z = \dfrac{\cot^2 z - 1}{2 \cot z}$$

$$= \tfrac{1}{2} \cot z - \tfrac{1}{2} \tan z.$$

Therefore

$$\tan z = \cot z - 2 \cot 2z. \tag{1}$$

Substituting (23) of Article 16.27 in (1), we find

$$\tan z = \dfrac{1}{z} + \sum_{-\infty}^{\infty}{}' \left(\dfrac{1}{z - n\pi} + \dfrac{1}{n\pi} \right)$$

$$- \dfrac{2}{2z} - 2 \sum_{-\infty}^{\infty}{}' \left(\dfrac{1}{2z - n\pi} + \dfrac{1}{n\pi} \right)$$

$$= \sum_{-\infty}^{\infty}{}' \left[\dfrac{1}{z - n\pi} - \dfrac{1}{z - \dfrac{n\pi}{2}} - \dfrac{1}{n\pi} \right]$$

$$= \sum_{-\infty}^{\infty}{}' \left[\dfrac{1}{(n + \tfrac{1}{2})\pi - z} - \dfrac{1}{n\pi} \right] + \dfrac{1}{\dfrac{\pi}{2} - z}, \quad z \neq (n + \tfrac{1}{2})\pi \tag{2}$$

$$= \sum_1^\infty \left[\frac{1}{(n + \frac{1}{2})\pi - z} + \frac{1}{(-n + \frac{1}{2})\pi - z} \right] + \frac{1}{\frac{\pi}{2} - z}$$

$$= \sum_0^\infty \left[\frac{1}{(n + \frac{1}{2})\pi - z} - \frac{1}{(n + \frac{1}{2})\pi + z} \right] + \frac{1}{\frac{\pi}{2} - z} - \frac{1}{\frac{\pi}{2} - z}$$

$$= 2z \sum_0^\infty \frac{1}{(n + \frac{1}{2})^2 \pi^2 - z^2} \tag{3}$$

16.30. THEOREM.

$$\csc z = \frac{1}{z} + \sum_{-\infty}^{\infty}{}' (-1)^n \left(\frac{1}{z - n\pi} + \frac{1}{n\pi} \right), \quad (z \neq n\pi).$$

Proof: Use the identity

$$\csc z = \tan \frac{z}{2} + \cot z.$$

CHAPTER 17

Miscellaneous Theorems

CAUCHY-GOURSAT THEOREM

17.01. THEOREM. If $f(z)$ is continuous in a domain D and if $\int_\Gamma f(z)dz = 0$, where Γ is an arbitrary rectangle with sides parallel to the coordinate axes and lying entirely inside D, then $f(z)$ is analytic in D. (This is an extension of *Morera's Theorem*, Art. 11.34, Vol. I.)

Proof: Take z_0 *any* point in D and draw a rectangle in D with its sides parallel to the coordinate axes and having z_0: (ξ, η) as upper right corner (see Figure 17.1). Let $\omega:(a, b)$ be the lower left corner of the rectangle and let L_1 and L_2 be the broken lines shown in the figure connecting (a, b) with (ξ, η). Then define

$$F(z_0) = \int_{\substack{\omega \\ L_1}}^{z_0} f(z)dz.$$

This integral exists because $f(z)$ is continuous in D and L_1 is a regular curve in D (Art. 11.02, Vol. I). Hence

$$F(z_0) = \int_a^\xi f(x + ib)dx + i \int_b^\eta f(\xi + iy)dy \tag{1}$$

$$= U(\xi, \eta) + iV(\xi, \eta).$$

Therefore

$$\frac{\partial F}{\partial \eta} = 0 + if(\xi + i\eta), \tag{2}$$

since f is continuous.

Again (because of the hypothesis),

$$F(z_0) = \int_{\substack{\omega \\ L_2}}^{z_0} f(z)dz$$

$$= i \int_b^\eta f(a + iy)dy + \int_a^\xi f(x + i\eta)dx. \tag{3}$$

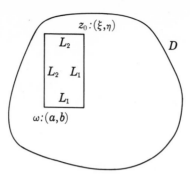

Figure 17.1

Therefore

$$\frac{\partial F}{\partial \xi} = 0 + f(\xi + i\eta).$$ (4)

Hence from (2) and (4) we have

$$\frac{1}{i}\frac{\partial F}{\partial \eta} = \frac{\partial F}{\partial \xi}.$$

That is,

$$\frac{U_\eta + iV_\eta}{i} = U_\xi + iV_\xi,$$

or

$$U_\xi = V_\eta,$$ (5)
$$V_\xi = -U_\eta,$$

and the $C\text{--}R$ equations hold for $F(z_0)$. Moreover, from (4)

$$U_\xi + iV_\xi = f(\xi + i\eta),$$

a continuous function. Hence U_ξ and V_ξ are continuous. Similarly, U_η and V_η are continuous. Therefore $F(z_0)$ is analytic (Art. 9.34, Vol. I).
But $F'(z_0) = f(z_0)$. Hence $f(z_0)$ is analytic in D.

17.02. GOURSAT'S THEOREM.   If $f(z)$ has a derivative in a domain D, then that derivative is continuous there and $f(z)$ is analytic in D (see Art. 9.32, Vol. I).

Proof: Since $f'(z)$ exists in D, then $f(z)$ is continuous in D. We let Γ be *any* rectangle with sides parallel to the coordinate axes and lying entirely within D. We *suppose*

$$\left| \int_\Gamma f(z)dz \right| = g > 0.$$ (1)

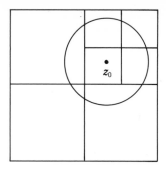

Figure 17.2

We divide the rectangle Γ (see Figure 17.2) into four congruent rectangles Γ_1, Γ_2, Γ_3, Γ_4. Then we have for at least one of these rectangles, γ_1, say,

$$\left| \int_{\gamma_1} f(z)\,dz \right| \geq g/4. \tag{2}$$

For we have

$$\int_\Gamma = \int_{\Gamma_1} + \int_{\Gamma_2} + \int_{\Gamma_3} + \int_{\Gamma_4}.$$

Hence

$$\left| \int_\Gamma \right| \leq \left| \int_{\Gamma_1} \right| + \left| \int_{\Gamma_2} \right| + \left| \int_{\Gamma_3} \right| + \left| \int_{\Gamma_4} \right|. \tag{3}$$

Now, if each term on the right of (3) is $<g/4$, then we would have

$$g < g/4 + g/4 + g/4 + g/4 = g,$$

which is impossible. Hence (2) must hold.

Treating rectangle γ_1 in a similar fashion, we have

$$\left| \int_{\gamma_2} f(z)\,dz \right| \geq g/4^2.$$

Continuing this process indefinitely, we have

$$\left| \int_{\gamma_n} f(z)\,dz \right| \geq g/4^n.$$

But this sequence of rectangles converges to some point z_0 inside or on the boundary of each rectangle γ_n.

Now set

$$\varphi(z) = \frac{f(z) - f(z_0)}{z - z_0} - f'(z_0). \tag{4}$$

Then

$$\lim_{z \to z_0} \varphi(z) = 0. \tag{5}$$

Solving (4) for $f(z)$, we have

$$f(z) = (z - z_0)\varphi(z) + f(z_0) + f'(z_0)(z - z_0).$$

Hence

$$\int_{\gamma_n} f(z)dz = \int_{\gamma_n} \varphi(z)(z - z_0)dz + 0 + 0.$$

Now, by (5), there exists a $\delta > 0$ such that, for any given $\epsilon > 0$,

$$|\varphi(z)| < \epsilon \text{ when } |z - z_0| < \delta.$$

Geometrically this claims that $|\varphi(z)| < \epsilon$ in some circle $|z - z_0| < \delta$. We now certainly can find an m such that γ_n is inside this circle $|z - z_0| < \delta$ for all $n > m$. Hence we have

$$g/4^n \leq \left| \int_{\gamma_n} f(z)dz \right|$$

$$= \left| \int_{\gamma_n} \varphi(z)(z - z_0)dz \right|$$

$$\leq \int_{\gamma_n} |\varphi(z)||z - z_0|ds$$

$$< \epsilon \frac{h}{2^n} \sqrt{2} \left(\frac{h}{2^n} 4 \right), \tag{6}$$

where h is the longer side of Γ. For then the longer side of γ_n is $h/2^n$ and the largest value of $|z - z_0|$ for z on the boundary of γ_n is $< (h/2^n)\sqrt{2}$. From (6) we have

$$g < 4\sqrt{2}h^2\epsilon. \tag{7}$$

But this is impossible if $g > 0$, for we may take ϵ as small as we please. Therefore the supposition (1) is at fault, and we must have

$$\int_{\Gamma} f(z)dz = 0$$

for *any* rectangle Γ with sides parallel to the coordinate axes and lying entirely within D. Thus we may apply Article 17.01, which proves that $f(z)$ is analytic in D.

HURWITZ'S THEOREM

17.03. HURWITZ'S THEOREM. If $f_n(z)$, $(n = 0, 1, 2, \cdots)$, are analytic in D, and if

$$\lim_{n \to \infty} f_n(z) = f(z)$$

uniformly in D, and if C is any simple regular closed curve in D lying with its interior entirely inside D, and if $f(z) \neq 0$ on C, then there exists an integer m such that $f_n(z)$ and $f(z)$ have the same number of zeros inside C for $n > m$.

Proof: By hypothesis, we have

$$|f(z)| > 0 \text{ on } C.$$

Moreover, $f(z)$ is analytic in D and hence $|f(z)|$ is continuous on C. Thus there exists an $M > 0$ such that

$$|f(z)| > M \text{ on } C.$$

Now, since the sequence $f_n(z)$ converges uniformly to $f(z)$ in D, there exists an m independent of z on C such that

$$|f_n(z) - f(z)| < M < |f(z)|, \text{ on } C, \tag{1}$$

for all $n > m$.

Let us set

$$g(z) = f_n(z) - f(z).$$

Now $g(z)$ and $f(z)$ are analytic in and on the boundary of C, and, by (1),

$$|g(z)| < |f(z)| \text{ on } C.$$

Hence, by Rouché's Theorem (Art. 13.27), $f(z)$ and $f_n(z)$ have the same number of zeros inside C for $n > m$.

17.04. THEOREM. If $f_n(z)$, $(n = 0, 1, 2, \cdots)$, is analytic in D, and if $\lim_{n \to \infty} f_n(z) = f(z)$ uniformly in D, and if $f(z) \not\equiv 0$ in D, then z_0 is a zero of $f(z)$ if and only if it is a cluster point of zeros of the functions $f_n(z)$.

This theorem is also due to Hurwitz but will not be proved here.

UNIFORM CONTINUITY

17.05.   HEINE-BOREL THEOREM.   If S is a set of open intervals such that to each x of $a \leq x \leq b$ there corresponds an interval T_x of S containing x, then there exists a finite number of intervals of S,

$$T_{x_1}, T_{x_2}, \cdots, T_{x_n},$$

such that every point x of $a \leq x \leq b$ is in at least one of them.

17.06.   THEOREM.   If $f(x)$ is continuous in $a \leq x \leq b$, then

(a) $|f(x)| < N$ for $a \leq x \leq b$;

(b) $f(x) > 0$ in $a \leq x \leq b$ implies that $f(x) > M > 0$ for $a \leq x \leq b$;

(c) $f(x)$ has both a maximum and a minimum in $a \leq x \leq b$;

(d) $f(a) \gtreqless 0$ and $f(b) \lesseqgtr 0$ implies that $f(\xi) = 0$ for some ξ in $a < \xi < b$.

17.07.   DEFINITION. $f(x)$ is *uniformly continuous* in an interval I if to an arbitrary $\epsilon > 0$ there corresponds a $\delta > 0$ such that for every pair of numbers x', x'' in I for which $|x' - x''| < \delta$ we have

$$|f(x') - f(x'')| < \epsilon.$$

17.08.   THEOREM. $f(x)$ is uniformly continuous in an interval I if to an arbitrary $\epsilon > 0$ there corresponds a $\delta > 0$ independent of x in I such that

$$|f(x + h) - f(x)| < \epsilon, \quad 0 \leq h < \delta.$$

Proof: This theorem is equivalent to the definition in Article 17.07. For set

$$x + h = \max(x', x''), \quad x = \min(x', x'').$$

Note: The interval I in Articles 17.07 and 17.08 may be an infinite interval.

17.09.   EXAMPLES.   (a) $f(x) = x^2$, $(0 < x \leq 1)$. Here we have

$$|(x + h)^2 - x^2| = |2xh + h^2|$$

$$= 2xh + h^2 \qquad \text{since } x > 0, h > 0$$

$$\leq 2h + h^2.$$

But this latter may be made less than any ϵ by taking h sufficiently small. Hence $f(x) = x^2$ is uniformly continuous in $0 < x \leq 1$.

(b) $f(x) = 1/x$, $(0 < x \leq 1)$. Here we have

$$\left| \frac{1}{x+h} - \frac{1}{x} \right| = \left| \frac{h}{x(x+h)} \right|$$

$$= \frac{h}{x(x+h)} \qquad \text{since } x > 0, h > 0.$$

Hence $f(x) = 1/x$ is *not* uniformly continuous in $0 < x \leq 1$ (although it is continuous there). For suppose it is. Then there exists a δ independent of x such that

$$\frac{h}{x(x+h)} < \epsilon, \quad 0 \leq h < \delta,$$

for all x in $0 < x \leq 1$. But this is impossible, as is seen by letting $x \to 0$.

Hence *continuity in I does not necessarily imply uniform continuity in I.*

(c) $f(x) = x/\log x$, $(1 < x < \infty)$. Suppose $x/\log x$ is uniformly continuous in $1 < x < \infty$. Then, for given $\epsilon > 0$, there exists a $\delta > 0$ such that

$$\left| \frac{x+h}{\log(x+h)} - \frac{x}{\log x} \right| < \epsilon, \quad 0 \leq h < \delta, \tag{1}$$

for all x in the interval. Thus (1) must hold for some positive h. But this is impossible, for as $x \to 1$,

$$\frac{x+h}{\log(x+h)} \to \frac{1+h}{\log(1+h)} = c, \text{ a constant,}$$

and

$$\frac{x}{\log x} \to \infty.$$

Hence we may take x so near to 1 that the left side of (1) may be made as large as we please, and hence be larger than ϵ. Hence the initial assumption is false, and $x/\log x$ is *not* uniformly continuous in $1 < x < \infty$.

(d) $f(x) = x \log x$, $(0 < x < \infty)$. Suppose $x \log x$ is uniformly continuous in $0 < x < \infty$. Then, for given $\epsilon > 0$, there exists a $\delta > 0$ such that

$$|(x+h)\log(x+h) - x \log x| < \epsilon,$$

where $0 \leq h < \delta$ and for all x. Then, for some positive h,

$$|(x + h) \log(x + h) - x \log x| = \left| x \log \left(\frac{x + h}{x} \right) + h \log(x + h) \right|$$

$$= \left| x \log \left(1 + \frac{h}{x} \right) + h \log(x + h) \right| < \epsilon. \tag{2}$$

Now, taking $x > 1$, both terms in (2) are positive and hence, for $x > 1$,

$$\left| x \log \left(1 + \frac{h}{x} \right) + h \log(x + h) \right| > h \log(x + h). \tag{3}$$

But the right side of (3) may be made as great as we please by increasing x, and hence made greater than ϵ. Thus the initial assumption is incorrect and $x \log x$ is *not* uniformly continuous in $0 < x < \infty$.

17.10. THEOREM.   Uniform continuity in I implies ordinary continuity in I.

Proof: The proof follows from the definition in Article 17.07.

17.11. THEOREM.   If $f(x)$ is uniformly continuous in I, then it is uniformly continuous in any subinterval I' of I.

Proof: The proof follows from the definition in Article 17.07.

17.12. THEOREM.   If $f(x)$ is continuous in the *closed* interval $a \leq x \leq b$, then it is uniformly continuous there.

Proof: Since $f(x)$ is continuous in $[a, b]$, it is continuous at each point of $[a, b]$. That is, given any $\epsilon > 0$, there exists a $\delta_{\bar{x}}/2$ such that, for any point $\bar{x}$ of $[a, b]$,

$$|f(x) - f(\bar{x})| < \epsilon/2, \quad |x - \bar{x}| < \delta_{\bar{x}}, \quad x \text{ in } [a, b].$$

Thus for each point $\bar{x}$ in $[a, b]$ there is associated an open interval T_k, say, of length δ_k. Hence, by the Heine-Borel Theorem (Art. 17.05), a finite number of these intervals

$$T_{x_1}, T_{x_2}, \cdots, T_{x_n}$$

exist such that every point of $[a, b]$ is in at least one of them. To each of these intervals corresponds a $\delta/2$, say

$$\delta_{x_1}/2, \delta_{x_2}/2, \cdots, \delta_{x_n}/2.$$

Let

$$\delta = \min(\delta_{x_1}/2, \delta_{x_2}/2, \cdots, \delta_{x_n}/2).$$

Take an arbitrary point x' in $[a, b]$ and suppose it lies in T_{x_k}. Then

$$|x' - x_k| < \delta_{x_k}/2 \tag{1}$$

and

$$|f(x') - f(x_k)| < \epsilon/2. \tag{2}$$

Now take x'' such that

$$|x'' - x'| < \delta \leq \delta_{x_k}/2. \tag{3}$$

Then, from (1) and (3),

$$|x'' - x_k| < \delta_{x_k},$$

whence

$$|f(x'') - f(x_k)| < \epsilon/2. \tag{4}$$

Therefore, from (2) and (4), we have

$$|f(x') - f(x'')| < \epsilon, \quad |x' - x''| < \delta,$$

which proves the theorem.

Example: Show that $x \log x$ is uniformly continuous in $0 < x \leq 1$.

We know that both $\log x$ and x, and hence $x \log x$, are continuous in $0 < x < \infty$. Let us define

$$x \log x|_{x=0} = \lim_{x \to 0+} x \log x = 0.$$

Then $x \log x$ is also continuous at $x = 0$. Hence $x \log x$ is certainly continuous in the *closed* interval $0 \leq x \leq 1$, and therefore uniformly continuous there. *A fortiori*, then, is $x \log x$ uniformly continuous in $0 < x \leq 1$.

CHAPTER 18

Infinite Products

CONVERGENCE

18.01. DEFINITION. An *infinite product* is an expression of the form

$$\prod_{n=0}^{\infty} (1 + u_n) = (1 + u_0)(1 + u_1)(1 + u_2)\cdots, \qquad \text{(A)}$$

where the u_n are arbitrary complex constants.

18.02. DEFINITIONS. The infinite product (A) *converges* if and only if

(1) an integer m exists such that $u_n \neq -1$ for $n > m$,

(2) $\lim_{q \to \infty} (1 + u_{m+1})(1 + u_{m+2}) \cdots (1 + u_{m+q}) = U_m,$

(3) $U_m \neq 0, \neq \infty.$

The *value* of the infinite product is

$$(1 + u_0)(1 + u_1) \cdots (1 + u_m)U_m.$$

18.03. DEFINITION. The infinite product (A) *diverges* if it does not converge.

Ways in which (A) might diverge are

(1) $u_n = -1$ for infinitely many n,

(2) U_m does not exist,

(3) $U_m = 0.$

173

18.04. DEFINITION. If $U_m = 0$, then we say that (A) *diverges to zero.*

Examples

(a) $\displaystyle\prod_{1}^{\infty}\left(1 - \frac{1}{n}\right) = 0 \cdot \frac{1}{2} \cdot \frac{2}{3} \cdot \frac{3}{4} \cdots$ (1)

Now,

$$\frac{1}{2} \cdot \frac{2}{3} \cdot \frac{3}{4} \cdots \cdot \frac{(n-1)}{n} = \frac{1}{n}$$

and

$$U_1 = \lim_{n \to \infty} \frac{1}{n} = 0.$$

Hence (1) diverges to zero.

(b) $(1 - \tfrac{1}{2})(1 + \tfrac{1}{3})(1 - \tfrac{1}{4})(1 + \tfrac{1}{5}) \cdots = \tfrac{1}{2} \cdot \tfrac{4}{3} \cdot \tfrac{3}{4} \cdot \tfrac{6}{5} \cdot \tfrac{5}{6} \cdots.$ (2)

Now, if there are an odd number of factors, the partial product equals $\tfrac{1}{2}$. If there are an even number of factors, the product has the form

$$\frac{1}{2}\frac{2n}{2n-1} = \frac{n}{2n-1},$$

which in the limit as $n \to \infty$ is again $\tfrac{1}{2}$. Hence (2) converges to $\tfrac{1}{2}$.

If 0 were prefixed as the first factor of (2), then (2) would *converge* to zero.

18.05. THEOREM. A convergent infinite product has the value 0 if and only if one of its factors is 0.

Proof: This theorem follows immediately from Article 18.02.

18.06. ASSUMPTION. We shall assume from now on that our infinite product contains no zero factor.

18.07. THEOREM. If (A) converges, then $u_n \to 0$ (or $1 + u_n \to 1$).

Proof: Let

$$p_{n'} = (1 + u_0)(1 + u_1) \cdots (1 + u_n).$$

Then

$$\lim_{n \to \infty} p_n = p, \quad p \neq 0.$$

Similarly,

$$\lim_{n \to \infty} p_{n-1} = p.$$

Therefore

$$1 + u_n = \frac{p_n}{p_{n-1}} \to 1,$$

or

$$u_n \to 0.$$

Notes: (1) Thus the condition $u_n \to 0$ is a *necessary* condition for convergence. It is *not* a sufficient condition, as is seen by Example (a) of Article 18.04.

(2) It is because of this theorem that we prefer to represent an infinite product in the form $\Pi(1 + u_n)$ rather than Πa_n.

18.08. DEFINITION. The numbers u_n in (A) will be called the *terms* of the product (A).

18.09. THEOREM. If $u_n \geq 0$ (real) for all n, then $\displaystyle\prod_0^\infty (1 + u_n)$ converges or diverges with $\displaystyle\sum_0^\infty u_n$.

Proof: We shall make use of the inequality

$$1 + u_n \leq e^{\mu_n}. \tag{1}$$

From (1) we have, since $u_n \geq 0$,

$$u_0 + u_1 + \cdots + u_n \leq (1 + u_0)(1 + u_1) + \cdots + (1 + u_n) \tag{2}$$

$$\leq e^{u_0 + u_1 + \cdots + u_n}. \tag{3}$$

(1) Suppose $\sum u_n$ converges to M. Then

$$p_n \leq p_{n+1} \leq e^M.$$

Hence $\lim p_n$ exists and is not equal to 0. That is, the product also converges.

(2) Suppose $\sum u_n$ diverges. Then, from (2), we have

$$\infty \leq \lim_{n \to \infty} p_n,$$

and the product also diverges.

Examples

(a) $\qquad \frac{3}{2} \cdot \frac{4}{3} \cdot \frac{5}{4} \cdots = (1 + \frac{1}{2})(1 + \frac{1}{3})(1 + \frac{1}{4}) \cdots.$

Since the harmonic series $\frac{1}{2} + \frac{1}{3} + \frac{1}{4} + \cdots$ diverges, so does the product diverge.

(b)
$$\prod_{1}^{\infty} \left| 1 + \frac{i}{n} \right| = \prod_{1}^{\infty} \left(1 + \frac{1}{n^2} \right)^{1/2}.$$

Since the series $\sum 1/n^2$ converges, the product $\prod (1 + 1/n^2)$ converges, and hence the product $\prod (1 + 1/n^2)^{1/2}$ converges. (However, $\prod_{1}^{\infty} (1 + i/n)$ diverges.)

(c)
$$\prod_{1}^{\infty} \left(1 + \frac{1}{n(n+2)} \right) = \prod_{1}^{\infty} \frac{(n+1)^2}{n(n+2)}.$$

Here
$$\sum_{1}^{\infty} \frac{1}{n(n+2)} \ll \sum_{1}^{\infty} \frac{1}{n^2},$$

and hence converges. Therefore the product converges. The value of the product is given by

$$\lim_{n\to\infty} \left\{ \frac{2\cdot 2}{1\cdot 3} \cdot \frac{3\cdot 3}{2\cdot 4} \cdot \frac{4\cdot 4}{3\cdot 5} \cdots \frac{(n+1)\cdot(n+1)}{n(n+2)} \right\} = \lim_{n\to\infty} \left\{ \frac{2(n+1)}{n+2} \right\} = 2.$$

18.10. THEOREM. A necessary and sufficient condition that $\prod_{0}^{\infty} (1 + u_n)$, $(u_n \neq -1)$, converges is that to an arbitrary $\epsilon > 0$ corresponds an integer m such that

$$|(1 + u_{n+1})(1 + u_{n+2}) \cdots (1 + u_{n+k}) - 1| < \epsilon, \qquad (1)$$

for all $n > m$, $k = 1, 2, \cdots$.

Proof: (1) Suppose the product converges. Then

$$\lim_{n\to\infty} p_n = p \neq 0.$$

Also, by hypothesis,

$$p_n \neq 0, \text{ for all } n.$$

Therefore there exists an $M > 0$ such that

$$|p_n| > M, \text{ for all } n \qquad \text{(see note below)}.$$

Since the sequence $\{p_n\}$ converges, then, by Cauchy's Criterion, there exists an m such that, for a given $\epsilon > 0$,

$$|p_{n+k} - p_n| < M\epsilon, \quad n > m, k = 1, 2, \cdots. \qquad (2)$$

From (2) we have

$$\left| \frac{p_{n+k}}{p_n} - 1 \right| = |(1 + u_{n+1})(1 + u_{n+2}) \cdots (1 + u_{n+k}) - 1|$$

$$< \frac{M\epsilon}{|p_n|} < \epsilon.$$

(2) Conversely, suppose (1) holds. Then there exists an α such that, given $0 < r < 1$,

$$\left| \frac{p_{\alpha+k}}{p_\alpha} - 1 \right| < r, \quad k = 1, 2, \cdots, \tag{3}$$

or

$$1 - r < \left| \frac{p_{\alpha+k}}{p_\alpha} \right| < 1 + r, \quad k = 1, 2, \cdots. \tag{4}$$

Also by our supposition, given $\epsilon > 0$, there exists an $m > \alpha$ such that

$$\left| \frac{p_{m+l}}{p_m} - 1 \right| < \frac{\epsilon}{1+r}, \quad l = 1, 2, \cdots. \tag{5}$$

We may write (5) as

$$\left| \frac{\dfrac{p_{m+l}}{p_\alpha}}{\dfrac{p_m}{p_\alpha}} - 1 \right| < \frac{\epsilon}{1+r}, \quad l = 1, 2, \cdots,$$

or

$$\left| \frac{p_{m+l}}{p_\alpha} - \frac{p_m}{p_\alpha} \right| < \left| \frac{p_m}{p_\alpha} \right| \frac{\epsilon}{1+r} < (1+r)\frac{\epsilon}{1+r} = \epsilon \quad \text{by (4)}.$$
$$l = 1, 2, \cdots.$$

Hence, by the Cauchy Criterion,

$$\lim_{n\to\infty} \frac{p_n}{p_\alpha} \text{ exists,}$$

and hence

$$\lim_{n\to\infty} p_n \text{ exists.}$$

Moreover, by (4), this limit is not equal to 0. That is, the product $\prod_{0}^{\infty} (1 + u_n)$ converges.

Note: *Lemma.* If sequence $\{p_n\}$ converges and if $p_n \neq 0$ for all n, $\lim \{p_n\} \neq 0$, then there exists a constant $M > 0$ such that $|p_n| \geq M$ for every n.

Proof: Let $\lim \{p_n\} = p$. Then, by hypothesis, $\frac{1}{2}|p| > 0$, and there exists an integer m such that, for every $n > m$,

$$|p_n - p| < |p|/2,$$

and therefore

$$|p_n| > |p|/2, \quad n > m.$$

Now set

$$M = \max\{|p_0|, |p_1|, \cdots, |p_m|, |p|/2\}.$$

Then clearly

$$|p_n| \geq M$$

for all n.

18.11.   THEOREM.   If u_n are real for all n, $\sum u_n$ converges, $\sum u_n^2$ diverges, then

$$\Pi \, (1 + u_n) \text{ diverges to } 0.$$

Proof: Since $\sum u_n$ converges, then $\lim_{n \to \infty} |u_n| = 0$, and hence there exists an m such that

$$|u_n| < 1, \quad n > m.$$

We now assume the following inequalities:

$$\frac{\frac{1}{2}u^2}{1 + u} < u - \log(1 + u), \quad 0 < u < 1,$$

and   (1)

$$\tfrac{1}{2}u^2 < u - \log(1 + u), \quad -1 < u < 0.$$

By the inequalities (1), we have, since $\sum u_n^2$ diverges and hence must diverge to $+\infty$,

$$u_{n+1} + u_{n+2} + \cdots + u_{n+p} - \log(1 + u_{n+1})(1 + u_{n+2}) \cdots (1 + u_{n+p})$$

$$= \sum_{n+1}^{n+p} u_n - \log \prod_{n+1}^{n+p} (1 + u_n) > g \qquad (2)$$

for n sufficiently large and greater than m, and where g is any positive preassigned number, however large. Hence, from (2), we have

$$\lim_{p \to \infty} \sum_{n+1}^{n+p} u_n - \lim_{p \to \infty} \log \prod_{n+1}^{n+p} (1 + u_n)$$

$$= \sum_{n+1}^{\infty} u_n - \lim_{p \to \infty} \log \prod_{n+1}^{n+p} (1 + u_n) = +\infty.$$

Therefore

$$\lim_{p \to \infty} \log \prod_{n+1}^{n+p} (1 + u_n) = -\infty$$

and

$$\lim_{p \to \infty} \prod_{n+1}^{n+p} (1 + u_n) = 0.$$

Hence the product diverges to 0.

Example

$$(1 - 1/\sqrt{2})(1 + 1/\sqrt{3})(1 - 1/\sqrt{4}) \cdots \text{ diverges to } 0.$$

ABSOLUTE CONVERGENCE

18.12. DEFINITION. $\prod_0^\infty (1 + u_n)$ converges *absolutely* if and only if $\prod_0^\infty (1 + |u_n|)$ converges.

18.13. THEOREM. $\prod_0^\infty (1 + u_n)$ converges absolutely if and only if $\sum_0^\infty u_n$ converges absolutely.

Proof: By Article 18.09.

18.14. THEOREM. If $\prod_0^\infty (1 + u_n)$ converges absolutely, then it converges.

Proof: (1) Set

$$p_n = (1 + u_0)(1 + u_1) \cdots (1 + u_n),$$
$$P_n = (1 + |u_0|)(1 + |u_1|) \cdots (1 + |u_n|).$$

Now,

$$
\begin{aligned}
|p_{n+1} - p_n| &= |(1 + u_0)||(1 + u_1)| \cdots |(1 + u_n)||u_{n+1}| \\
&\leq (1 + |u_0|)(1 + |u_1|) \cdots (1 + |u_n|)|u_{n+1}| \\
&= P_{n+1} - P_n > 0.
\end{aligned}
$$

Therefore

$$p_0 + \sum_0^\infty (p_{n+1} - p_n) \ll P_0 + \sum_0^\infty (P_{n+1} - P_n).$$

But since

$$\lim_{n \to \infty} P_n = P,$$

the dominating series

$$P_0 + \sum_0^\infty (P_{n+1} - P_n)$$

converges. Therefore

$$p_0 + \sum_0^\infty (p_{n+1} - p_n)$$

converges, whence we have

$$\lim_{n \to \infty} p_n = p.$$

(2) Consider

$$\frac{1}{p_n} = \left(\frac{1}{1 + u_0}\right) \cdots \left(\frac{1}{1 + u_n}\right)$$

$$= \left(1 - \frac{u_0}{1 + u_0}\right) \cdots \left(1 - \frac{u_n}{1 + u_n}\right). \tag{1}$$

Now,

$$\sum_{n_0+1}^\infty \frac{|u_n|}{|1 + u_n|} \ll \sum_{n_0+1}^\infty 2|u_n|, \tag{2}$$

for

$$|1 + u_n| \geq 1 - |u_n|,$$

and, since our infinite product is absolutely convergent, $|u_n| \to 0$, and therefore

$$1 - |u_n| \geq \tfrac{1}{2}, \quad n > n_0, \text{ say.}$$

Therefore, from (2),

$$\sum_{n_0+1}^\infty \frac{|u_n|}{|1 + u_n|}$$

converges, whence, from (1), by part (1),

$$\lim_{n \to \infty} 1/p_n \text{ exists } (\neq \infty).$$

Therefore

$$\lim_{n \to \infty} p_n = p \neq 0,$$

and our theorem is proved.

Examples

(a) Prove convergence and find the value of

$$\prod_2^\infty \left(1 - \frac{2}{n(n+1)}\right). \tag{3}$$

Here

$$\sum_2^\infty \left| -\frac{2}{n(n+1)} \right| \ll \sum_2^\infty 2/n^2,$$

which converges. Thus the product (3) converges absolutely, and hence converges.

The value of the product is given by

$$\lim_{n\to\infty} \prod_2^n \left(1 - \frac{2}{n(n+1)}\right) = \lim_{n\to\infty} \prod_2^n \frac{(n-1)(n+2)}{n(n+1)}$$

$$= \lim_{n\to\infty} \left\{ \frac{1\cdot 4}{2\cdot 3} \cdot \frac{2\cdot 5}{3\cdot 4} \cdot \frac{3\cdot 6}{4\cdot 5} \cdots \frac{(n-1)(n+2)}{n(n+1)} \right\}$$

$$= \lim_{n\to\infty} \left\{ \frac{1}{3} \frac{n+2}{n} \right\} = 1/3. \qquad Ans.$$

(b) Prove convergence and find the value of

$$\prod_2^\infty \left(\frac{n^3-1}{n^3+1}\right) = \prod_2^\infty \left(1 - \frac{2}{n^3+1}\right). \tag{4}$$

Here

$$\sum_2^\infty \left| -\frac{2}{n^3+1} \right| \ll \sum_2^\infty 2/n^3,$$

which converges. Thus the product (4) converges absolutely, and hence converges.

The value of the product is given by

$$\lim_{n\to\infty} \prod_2^n \frac{(n-1)(n^2+n+1)}{(n+1)(n^2-n+1)}$$

$$= \lim_{n\to\infty} \left\{ \frac{1\cdot 7}{3\cdot 3} \cdot \frac{2\cdot 13}{4\cdot 7} \cdot \frac{3\cdot 21}{5\cdot 13} \cdot \frac{4\cdot 31}{6\cdot 21} \cdots \frac{(n-1)(n^2+n+1)}{(n+1)(n^2-n+1)} \right\}$$

$$= \lim_{n\to\infty} \left\{ \frac{1}{3\cdot 3} \cdot \frac{2}{4} \cdot \frac{3}{5} \cdot \frac{4}{6} \cdot \frac{5}{7} \cdots \frac{(n-1)(n^2+n+1)}{n+1} \right\}$$

$$= \lim_{n\to\infty} \left\{ \frac{1}{3} \cdot \frac{2(n^2+n+1)}{n(n+1)} \right\} = \frac{2}{3}. \qquad Ans.$$

18.15. *LEMMA.* If $\prod\limits_{0}^{\infty} (1 + u_n)$ converges absolutely, then corresponding to an arbitrary $\epsilon > 0$ there exists an integer m such that

$$|(1 + u_\alpha)(1 + u_\beta) \cdots (1 + u_\lambda) - 1| < \epsilon$$

for $\alpha, \beta, \cdots, \lambda > m$.

Proof:

$$|(1 + u_\alpha)(1 + u_\beta) \cdots (1 + u_\lambda) - 1|$$

$$\leq |(u_\alpha + u_\beta + \cdots + u_\lambda) + (u_\alpha u_\beta + \cdots) + \cdots + (u_\alpha u_\beta \cdots u_\lambda)|$$

$$\leq |u_\alpha| + |u_\beta| + \cdots + |u_\lambda| + |u_\alpha u_\beta| + \cdots + \cdots + |u_\alpha u_\beta \cdots u_\lambda|$$

$$= (1 + |u_\alpha|)(1 + |u_\beta|) \cdots (1 + |u_\lambda|) - 1$$

$$\leq e^{|u_\alpha| + |u_\beta| + \cdots + |u_\lambda|} - 1 \qquad \text{by (1) of Art. 18.09.}$$

Suppose $|u_\nu| = \min\{|u_\alpha|, |u_\beta|, \cdots, |u_\lambda|\}$, and take p large enough so that

$$\nu + p > \alpha, \beta, \cdots, \lambda.$$

Then

$$|(1 + u_\alpha)(1 + u_\beta) \cdots (1 + u_\lambda) - 1| \leq e^{|u_\nu| + |u_{\nu+1}| + \cdots + |u_{\nu+p}|} - 1.$$

Now, by hypothesis, $\sum |u_n|$ converges. Therefore there exists an m such that, given $\epsilon > 0$,

$$|u_n| + |u_{n+1}| + \cdots + |u_{n+p}| < \log(1 + \epsilon)$$

for all $n > m$ and any p. Hence, if $\alpha, \beta, \cdots, \lambda > m$, we have

$$|(1 + u_\alpha)(1 + u_\beta) \cdots (1 + u_\lambda) - 1| \leq e^{\log(1+\epsilon)} - 1 = \epsilon,$$

and the theorem is proved.

18.16. THEOREM.   The factors of an absolutely convergent product can be rearranged without affecting the value of the product.

Proof: We are given that

$$p = \prod (1 + u_n) \tag{1}$$

converges absolutely. That is,

$$\sum |u_n| \tag{2}$$

converges. Now consider any rearrangement of (1), namely

$$p' = \prod (1 + u_n').$$

This product certainly converges absolutely since

$$\sum |u_n'|$$

converges by virtue of (2). (The terms of any absolutely convergent series may be rearranged.) Now

$$p_k \to p, p_k' \to p', \quad k \to \infty.$$

Let $\epsilon > 0$ be any given positive number. Then, by Article 18.15, an m and a q exist such that, for all $k > m$,

$$\left| \frac{p_{k+q}'}{p_k} - 1 \right| = |(1 + u_\alpha)(1 + u_\beta) \cdots (1 + u_\lambda) - 1| < \epsilon,$$

where $\alpha, \beta, \cdots, \lambda > k$. ($q$ is taken so large that p_{k+q}' contains all the factors of p_k; then $\alpha, \beta, \cdots, \lambda > k$.) Taking the limit as $k \to \infty$, we have

$$|1 - p'/p| \le \epsilon,$$

whence

$$p' = p.$$

UNIFORM CONVERGENCE

18.17. DEFINITIONS. $\prod\limits_{0}^{\infty} [1 + u_n(z)]$ *converges uniformly* in a region R if and only if the series

$$p_0(z) + \sum_{1}^{\infty} [p_n(z) - p_{n-1}(z)] \tag{1}$$

converges uniformly in R to $p(z) \ne 0$, where

$$p_n(z) = [1 + u_0(z)][1 + u_1(z)] \cdots [1 + u_n(z)].$$

The series (1) is known as the *collapsing series* of the given product.

18.18. THEOREM. If $u_n(z)$ is analytic in D, and if $\prod\limits_{0}^{\infty} [1 + u_n(z)]$ converges uniformly in D to $f(z)$, then $f(z)$ is analytic in D.

Proof: If $u_n(z)$ is analytic in D, so is $p_n(z)$ analytic in D. Hence the terms of the collapsing series are analytic in D. But the collapsing series converges uniformly to $f(z)$. Hence, by Article 14.82, $f(z)$ is analytic in D.

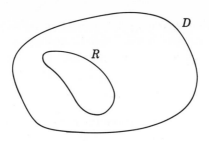

Figure 18.1

18.19. THEOREM.   If $u_n(z)$ is analytic in D, and if $\sum\limits_{0}^{\infty} |u_n(z)|$ converges uniformly in every *closed* region R of D, then

$$\prod_{0}^{\infty} [1 + u_n(z)]$$

converges uniformly to $f(z)$ in every such R and $f(z)$ is analytic in D (see Figure 18.1).

Proof: We wish to show that the collapsing series approaches $f(z) \neq 0$ uniformly in R. To this end, we have

$$p_0(z) + \sum_{1}^{\infty} [p_n(z) - p_{n-1}(z)]$$

$$\ll |p_0(z)| + \sum_{1}^{\infty} |1 + u_0(z)| \cdots |1 + u_{n-1}(z)||u_n(z)|$$

$$\ll |p_0(z)| + \sum_{1}^{\infty} (1 + |u_0(z)|) \cdots (1 + |u_{n-1}(z)|)|u_n(z)|$$

$$\ll |p_0(z)| + \sum_{1}^{\infty} e^{|u_0(z)| + \cdots + |u_{n-1}(z)|}|u_n(z)|$$

by (1), Art. 18.09.

We let

$$g(z) = \sum_{0}^{\infty} |u_n(z)|.$$

Then $g(z) \geqq 0$ and also, by Article 14.79, is continuous in any *closed* region R of D. Hence $g(z)$ has an upper bound M in R. That is,

$$g(z) < M \text{ in } R.$$

Therefore, returning to our dominant series, we have

$$p_0(z) + \sum_{1}^{\infty} [p_n(z) - p_{n-1}(z)] \ll |p_0(z)| + e^M \sum_{1}^{\infty} |u_n(z)|, \quad z \text{ in } R.$$

Now this series converges uniformly in R. But if a series is dominated by a uniformly convergent series, then the first series is uniformly convergent (see Art. 14.78). That is, the collapsing series converges uniformly in R. Hence, with the aid of Article 18.18, our theorem is established.

18.20.   EXERCISES.   (a) From the product development of $\sin z$, prove its periodicity.

We are given that

$$\sin z = z \prod_1^\infty (1 - z^2/n^2\pi^2) \qquad \text{(see Art. 19.07).} \qquad (1)$$

Therefore

$$\frac{\sin \pi z}{\pi} = z \prod_1^\infty (1 - z^2/n^2). \qquad (2)$$

We may take for p_n of (2)

$$p_n(z) = \left(1 - \frac{z}{n}\right)\left(1 - \frac{z}{n-1}\right) \cdots (1-z)z(1+z) \cdots \left(1 + \frac{z}{n}\right)$$

$$= \left(\frac{n-z}{n}\right)\left(\frac{n-1-z}{n-1}\right) \cdots (1-z)z(1+z) \cdots \left(\frac{n+z}{n}\right). \qquad (3)$$

Substituting $z + 1$ in (3) for z, we have

$$p_n(z+1)$$

$$= \left(\frac{n-1-z}{n}\right)\left(\frac{n-2-z}{n-1}\right) \cdots (-z)(1+z)(2+z) \cdots \left(\frac{n+1+z}{n}\right)$$

$$= -p_n(z)\frac{n+1+z}{n-z}. \qquad (4)$$

Hence, letting $n \to \infty$, we find that

$$z \prod_1^\infty \left(1 - \frac{z^2}{n^2}\right) = -(z+1)\prod_1^\infty \left(1 - \frac{(z+1)^2}{n^2}\right),$$

or

$$\sin \pi z = -\sin \pi(z+1),$$

or, putting z in place of πz,

$$\sin z = -\sin (z + \pi).$$

Hence

$$\sin z = \sin(z + 2\pi),$$

and $\sin z$ has the period 2π.

(b) Find the product development of $\cos z$.
We have

$$\sin 2z = 2 \sin z \cos z,$$

or

$$\cos z = \frac{\sin 2z}{2 \sin z}, \quad \sin z \neq 0$$

$$= \frac{2z \, \Pi \left(1 - \dfrac{4z^2}{n^2 \pi^2}\right)}{2z \, \Pi \left(1 - \dfrac{z^2}{n^2 \pi^2}\right)}$$

$$= \frac{\Pi \left(1 - \dfrac{4z^2}{n^2 \pi^2}\right)}{\Pi \left(1 - \dfrac{4z^2}{(2n)^2 \pi^2}\right)} \tag{5}$$

$$= \prod_{k=1}^{\infty} \left(1 - \frac{4z^2}{(2k-1)^2 \pi^2}\right), \tag{6}$$

for all the factors in the numerator of (5) which correspond to even n's cancel out by the denominator, leaving only factors corresponding to odd n's.

Problem: Justify the factor-by-factor division above in passing from (5) to (6).

CHAPTER 19

Entire Functions

19.01. DEFINITION. $f(z)$ is *entire* (or *integral*) if it is analytic in the unextended plane.

19.02. THEOREM. If $f(z)$ is entire and has no zeros, then it is of the form

$$f(z) = e^{E(z)},$$

where $E(z)$ is entire.

Proof: Since $f(z)$ is entire, so is $f'(z)$ entire, and therefore, since further $f(z)$ has no zeros, $f'(z)/f(z)$ is entire. Hence the Maclaurin expansion

$$f'(z)/f(z) \equiv c_0 + c_1 z + c_2 z^2 + \cdots \tag{1}$$

holds throughout the unextended plane. Now define K by means of the relation

$$e^K = f(0) \tag{2}$$

[select any particular value of K which satisfies (2)] and consider the function

$$E(z) = K + c_0 z + c_1 z^2/2 + c_2 z^3/3 + \cdots. \tag{3}$$

Clearly, $E(z)$ is entire. Set

$$g(z) = e^{E(z)}.$$

Then, since $g(z) \neq 0$,

$$g'(z)/g(z) = E'(z)$$
$$= c_0 + c_1 z + c_2 z^2 + \cdots \quad \text{by (3)}$$
$$= f'(z)/f(z) \quad \text{by (1).} \tag{4}$$

Hence, from (4),

$$(fg' - gf')/f^2 = 0,$$

or

$$\frac{d}{dz}(g/f) = 0.$$

187

Therefore

$$g/f = c, \text{ a constant.} \tag{5}$$

Putting $z = 0$, we see that

$$c = \frac{g(0)}{f(0)} = \frac{e^{E(0)}}{f(0)} = \frac{e^K}{f(0)} = 1 \qquad \text{by (2).}$$

Hence, from (5), we see that

$$f(z) = g(z) = e^{E(z)}.$$

19.03.   THEOREM.   If $f(z)$ is entire and has zeros only at the points $a_0, a_1, \cdots, a_m$, where

$$a_n = 0, \quad n \leq k - 1, \quad a_n \neq 0, \quad n \geq k,$$

then

$$f(z) = e^{E(z)} z^k \prod_k^m (1 - z/a_n),$$

where $E(z)$ is entire.

Proof: Consider the function

$$F(z) \equiv \frac{f(z)}{z^k \prod_k^m (1 - z/a_n)}. \tag{1}$$

(a) For $z \neq a_p$, both numerator and denominator of (1) are analytic. Hence the quotient $F(z)$ is analytic.

(b) For $z = a_p$, we have a_p as a root of the same order of both the numerator and the denominator. That is, we have

$$F(z) = \frac{(z - a_p)^{n_p} \varphi_p(z)}{(z - a_p)^{n_p} \psi_p(z)},$$

where n_p is an integer, $\varphi_p(z)$ and $\psi_p(z)$ are analytic and not equal to 0 at a_p. Hence, if we define

$$F(a_p) = \varphi_p(a_p)/\psi_p(a_p),$$

then $F(z)$ is analytic at a_p and not equal to 0 there.

Hence, combining (a) and (b), we see that $F(z)$ is entire with no zeros. Therefore, by Article 19.02,

$$F(z) = e^{E(z)},$$

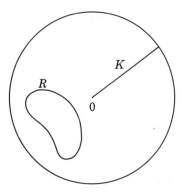

Figure 19.1

or, by virtue of (1),

$$f(z) = e^{E(z)} z^k \prod_{k}^{m} (1 - z/a_n).$$

Note: $f(z) = e^{E(z)} \prod_{0}^{m} (z - a_n)$ is equally general.

19.04. THEOREM. If $f(z)$ is entire and has zeros only at the points $a_0, a_1, \cdots$, where

$$a_n = 0, \quad n \leq k - 1, \quad a_n \neq 0, \quad n \geq k,$$

and if $\sum_{k}^{\infty} 1/|a_n|$ converges, then

$$f(z) = e^{E(z)} z^k \prod_{k}^{\infty} (1 - z/a_n),$$

where $E(z)$ is entire.

Proof: As shown in Figure 19.1, draw a circle with arbitrarily large radius K and with center at the origin. Suppose a_{N-1} is the last zero *inside* this circle. Set

$$f_1(z) = z^k \prod_{k}^{N-1} (1 - z/a_n), \tag{1}$$

$$f_2(z) = \prod_{N}^{\infty} (1 - z/a_n). \tag{2}$$

Take an arbitrary *closed* region R inside the circle. Then in R.

$$\sum_{n}^{\infty} \left| \frac{z}{a_n} \right| \ll \sum_{N}^{\infty} \frac{K}{|a_n|}. \tag{3}$$

But, by hypothesis, the dominant series in (3) converges. Hence, by Article 18.19, $f_2(z)$ is analytic inside the circle. Furthermore, by our choice of N, $f_2(z) \neq 0$ inside the circle.

Now, $f_1(z)$ has the same zeros inside the circle as has $f(z)$. Hence, by cancellation of these common roots, we see that

$$f(z)/f_1(z)f_2(z)$$

is analytic and not equal to 0 inside the circle. Hence, by Article 19.02, it equals $e^{E(z)}$. That is, we have

$$f(z) = e^{E(z)} z^k \prod_k^\infty (1 - z/a_n)$$

inside the circle. But the radius K of the circle was arbitrarily large. Hence the theorem.

Note: There are only a finite number of a_p's inside the circle, owing to the fact that $\sum 1/|a_n|$ converges.

19.05. LEMMA.   If $|u| < 1$, and if $1 + r = (1 - u)e^u$, then

$$|r| \leq \frac{|u|^2}{1 - |u|}.$$

Proof: We have

$$e^u = 1 + u + u^2/2 + \cdots + u^n/n! + \cdots,$$
$$-ue^u = -u - u^2 - u^3/2 - \cdots - u^{n+1}/n! - \cdots.$$

Hence

$$(1 - u)e^u = 1 - u^2/2 - \cdots - (1 - 1/n)u^n/(n - 1)! - \cdots.$$

Therefore

$$|r| \leq \frac{|u|^2}{2} + \cdots + \frac{1}{(n - 1)!}\frac{(n - 1)}{n}|u|^n + \cdots$$

$$\ll |u|^2 + \cdots + |u|^n + \cdots$$

$$= \frac{|u|^2}{1 - |u|}, \qquad \text{since } |u| < 1.$$

19.06. THEOREM.   If $f(z)$ is entire and has zeros only at the points $a_0, a_1, \cdots$, where

$$a_n = 0, \quad n \leq k - 1, \quad a_n \neq 0, \quad n \geq k,$$

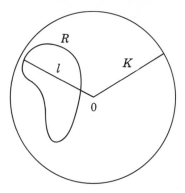

Figure 19.2

and if

$$\sum_{k}^{\infty} 1/|a_n|^2 \text{ converges,}$$

then

$$f(z) = e^{E(z)} z^k \prod_{k}^{\infty} [(1 - z/a_n)e^{z/a_n}],$$

where $E(z)$ is entire.

Proof: As shown in Figure 19.2, draw a circle with arbitrarily large radius K and with center at the origin. Suppose a_{N-1} is the last zero *inside* this circle.   Set

$$f_1(z) = z^k \prod_{k}^{N-1} [(1 - z/a_n)e^{z/a_n}],$$

$$f_2(z) = \prod_{N}^{\infty} [(1 - z/a_n)e^{z/a_n}],$$

and take an arbitrary *closed* region R inside the circle. Set

$$u_n(z) = (1 - z/a_n)e^{z/a_n} - 1.$$

Then, by Article 19.05, for z in R, $n \geq N$,

$$|u_n(z)| \leq \frac{\left|\dfrac{z}{a_n}\right|^2}{1 - \left|\dfrac{z}{a_n}\right|},$$

since $|z/a_n| < 1$ for z in R and $n \geq N$. Therefore

$$\sum_N^\infty |u_n(z)| \ll \sum_N^\infty \frac{\left|\dfrac{z}{a_n}\right|^2}{1 - \left|\dfrac{z}{a_n}\right|}$$

$$\ll \frac{K^2}{1 - l/K} \sum_N^\infty 1/|a_n|^2, \tag{1}$$

where l is the greatest distance of points in R from the origin. But the final dominant series in (1) is convergent, by hypothesis, and hence $\sum_n^\infty |u_n(z)|$ converges uniformly in R. Therefore, by Article 18.19, $f_2(z)$ is analytic inside the circle.

Now, $f_1(z)$ has the same zeros inside the circle as has $f(z)$. Hence we see that

$$f(z)/f_1(z)f_2(z)$$

is analytic and not equal to 0 inside the circle. Therefore, by Article 19.02,

$$f(z) = e^{E(z)} z^k \prod_k^\infty [(1 - z/a_n)e^{z/a_n}]$$

inside the circle. But the radius K of the circle was arbitrarily large. Hence the theorem.

19.07.   THEOREM. $\sin z = z \prod_1^\infty (1 - z^2/n^2\pi^2)$.

Proof: Sin z has zeros, all of the first order, at

$$\cdots -2\pi, -\pi, 0, \pi, 2\pi, \cdots,$$

$$\cdots a_4, a_2, a_0, a_1, a_3, \cdots.$$

Moreover, $\sum_1^\infty 1/n\pi$ diverges, but $\sum_1^\infty 1/(n\pi)^2$ converges. Hence, by Article 19.06, we have

$$\sin z = e^{E(z)} z \left[\left(1 - \frac{z}{\pi}\right)e^{z/\pi}\right]\left[\left(1 + \frac{z}{\pi}\right)e^{-z/\pi}\right]\left[\left(1 - \frac{z}{2\pi}\right)e^{z/2\pi}\right]\cdots$$

$$= e^{E(z)} z \left(1 - \frac{z^2}{\pi^2}\right)\left(1 - \frac{z^2}{(2\pi)^2}\right)\cdots$$

$$= e^{E(z)} z \prod_1^\infty \left(1 - \frac{z^2}{n^2\pi^2}\right). \tag{1}$$

We now show that $E(z) = 0$. To this end, we set

$$p_m = e^{E(z)} z \prod_1^m \left(1 - \frac{z^2}{n^2\pi^2}\right). \qquad (2)$$

Then $p_m(z) \to \sin z$ uniformly in any finite domain D. Hence, differentiating, we have

$$p_m'(z) \to \cos z,$$

and

$$p_m'(z)/p_m(z) \to \cot z, \quad z \neq n\pi, n = 0, \pm 1, \cdots.$$

Therefore, from (2),

$$\frac{p_m'(z)}{p_m(z)} = E'(z) + \frac{1}{z} + \sum_1^m \left[\frac{1}{z - n\pi} + \frac{1}{z + n\pi}\right],$$

and hence

$$\cot z = E'(z) + \frac{1}{z} + \sum_1^\infty \left[\frac{1}{z - n\pi} + \frac{1}{z + n\pi}\right]. \qquad (3)$$

But, by Article 16.28,

$$\cot z = \frac{1}{z} + \sum_1^\infty \frac{2z}{z^2 - n^2\pi^2}, \quad z \neq n\pi. \qquad (4)$$

Therefore, comparing (3) and (4), we see that

$$E'(z) = 0 \quad \text{or} \quad E(z) = \text{constant } C.$$

Hence we have, from (1),

$$\frac{\sin z}{z} = e^C \prod_1^\infty \left(1 - \frac{z^2}{n^2\pi^2}\right).$$

Now, letting $z \to 0$, we have

$$1 = e^C \quad \text{or} \quad C = 0.$$

Hence

$$\sin z = z \prod_1^\infty \left(1 - \frac{z^2}{n^2\pi^2}\right), \quad z \neq n\pi.$$

For the case $z = n\pi$, the proof is trivial.

19.08. WALLIS' PRODUCT.   In Article 19.07 we set $z = \pi/2$. We get

$$1 = \frac{\pi}{2} \prod_1^\infty \left(1 - \frac{1}{4n^2} \right),$$

or

$$\frac{\pi}{2} = 1 / \prod_1^\infty \left[\frac{(2n - 1) \cdot (2n + 1)}{2n \cdot 2n} \right]$$

$$= \prod_1^\infty \left[\frac{2n}{2n - 1} \cdot \frac{2n}{2n + 1} \right]$$

$$= \left(\frac{2 \cdot 2}{1 \cdot 3} \right) \left(\frac{4 \cdot 4}{3 \cdot 5} \right) \left(\frac{6 \cdot 6}{5 \cdot 7} \right) \cdots. \qquad (1)$$

Now we consider

$$p = \frac{2}{1} \cdot \frac{2}{3} \cdot \frac{4}{3} \cdot \frac{4}{5} \cdot \frac{6}{5} \cdot \frac{6}{7} \cdot \cdots \cdot a_n \cdots.$$

Then, by (1), we see that

$$p_1, p_3, p_5, \cdots \to \frac{\pi}{2}.$$

Also,

$$p_{2n} = p_{2n-1} a_n \to \left(\frac{\pi}{2} \right)(1) = \frac{\pi}{2}.$$

Therefore we may remove the parentheses in (1), thus obtaining *Wallis' Product,*

$$\frac{\pi}{2} = \frac{2}{1} \cdot \frac{2}{3} \cdot \frac{4}{3} \cdot \frac{4}{5} \cdot \frac{6}{5} \cdot \frac{6}{7} \cdot \cdots.$$

19.09. LEMMA.   If $|u| < 1$ and if

$$1 + r = (1 - u)e^{u + u^2/2 + \cdots + u^k/k},$$

then

$$|r| \le \frac{|u|^{k+1}}{1 - |u|}.$$

Proof: We have

$$e^u = (1 + u + u^2/2 + \cdots + u^n/n! + \cdots),$$

and therefore

$$
\begin{aligned}
e^{u+u^2/2+\cdots+u^k/k} &= 1 + (u + u^2/2 + \cdots + u^k/k) \\
&\quad + (\quad)^2/2! + (\quad)^3/3! + \cdots \\
&= 1 + \beta_1 u + \beta_2 u^2 + \beta_3 u^3 + \cdots, \text{ say.}
\end{aligned} \tag{1}
$$

Now, since $e^{u+u^2/2+\cdots+u^k/k}$ is entire, series (1) must converge for all u. Also, clearly,

$$
\beta_n > 0, \quad \beta_n \geq \beta_{n+1}.
$$

Multiplying (1) by $(1 - u)$, we have

$$
(1 - u)e^{u+u^2/2+\cdots+u^k/k} = 1 + (\beta_1 - 1)u + (\beta_2 - \beta_1)u^2 + \cdots. \tag{2}
$$

Now,

$$
1/(1 - u) = e^{\log(1-u)^{-1}} = e^{u+u^2/2+u^3/3+\cdots}. \tag{3}
$$

Hence, from (2) and (3), we see that when $k = \infty$ the β's all equal 1. Hence, when $k \neq 0$, we surely have

$$
\beta_n \leq 1.
$$

Therefore, from (2),

$$
\begin{aligned}
(1 - u)e^{u+u^2/2+\cdots+u^k/k} &= 1 + \alpha_1 u + \alpha_2 u^2 + \cdots, \quad |\alpha_n| \leq 1, \tag{4} \\
&= e^{\log(1-u)}e^{u+u^2/2+\cdots+u^k/k} \\
&= e^{-u-u^2/2-\cdots}e^{u+u^2/2+\cdots+u^k/k} \\
&= e^{-u^{k+1}/(k+1)-u^{k+2}/(k+2)-\cdots} \\
&= 1 + \alpha_{k+1}u^{k+1} + \alpha_{k+2}u^{k+2} + \cdots.
\end{aligned}
$$

Thus the first k α's in (4) are zero. [This can also be seen by differentiating (4).] Therefore we have

$$
r = \alpha_{k+1}u^{k+1} + \alpha_{k+2}u^{k+2} + \cdots.
$$

Hence

$$
\begin{aligned}
|r| &\leq |\alpha_{k+1}||u|^{k+1} + |\alpha_{k+2}||u|^{k+2} + \cdots \\
&\leq |u|^{k+1} + |u|^{k+2} + \cdots \quad \text{since } |\alpha_n| \leq 1 \\
&= \frac{|u|^{k+1}}{1 - |u|} \quad \text{since } |u| < 1.
\end{aligned}
$$

19.10. THEOREM. If $f(z)$ is entire and has zeros only at the points $a_0, a_1, a_2, \cdots$, where

$$
a_n = 0, \quad n \leq k - 1, \quad a_n \neq 0, \quad n \geq k,
$$

and if

$$\sum_{k}^{\infty} 1/|a_n|^{\lambda+1} \text{ converges,}$$

then

$$f(z) = e^{E(z)} z^k \prod_{k}^{\infty} \left[\left(1 - \frac{z}{a_n} \right) e^{z/a_n + (1/2)(z/a_n)^2 + \cdots + (1/\lambda)(z/a_n)^\lambda} \right]$$

where $E(z)$ is entire.

Proof: The proof of this theorem is similar to that of Article 19.06, only here we use the lemma of Article 19.09 in place of the lemma of Article 19.05.

19.11 DEFINITION.   A *primary function* is a function of the form

$$(1 - u)e^{u + u^2/2 + \cdots + u^l/l}.$$

We denote this primary function by the symbol

$$E(u, l).$$

19.12. THEOREM (due to Weierstrass).   If $f(z)$ is entire and has zeros only at the points $a_0, a_1, \cdots$, where

$$a_n = 0, \quad n \leq k - 1, \quad a_n \neq 0, \quad n \geq k,$$

then

$$f(z) = e^{E(z)} z^k \prod_{k}^{\infty} E(z/a_n, n),$$

where $E(z)$ is entire.

Proof: As shown in Figure 19.3, draw a circle with arbitrarily large radius K and with center at the origin. Suppose a_{N-1} is the last zero inside this circle. There must be such a last zero because, if there were not, the zeros would have a finite limit point. But such a point is a singularity (see Art. 11.66, Vol. I).

Set

$$f_1(z) = z^k \prod_{k}^{N-1} E(z/a_n, n),$$

$$f_2(z) = \prod_{N}^{\infty} E(z/a_n, n),$$

and take an arbitrary closed region R inside the circle.

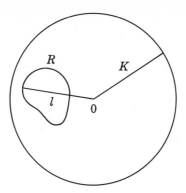

Figure 19.3

By Article 19.09, we have

$$|u_n| = E(z/a_n, n) - 1 \leqq \frac{\left|\dfrac{z}{a_n}\right|^{n+1}}{1 - \left|\dfrac{z}{a_n}\right|}, \quad n \geqq N.$$

Therefore

$$\sum_N^\infty |u_n| \ll \sum_N^\infty \frac{\left|\dfrac{z}{a_n}\right|^{n+1}}{1 - \left|\dfrac{z}{a_n}\right|}$$

$$\ll \frac{1}{1 - l/K} \sum_N^\infty \left\{\frac{K}{|a_n|}\right\}^{n+1}, \tag{1}$$

where l is the maximum distance from the origin to a point in R. Now,

$$|a_n| \to \infty,$$

and hence

$$K/|a_n| \to 0,$$

and we have

$$K/|a_n| < \tfrac{1}{2}, \text{ for all } n > n_0, \text{ say.}$$

Hence

$$\sum_{n_0+1}^\infty \left\{\frac{K}{|a_n|}\right\}^{n+1} \ll \sum_{n_0+1}^\infty (\tfrac{1}{2})^{n+1}. \tag{2}$$

But the dominant series in (2) is a convergent geometric series. Hence, from (1),

$$\sum_{N}^{\infty} |u_n|$$

converges uniformly in R, and therefore (Art. 18.19) $f_2(z)$ is analytic inside the circle.

Now, $f_1(z)$ has the same zeros inside the circle as has $f(z)$. Hence we see that

$$f(z)/f_1(z)\,f_2(z)$$

is analytic inside the circle and not equal to 0 there. Hence, by Article 19.02,

$$f(z) = e^{E(z)} z^k \prod_{k}^{\infty} E(z/a_n, n).$$

But the radius K of the circle was arbitrarily large. Hence the theorem.

19.13. SUMMARY.   If $f(z)$ is entire and has zeros only at the points a_n, then with
(1) no zeros

$$f(z) = e^{E(z)},$$

(2) finite number of zeros

$$f(z) = e^{E(z)} z^k \prod_{k}^{m} E(z/a_n, 0),$$

(3) infinite number of zeros, $\sum_{k}^{\infty} 1/|a_n|$ converging,

$$f(z) = e^{E(z)} z^k \prod_{k}^{\infty} E(z/a_n, 0),$$

(4) infinite number of zeros, $\sum_{k}^{\infty} 1/|a_n|^{l+1}$ converging,

$$f(z) = e^{E(z)} z^k \prod_{k}^{\infty} E(z/a_n, l),$$

(5) infinite number of zeros, no restriction,

$$f(z) = e^{E(z)} z^k \prod_{k}^{\infty} E(z/a_n, n).$$

Or

Case	No. of Zeros m	k	u	l	$E(u, l)$
(1)	0	0	0	0	$E(0, 0)$
(2)	m	k	z/a_n	0	$E(z/a_n, 0)$
(3)	∞	k	z/a_n	0	$E(z/a_n, 0)$
(4)	∞	k	z/a_n	l	$E(z/a_n, l)$
(5)	∞	k	z/a_n	n	$E(z/a_n, n)$

$$f(z) = e^{E(z)} z^k \prod_{k}^{m} E(u, l).$$

19.14. DEFINITION. The product

$$z^k \prod_{k}^{\infty} E(z/a_n, \lambda),$$

where λ is the *smallest integer* that makes the series

$$\sum_{k}^{\infty} 1/|a_n|^{\lambda+1}$$

converge, is known as a *canonical product*.

Note: If $a_n = \log n$, then there is no canonical product since no λ exists.

19.15. DEFINITION. If

$$f(z) = e^{P_m(z)} z^k \prod_{k}^{\infty} E(z/a_n, \lambda),$$

where $P_m(z)$ is a polynomial of degree m, then the *genus* of $f(z)$ is given by

$$g = \max(m, \lambda).$$

If $f(z)$ cannot be represented in this form, then the genus is said to be ∞. Thus the genus is ∞ if λ does not exist or if a $P_m(z)$ does not exist.

Thus, for sin z, we have

$$\sin z = z.\prod_{1}^{\infty} (1 - z^2/n^2\pi^2).$$

Here $m = 1, \lambda = 1$. Hence $g = 1$.

Again, in

$$f(z) = \prod_{0}^{\infty} (1 - z/n^2),$$

$m = 0, \lambda = 0$. Hence $g = 0$.

19.16. DEFINITION.   The smallest λ, or the greatest lower bound of λ, such that

$$\sum 1/|a_n|^{\lambda}$$

converges, is known as the *exponent of convergence*. This λ is not necessarily an integer.

19.17. THEOREM.   If $f(z)$ is meromorphic and has zeros only at the points $a_0, a_1, a_2, \cdots$, where

$$a_n = 0, \quad n \leq k - 1, \quad a_n \neq 0, \quad n \geq k,$$

and poles only at the points $b_0, b_1, b_2, \cdots$, where

$$b_n = 0, \quad n \leq l - 1, \quad b_n \neq 0, \quad n \geq l,$$

then

$$f(z) = e^{E(z)} \left\{ \frac{z^k \prod\limits_{k}^{\infty} E(z/a_n, n)}{z^l \prod\limits_{l}^{\infty} E(z/b_n, n)} \right\},$$

where $E(z)$ is entire.

Proof: If we call the brace $h(z)$, then $f(z)/h(z)$ has only removable singularities and no zeros. Therefore, by Article 19.02,

$$f(z)/h(z) = e^{E(z)}.$$

Hence the theorem.

Note: Thus a meromorphic function is the ratio of two entire functions.

CHAPTER 20

The Gamma Function

20.01. DEFINITION.   We define the *gamma function* $\Gamma(z)$ as

$$\Gamma(z) = \lim_{n \to \infty} \frac{n! n^z}{z(z+1) \cdots (z+n)},$$

where

$$n^z = e^{z \log n}$$

and $\log n$ is taken as real.

Note: This definition is due to Gauss.

20.02. DEFINITION.   We define γ, known as *Euler's constant*, by

$$\gamma = \lim_{n \to \infty} \left(1 + \frac{1}{2} + \frac{1}{3} + \cdots + \frac{1}{n} - \log n \right).$$

20.03. THEOREM. γ exists.

Proof: Take x such that $n \le x \le n + 1$. Then

$$1/(n+1) \le 1/x \le 1/n,$$

or

$$\int_n^{n+1} dx/(n+1) \le \int_n^{n+1} dx/x \le \int_n^{n+1} dx/n,$$

or

$$1/(n+1) \le \int_n^{n+1} dx/x \le 1/n,$$

or

$$0 \le \frac{1}{n} - \int_n^{n+1} \frac{dx}{x} \le \frac{1}{n} - \frac{1}{n+1}. \tag{1}$$

Hence, in particular,

$$0 \leq 1 - \int_1^2 \frac{dx}{x} \leq 1 - \frac{1}{2}$$

$$0 \leq \frac{1}{2} - \int_2^3 \frac{dx}{x} \leq \frac{1}{2} - \frac{1}{3}$$

. . . .

$$0 \leq \frac{1}{n-1} - \int_{n-1}^n \frac{dx}{x} \leq \frac{1}{n-1} - \frac{1}{n}.$$

Adding these inequalities, we obtain

$$0 \leq \left(1 + \frac{1}{2} + \cdots + \frac{1}{n-1} - \int_1^n \frac{dx}{x} \right) \leq 1 - \frac{1}{n} < 1. \qquad (2)$$

Now let us call the parenthesis in (2), u_n. Then,

$$u_{n+1} - u_n = \frac{1}{n} - \int_n^{n+1} \frac{dx}{x} \geq 0 \qquad \text{by (1)}.$$

Hence

$$u_n \leq u_{n+1}.$$

Also,

$$u_n < 1 \qquad \text{by (2)}.$$

Hence $\lim_{n \to \infty} u_n$ exists and is ≤ 1. But

$$\gamma = \lim_{n \to \infty} \left(1 + \frac{1}{2} + \cdots + \frac{1}{n} - \log n \right)$$

$$= \lim_{n \to \infty} \left(u_n + \frac{1}{n} \right)$$

$$= \lim_{n \to \infty} u_n.$$

Thus γ exists and is ≤ 1.

  Note: $\gamma = 0.5772156649 \cdots$.

20.04.   THEOREM. $\Gamma(z)$ exists, $(z \neq 0, -1, -2, \cdots)$.

  Proof: We have

$$\frac{z(z+1)\cdots(z+n)}{n!n^z} = \frac{z}{1}\frac{(1+z)}{1}\frac{(2+z)}{2}\cdots\frac{(n+z)}{n}e^{-z\log n}$$

$$= z(1+z)\left(1+\frac{z}{2}\right)\cdots\left(1+\frac{z}{n}\right)e^{-z\log n}$$

$$= z\prod_1^n\left[\left(1+\frac{z}{k}\right)e^{-z/k}\right]e^{z+z/2+\cdots+z/n-z\log n}.$$

Taking the limit as $n \to \infty$, we have (Art. 20.02)

$$\frac{1}{\Gamma(z)} = z\prod_1^\infty\left[\left(1+\frac{z}{k}\right)e^{-z/k}\right]e^{z\gamma}. \qquad (1)$$

We know from our study of infinite products that this limit (1) exists. Moreover, since this limit vanishes only at $z = 0, -1, -2, \cdots$, the reciprocal, or $\Gamma(z)$, exists except at these points.

Notes: (1) We thus see, by Article 19.06, that $1/\Gamma(z)$ is entire with zeros at $0, -1, -2, -3, \cdots$.

(2)

$$\Gamma(z) = \frac{1}{ze^{\gamma z}\prod_1^\infty[(1+z/k)e^{-z/k}]}, \quad z \neq 0, -1, -2, \cdots.$$

20.05. THEOREM. $\Gamma(z)$ is meromorphic with its only poles (which are all of the first order) at the points $z = 0, -1, -2, \cdots$. $1/\Gamma(z)$ is entire.

20.06. THEOREM. $\Gamma(z+1) = z\Gamma(z)$ for all $z \neq 0, -1, -2, \cdots$.

Proof: $\Gamma(z+1) = \lim_{n\to\infty}\dfrac{n!n^{z+1}}{(z+1)(z+2)\cdots(z+n+1)}$

$$= z\lim_{n\to\infty}\frac{n!n^z}{z(z+1)\cdots(z+n)}\lim_{n\to\infty}\frac{n}{z+n+1}$$

$$= z\Gamma(z).$$

20.07. THEOREM. $\Gamma(n+1) = n!, (n = 0, 1, 2, \cdots)$.

Proof: $\Gamma(1) = \lim_{n\to\infty}\dfrac{n!n}{(n+1)!} = \lim_{n\to\infty}\dfrac{n}{n+1} = 1.$

$\left.\begin{array}{l} \Gamma(2) = 1\Gamma(1) = 1 \\ \Gamma(3) = 2\Gamma(2) = 2 \\ \cdot\ \cdot\ \cdot\ \cdot\ \cdot\ \cdot\ \cdot\ \cdot\ \cdot \\ \Gamma(n+1) = n\Gamma(n) = n(n-1)! = n! \end{array}\right\}$ by Art. 20.06.

20.08.   THEOREM. $\lim\limits_{n\to\infty} \dfrac{\Gamma(z+n+1)}{n!n^z} = 1$, for all z.

Proof: (1) $z \neq 0, -1, -2, \cdots$.

$$\Gamma(z+n+1) = (z+n)\Gamma(z+n)$$
$$= (z+n)(z+n-1)\Gamma(z+n-1)$$

$$\cdot \quad \cdot \quad \cdot \quad \cdot \quad \cdot \quad \cdot \quad \cdot \quad \cdot \quad \cdot \quad \cdot$$

$$= (z+n)\cdots(z)\Gamma(z).$$

Therefore

$$\lim_{n\to\infty} \frac{\Gamma(z+n+1)}{n!n^z}$$

$$= \lim_{n\to\infty} \left\{ \frac{(z+n)\cdots(z)}{n!n^z} \right\} \Gamma(z)$$

$$= \frac{1}{\Gamma(z)} \Gamma(z) = 1, \quad z \neq 0, -1, -2, \cdots.$$

(2) $z = -k$. Take $n \geq k$. Then

$$\lim_{n\to\infty} \frac{\Gamma(-k+n+1)}{n!n^{-k}} = \lim_{n\to\infty} \frac{(n-k)!}{n!n^{-k}} \qquad \text{by Art. 20.07}$$

$$= \lim_{n\to\infty} \frac{n^k}{(n-k+1)\cdots(n)}$$

$$= \lim_{n\to\infty} \frac{n}{n-k+1} \cdots \frac{n}{n}$$

$$= 1.$$

20.09.   THEOREM.

$$\Gamma(z)\Gamma(1-z) = \pi/\sin \pi z, \quad (z \neq 0, \pm 1, \pm 2, \cdots).$$

Proof: $\dfrac{1}{\Gamma(z)} = \lim\limits_{n\to\infty} \dfrac{z(z+1)\cdots(z+n)}{n!n^z},$

$$\frac{1}{\Gamma(1-z)} = \lim_{n\to\infty} \frac{(1-z)(2-z)\cdots(n+1-z)}{n!n^{(1-z)}}.$$

Hence

$$\frac{1}{\Gamma(z)\Gamma(1-z)}$$

$$= \lim_{n\to\infty}\left\{z[1-z^2]\left[1-\left(\frac{z}{2}\right)^2\right]\cdots\left[1-\left(\frac{z}{n}\right)^2\right]\right\}\lim_{n\to\infty}\frac{n+1-z}{n}$$

$$= z\prod_1^\infty\left[1-\left(\frac{z}{n}\right)^2\right]$$

$$= \frac{\sin\pi z}{z}\quad\text{by Art. 19.07.}$$

20.10. THEOREM (due to Euler).

$$\Gamma(z) = \frac{1}{z}\prod_1^\infty\left[\left(1+\frac{1}{n}\right)^z\left(1+\frac{z}{n}\right)^{-1}\right],\quad z\neq 0,-1,-2,\cdots.$$

Proof:

$$\frac{1}{\Gamma(z)} = \lim_{n\to\infty}\frac{z(z+1)\cdots(z+n)}{n!n^z}$$

$$= \lim_{n\to\infty}\frac{z(1+z)\left(1+\frac{z}{2}\right)\cdots\left(1+\frac{z}{n}\right)}{(1+1)^z\left(1+\frac{1}{2}\right)^z\cdots\left(1+\frac{1}{n}\right)^z}\lim_{n\to\infty}\left(1+\frac{1}{n}\right)^z,$$

because

$$n = 2\cdot\frac{3}{2}\cdot\frac{4}{3}\cdot\cdots\cdot\frac{n}{n-1} = \frac{(1+1)\left(1+\frac{1}{2}\right)\cdots\left(1+\frac{1}{n-1}\right)\left(1+\frac{1}{n}\right)}{1+\frac{1}{n}}.$$

Therefore

$$\frac{1}{\Gamma(z)} = z\prod_1^\infty\left[\left(1+\frac{z}{n}\right)\left(1+\frac{1}{n}\right)^{-z}\right].$$

We reciprocate and obtain the theorem for $z\neq 0,-1,-2,\cdots.$

20.11. LEMMA 1. $\displaystyle\int_0^\infty e^{-t}t^{x-1}dt$ converges for $0 < x < \infty$.

Proof: This integral will converge if each of the integrals

$$\int_0^1 e^{-t}t^{x-1}dt\quad\text{and}\quad\int_1^\infty e^{-t}t^{x-1}dt,\quad 0 < x < \infty,$$

converges. Now, since

$$\lim_{t \to \infty} t^2(e^{-t}t^{x-1}) = 0, \text{ for all } x > 0,$$

then the second integral converges for all x. Also, the first integral converges for $x \geq 1$, since for such x it is an ordinary proper integral. The first integral also converges for $0 < x < 1$. For

$$\lim_{t \to 0} t^k(e^{-t}t^{x-1}) = 0 \quad \text{if} \quad k + x - 1 > 0,$$

and this condition is surely satisfied if

$$1 - x < k < 1.$$

Hence the first integral converges for $0 < x < \infty$. This proves the theorem.

20.12.   LEMMA 2. $\dfrac{n!}{z(z+1)\cdots(z+n)} = \sum\limits_{k=0}^{n} \binom{n}{k} \dfrac{(-1)^k}{z+k}.$

Proof: The residue of

$$\frac{n!}{z(z+1)\cdots(z+n)} \tag{1}$$

at $z = -k$ is given by

$$\lim_{z \to -k} \frac{(z+k)n!}{z(z+1)\cdots(z+n)}$$

$$= \lim_{z \to -k} \frac{n!}{z(z+1)\cdots(z+k-1)(z+k+1)\cdots(z+n)}$$

$$= \frac{n!}{-k(-k+1)\cdots(-1)(+1)\cdots(n-k)}$$

$$= \frac{n!}{k!(n-k)!(-1)^k}$$

$$= \binom{n}{k}(-1)^k.$$

Hence the principal part of (1) at $z = -k$ is

$$\binom{n}{k}\frac{(-1)^k}{z+k}.$$

Therefore, by the partial fraction development, we have

$$\frac{n!}{z(z+1)\cdots(z+n)} = \sum_{k=0}^{n} \binom{n}{k}\frac{(-1)^k}{z+k} + C \tag{2}$$

for all $z \neq 0, -1, -2, \cdots, -n$. (See Article 12.32.) We now show that $C = 0$. To this end, we set

$$\frac{z(z+1)\cdots(z+n)}{z+k} = N_k.$$

$N_k, (k = 0, 1, \cdots, n)$, is, then, a polynomial in z of degree $n - 1$. From (2) we have

$$\frac{n!}{z(z+1)\cdots(z+n)} = \frac{\binom{n}{0}}{z} - \frac{\binom{n}{1}}{z+1} + \cdots \pm \frac{\binom{n}{n}}{z+n} + C$$

$$= \frac{\binom{n}{0}N_0 - \binom{n}{1}N_1 + \cdots \pm \binom{n}{n}N_n + CzN_0}{z(z+1)\cdots(z+n)}. \qquad (3)$$

Now, each term but the last one of the numerator of the right side of (3) is of degree $n - 1$ in z. The last term, if $C \neq 0$, is of degree n. Since this is impossible, it follows that $C = 0$ and our theorem is established.

Note: We obtain an interesting identity from (2) by setting $z = 1$. We get

$$\frac{1}{1+n} = \binom{n}{0} - \frac{1}{2}\binom{n}{1} + \frac{1}{3}\binom{n}{2} - \cdots \pm \frac{1}{1+n}\binom{n}{n}.$$

20.13.   LEMMA 3. $\Gamma(x) = \lim\limits_{n \to \infty} \int_0^n \left(1 - \frac{t}{n}\right)^n t^{x-1} dt.$

Proof: Make the transformation

$$t = nu, \quad dt = n\,du.$$

Then

$$\int_0^n \left(1 - \frac{t}{n}\right)^n t^{x-1} dt = n^x \int_0^1 (1-u)^n u^{x-1} du$$

$$= n^x \int_0^1 \sum_{k=0}^n \binom{n}{k}(-1)^k u^{k+x-1} du \qquad \text{(binomial exp.)}$$

$$= n^x \sum_{k=0}^n (-1)^k \binom{n}{k}\frac{u^{k+x}}{k+x}\Big|_0^1$$

$$= n^x \sum_{k=0}^n \binom{n}{k}\frac{(-1)^k}{x+k}$$

$$= \frac{n^x n!}{x(x+1)\cdots(x+n)} \qquad \text{by Lemma 2.} \qquad (1)$$

Taking $\lim\limits_{n \to \infty}$ of both sides of (1), we obtain the desired result.

20.14.   LEMMA 4. $0 \leq e^{-t} - \left(1 - \dfrac{t}{n}\right)^n \leq \dfrac{t^2 e^{-t}}{n}$, for $0 \leq t \leq n$.

Proof: We have

$$1 + u \leq e \text{ , for all } u. \tag{1}$$

Therefore

$$1 - u \leq e^{-u}. \tag{2}$$

Hence, certainly,

$$1 + t/n \leq e^{t/n}, \tag{3}$$

$$1 - t/n \leq e^{-t/n}. \tag{4}$$

Now, since $0 \leq t \leq n$,

$$1 + t/n > 0, \quad 1 - t/n \geq 0.$$

Hence

$$(1 + t/n)^n \leq e^t, \tag{5}$$

$$(1 - t/n)^n \leq e^{-t}. \tag{6}$$

From (6) we have

$$0 \leq e^{-t} - (1 - t/n)^n, \tag{7}$$

and from (5) we have

$$1 \geq e^{-t}(1 + t/n)^n,$$

or

$$(1 - t/n)^n \geq e^{-t}(1 - t^2/n^2)^n,$$

or

$$e^{-t} - (1 - t/n)^n \leq e^{-t} - e^{-t}(1 - t^2/n^2)^n$$

$$= e^{-t}[1 - (1 - t^2/n^2)^n]$$

$$\leq e^{-t}[1 - (1 - t^2/n)] \tag{7'}$$

$$= e^{-t} \frac{t^2}{n} \cdot \tag{8}$$

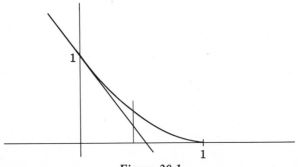

Figure 20.1

Results (7) and (8) establish the lemma. Step (7′) is shown as follows. As shown in Figure 20.1, the graph of the curve

$$y = (1 - x)^n$$

lies above its tangent at $(0, 1)$. The equation of this tangent is

$$y - 1 = -nx.$$

Hence

$$(1 - x)^n \geq 1 - nx. \tag{9}$$

Substituting $t^2/n^2 = x$ in (9), we find

$$(1 - t^2/n^2)^n \geq 1 - t^2/n.$$

This inequality establishes (7′).

20.15.   THEOREM. $\Gamma(x) = \displaystyle\int_0^\infty e^{-t}t^{x-1}dt$, for $0 < x < \infty$.

Proof: We have

$$\Gamma(x) - \int_0^\infty e^{-t}t^{x-1}dt$$

$$= \lim_{n\to\infty} \int_0^n \left(1 - \frac{t}{n}\right)^n t^{x-1}dt \qquad \text{by Lemma 3}$$

$$- \lim_{n\to\infty} \int_0^n e^{-t}t^{x-1}dt \qquad \text{by Lemma 1}$$

$$= \lim_{n\to\infty} \int_0^n t^{x-1}\left[\left(1 - \frac{t}{n}\right)^n - e^{-t}\right]dt. \tag{1}$$

Also,

$$\left|\int_0^n t^{x-1}\left[\left(1 - \frac{t}{n}\right)^n - e^{-t}\right]dt\right| \leq \int_0^n t^{x-1}\frac{t^2}{n}e^{-t}dt \qquad \text{by Lemma 4}$$

$$\leq \frac{1}{n}\int_0^\infty t^{x+1}e^{-t}dt \qquad \text{since integrand} > 0$$

$$= A/n,$$

where, by Lemma 1, A is some definite function of x. Hence

$$\lim_{n\to\infty} \int_0^n t^{x-1}\left[\left(1 - \frac{t}{n}\right)^n - e^{-t}\right]dt = 0.$$

Therefore we have, returning to (1),

$$\Gamma(x) = \int_0^\infty e^{-t} t^{x-1} dt.$$

Note: This links up Gauss's definition of the gamma function with the customary definition given for reals.

20.16.   THEOREM.   The residue of $\Gamma(z)$ at $z = -k$ is $(-1)^k/k!$, (k a positive integer).

Proof:

$$(z + k)\Gamma(z) = (z + k)\frac{\Gamma(z + 1)}{z} \qquad \text{by Art. 20.06}$$

$$= \frac{(z + k)\Gamma(z + 2)}{z(z + 1)}$$

$$\cdot \quad \cdot \quad \cdot \quad \cdot \quad \cdot \quad \cdot \quad \cdot \quad \cdot$$

$$= \frac{(z + k)\Gamma(z + k)}{z(z + 1)\cdots(z + k - 1)}$$

$$= \frac{\Gamma(z + k + 1)}{z(z + 1)\cdots(z + k - 1)}.$$

Therefore

$$\lim_{z \to -k} (z + k)\Gamma(z) = \frac{1}{-k(-k + 1)\cdots(-1)} = (-1)^k/k!.$$

The *principal part* at $z = -k$ is then

$$P = \frac{(-1)^k}{k!(z + k)}.$$

CHAPTER 21

Periodic Functions

SINGLY AND DOUBLY PERIODIC FUNCTIONS

21.01. AGREEMENT. In the following, $f(z)$ will always represent a single-valued function analytic except perhaps for isolated singularities.

21.02. DEFINITIONS. $f(z)$ is *periodic* if a complex number $\omega \neq 0$ exists such that

$$f(z + \omega) = f(z)$$

for all z not on the singularities.

Examples

$$
\begin{array}{ll}
\sin z & \omega = 2\pi \ (\text{or } 2n\pi), \\
\tan z & \omega = 2\pi, \\
e^z & \omega = 2\pi i, \\
17 & \omega = 23.
\end{array}
$$

ω is known as a *period* of $f(z)$. Note that every constant is a periodic function with any nonzero complex number as period.

21.03. THEOREM. If ω_1 and ω_2 are periods of a periodic function $f(z)$, then $n_1\omega_1 + n_2\omega_2$ is a period, where n_1 and n_2 are any integers.

Proof: This is obvious by successive applications of the definition in Article 21.02.

21.04. DEFINITION. The plane in which we plot the values of the periods ω will be known as the *period plane*.

21.05. THEOREM. If $f(z)$ is periodic and not constant, its periods are isolated in the unextended period plane.

Proof: Suppose there is a cluster point of the ω's. Then there is a set of ω's,

$$\omega_1, \omega_2, \omega_3, \cdots,$$

211

such that

$$\lim_{n \to \infty} \omega_n = \omega,$$

where ω is the cluster point. Thus the series

$$\omega_1 + (\omega_2 - \omega_1) + (\omega_3 - \omega_2) + \cdots$$

converges to ω. Set

$$\Omega_n = \omega_n - \omega_{n-1}.$$

Certainly,

$$\Omega_n \to 0 \quad \text{as} \quad n \to \infty. \tag{1}$$

But, by Article 21.03, Ω_n itself is a period.

Returning to the z-plane, let z_0 be a point at which $f(z)$ is analytic. Form

$$F(z) = f(z) - f(z_0).$$

Then $F(z)$ is analytic and not constant and vanishes at z_0. Hence, since z_0 is a zero of an analytic nonconstant function, it is an isolated zero of $F(z)$. Now,

$$\begin{aligned} F(z_0 + \Omega_n) &= f(z_0 + \Omega_n) - f(z_0) \\ &= f(z_0) - f(z_0) \\ &= 0. \end{aligned}$$

Hence $z_0 + \Omega_n$ is also a zero of $F(z)$. But, because of (1), we see that z_0 cannot be an isolated zero of $F(z)$. This is a contradiction.

Hence there is no cluster point of the ω's in the unextended period plane. This proves the theorem.

21.06.   DEFINITION.   A periodic function $f(z)$ is said to be *simply periodic* if all its periods are integral multiples of a single period.

Notes: (1) Thus a simply periodic function is nonconstant.
(2) Simply periodic functions exist, e.g., $\sin z$ and e^z.

21.07.   THEOREM.   If $f(z)$ is periodic, then it is simply periodic if and only if all its periods lie on a straight line through the origin in the period plane.

Proof: (1) Suppose $f(z)$ is simply periodic. Then an $\omega_1 \neq 0$ exists such that

$$f(z + \omega_1) = f(z),$$

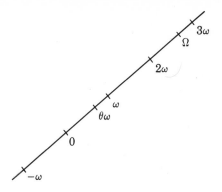

Figure 21.1

z not on a singularity, and all the periods of $f(z)$ are given by

$$\omega = n\omega_1, \quad n \text{ an integer.}$$

Plotting these points, we find that they all lie on a line through the origin in the period plane.

(2) Suppose the periods ω all lie on a line through the origin (see Figure 21.1). Now, by Article 21.05, these periods are isolated. Hence there exists an ω on the line nearest to the origin. Plot the points $n\omega$, n integral. These, by Article 21.03, are certainly periods. Moreover, these are all the periods. For suppose they are not and that

$$\Omega = n\omega + \theta\omega, \quad 0 < \theta < 1,$$

is one. Then, by Article 21.03, $\theta\omega$ is also one. But $\theta\omega$ is nearer the origin than ω, which is a contradiction. Hence Ω is not a period.

21.08. DEFINITION.   That period of which all other periods of a simply periodic function are integral multiples is known as a *primitive period*.

There are two primitive periods, ω and $-\omega$. They are the nonzero periods of least absolute value.

21.09. DEFINITIONS.   A periodic function $f(z)$ is said to be *doubly periodic* if all of its periods are expressible in terms of two particular periods ω_1 and ω_2 by the equation

$$\omega = n_1\omega_1 + n_2\omega_2,$$

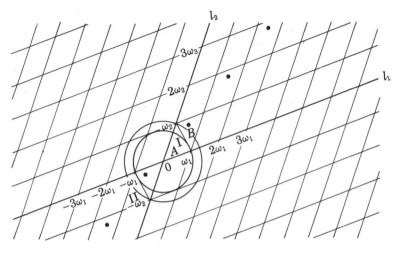

Figure 21.2

where n_1 and n_2 are integers, and if $f(z)$ is not simply periodic. We see that a doubly periodic function is nonconstant.

ω_1 and ω_2 are called the *primitive periods* of the doubly periodic function $f(z)$.

21.10.   THEOREM (due to Jacobi).   Any nonconstant periodic function $f(z)$ is either simply or doubly periodic.

Proof: Since $f(z)$ is nonconstant, the periods are isolated. Plot them. There are two cases.

(1) If the periods are all multiples of a single period, then they are all collinear with the origin, and the function is simply periodic (Art. 21.07).

(2) Now consider the case where the periods are not all multiples of a single period. Since the periods are isolated, there is a circle C_1 with center at the origin and which passes through that period nearest to the origin (see Figure 21.2). There are at least two periods on this circle (reflections of one another in the origin). Pick one of them and call it ω_1. Plot all the points $n\omega_1$, (n an integer). Now remove these points and begin again, drawing a circle C_2 (possibly coinciding with the first) with center at the origin and passing through the period nearest to the origin and not on the removed line l_1. Go from the origin to ω_1, to circle C_2, then around C_2 counterclockwise till you come to the first period on C_2 not on l_1. Call this point ω_2. Plot the points $n\omega_2$, (n an integer).

Now plot all the points

$$n_1\omega_1 + n_2\omega_2, \quad n_1 \text{ and } n_2 \text{ integers.} \tag{1}$$

This fills the plane with a set of parallelograms whose vertices are the periods (1). Suppose now that an ω exists different from these vertices, say

$$\omega = (n_1 + \theta_1)\omega_1 + (n_2 + \theta_2)\omega_2, \qquad (2)$$

where

$$0 \leq \theta_1 \leq 1 \quad \text{and} \quad 0 \leq \theta_2 \leq 1,$$

equality not holding for both θ_1 and θ_2. Then the ω's gotten by giving n_1 and n_2 all integral values in (2) are also periods. Thus there must be one within (or on) the parallelogram I. It will either be within (or on) $\triangle A$ or $\triangle B$. But it cannot be in or on $\triangle A$ by our choice of ω_1 and ω_2. Hence it must be in or on $\triangle B$. But if it is in $\triangle B$, then there exists a period in the corresponding $\triangle B$ of parallelogram II, and hence, by reflection in the origin, a period in $\triangle A$ of parallelogram I. But this we have just seen to be impossible. Hence there are no other periods than those given by (1). This proves the theorem.

21.11 THEOREM.   There are two, four, or six, and no more, periods on the circle C_1 of Article 21.10.

Proof: Clearly, there must be an even number of periods on C_1, for if ω is a period, so is $-\omega$ a period. It is also clear from Figure 21.3 that we may have two, four, or six periods on the circle. If eight or more periods were on the circle, then we would have a case of at least three collinear periods on the circle, which is impossible.

21.12. THEOREM.   The imaginary part of ω_2/ω_1 is positive. That is, $I(\omega_1/\omega_2) > 0$.

Proof: From our geometrical choice of ω_1 and ω_2, we see that

$$0 < \theta < \pi,$$

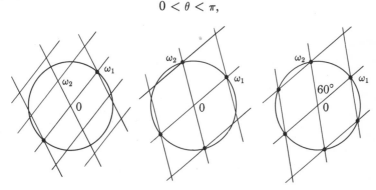

Figure 21.3

where θ is the angle from l_1 to l_2. Now we set

$$\omega_2 = r_2 e^{i\theta_2} \quad \text{and} \quad \omega_1 = r_1 e^{i\theta_1}.$$

Then

$$\frac{\omega_2}{\omega_1} = \frac{r_2}{r_1} e^{i(\theta_2-\theta_1)} = \frac{r_2}{r_1} e^{i\theta}.$$

Hence

$$I(\omega_2/\omega_1) = \frac{r_2}{r_1} \sin \theta > 0.$$

21.13. THEOREM. There are infinitely many pairs of primitive periods of a doubly periodic function $f(z)$. If ω_1, ω_2 is one pair, then all others are given by

$$\Omega_1 = l_1\omega_1 + l_2\omega_2, \quad \Omega_2 = k_1\omega_1 + k_2\omega_2,$$

where

$$\begin{vmatrix} l_1 & l_2 \\ k_1 & k_2 \end{vmatrix} = \pm 1,$$

l_1, l_2, k_1, k_2 integers.

Proof:

Necessary: Suppose Ω_1 and Ω_2 are primitive periods. Since they are periods, then integers l_1, l_2, k_1, k_2 exist such that

$$\Omega_1 = l_1\omega_1 + l_2\omega_2, \quad \Omega_2 = k_1\omega_1 + k_2\omega_2. \tag{1}$$

Solving these equations for ω_1 and ω_2 in terms of Ω_1 and Ω_2, we have

$$\omega_1 = \frac{k_2\Omega_1}{\Delta} - \frac{l_2\Omega_2}{\Delta},$$

$$\omega_2 = -\frac{k_1\Omega_1}{\Delta} + \frac{l_1\Omega_2}{\Delta}, \tag{2}$$

where

$$\Delta = \begin{vmatrix} l_1 & l_2 \\ k_1 & k_2 \end{vmatrix}.$$

But, since Ω_1 and Ω_2 are *primitive* periods, it follows that

$$k_2/\Delta, \quad -l_2/\Delta, \quad -k_1/\Delta, \quad l_1/\Delta$$

are integers. Hence the following determinant must also be an integer:

$$\begin{vmatrix} l_1/\Delta & -l_2/\Delta \\ -k_1/\Delta & k_2/\Delta \end{vmatrix} = \begin{vmatrix} l_1 & l_2 \\ k_1 & k_2 \end{vmatrix}/\Delta^2 = 1/\Delta.$$

Thus we must have

$$\Delta = \pm 1.$$

Sufficient: Suppose $\Delta = \pm 1$. Let ω be any period. Then

$$\omega = n_1\omega_1 + n_2\omega_2. \tag{3}$$

But, from (2), since $\Delta = \pm 1$, ω_1 and ω_2 are integral linear combinations of Ω_1 and Ω_2. Hence, from (3), ω is an integral linear combination of Ω_1 and Ω_2. That is, Ω_1 and Ω_2 are primitive periods.

21.14. DEFINITION. The parallelogram with vertices $0, \omega_1, \omega_1 + \omega_2, \omega_2$, where ω_1 and ω_2 are primitive periods, is called a *primitive parallelogram*, denoted by

$$\text{parallelogram } \omega_1, \omega_2.$$

21.15. THEOREM. The areas of all primitive parallelograms are equal for a given doubly periodic function $f(z)$.

Proof: Let

$$\omega_1 = a_1 + ib_1 \quad \text{and} \quad \omega_2 = a_2 + ib_2$$

be a pair of primitive periods. Also, let Ω_1 and Ω_2 be another pair of primitive periods. Then

$$\Omega_1 = l_1(a_1 + ib_1) + l_2(a_2 + ib_2),$$

$$\Omega_2 = k_1(a_1 + ib_1) + k_2(a_2 + ib_2),$$

where

$$\begin{vmatrix} l_1 & l_2 \\ k_1 & k_2 \end{vmatrix} = \pm 1 \qquad \text{by Art. 21.13.}$$

Now,

$$\text{parallelogram } \Omega_1, \Omega_2 = \pm \begin{vmatrix} l_1a_1 + l_2a_2 & l_1b_1 + l_2b_2 \\ k_1a_1 + k_2a_2 & k_1b_1 + k_2b_2 \end{vmatrix}$$

$$= \pm \begin{vmatrix} l_1 & l_2 \\ k_1 & k_2 \end{vmatrix} \cdot \begin{vmatrix} a_1 & b_1 \\ a_2 & b_2 \end{vmatrix}$$

$$= \pm \begin{vmatrix} a_1 & a_2 \\ b_1 & b_2 \end{vmatrix}$$

$$= \pm \text{ parallelogram } \omega_1, \omega_2.$$

FAREY'S SERIES

21.16. DEFINITION.   *Farey's series* of order n is the sequence composed of all the rational fractions in lowest terms between 0 and 1 and with denominators less than or equal to n, arranged in the order of increasing magnitude.

Examples

(a) $n = 3$:

$$\frac{0}{1}, \frac{1}{3}, \frac{1}{2}, \frac{2}{3}, \frac{1}{1}.$$

(b) $n = 7$:

$$\frac{0}{1}, \frac{1}{7}, \frac{1}{6}, \frac{1}{5}, \frac{1}{4}, \frac{2}{7}, \frac{1}{3}, \frac{2}{5}, \frac{3}{7}, \frac{1}{2}, \frac{4}{7}, \frac{3}{5}, \frac{2}{3}, \frac{5}{7}, \frac{3}{4}, \frac{4}{5}, \frac{5}{6}, \frac{6}{7}, \frac{1}{1}.$$

21.17. THEOREM.   If $p/q, p'/q', p''/q''$ are successive terms of a Farey's series, then

(a) $p'q - pq' = 1$,

(b) $p'/q' = (p + p'')/(q + q'')$.

Proof: (a) Assume $f(z)$ doubly periodic with primitive periods $1, i$. The periods are then the vertices of a lattice of squares. As shown in Figure 21.4, plot the points $q + ip$, $q' + ip'$ and construct the parallelogram determined by them and the origin. Now there is no period in this

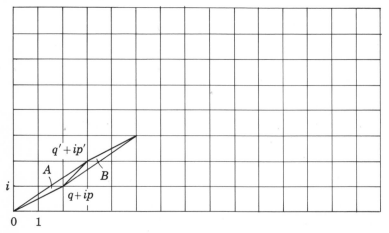

(fig. for case $n = 3$)

Figure 21.4

parallelogram. For suppose there were. Then it must be in triangle A or triangle B. If it is in triangle B, then (as in Art. 21.10) there is a period in triangle A. Thus, in either case, there is a period in triangle A. Since the line joining this period to the origin lies between those joining $q + ip$ and $q' + ip'$ to the origin, then, if a and b are the components of the period,

$$p/q < a/b < p'/q', \quad b < \max(q, q').$$

That is, the fraction a/b reduced would be a number of the Farey's series coming between p/q and p'/q'. But this is impossible since p/q and p'/q' are successive. Thus there are no periods in the parallelogram. Also, since p/q and p'/q' are in lowest terms, no period lies on the sides of the parallelogram. Hence the lattice of parallelograms must take in every period as a vertex, for the lattice fills the plane and each period must be in a parallelogram, or on a side of a parallelogram, or at a vertex of a parallelogram. The first two possibilities have been eliminated. Therefore the parallelogram in Figure 21.4 is a primitive parallelogram. Therefore

$$\text{area parallelogram}_{q+ip,q'+ip'} = \text{area parallelogram}_{1,i},$$

or

$$p'q - pq' = +1.$$

(b) By part (a),

$$p'q - q'p = 1,$$
$$-p'q'' + q'p'' = 1.$$

Therefore

$$p' = \frac{\begin{vmatrix} 1 & -p \\ 1 & p'' \end{vmatrix}}{\begin{vmatrix} q & -p \\ -q'' & p'' \end{vmatrix}}, \qquad q' = \frac{\begin{vmatrix} q & 1 \\ -q'' & 1 \end{vmatrix}}{\begin{vmatrix} q & -p \\ -q'' & p'' \end{vmatrix}}.$$

Hence

$$p'/q' = (p + p'')/(q + q'').$$

CHAPTER 22

Elliptic Functions

Note: In this chapter we shall use the notation of Chapter 21.

22.01. DEFINITION. z_0 *is congruent to z_1 modulo ω_1, ω_2,*

$$z_0 \equiv z_1 \bmod(\omega_1, \omega_2),$$

if integers n_1 and n_2 exist such that

$$z_1 = z_0 + n_1\omega_1 + n_2\omega_2.$$

22.02. DEFINITION. A *fundamental region R* is the interior of the parallelogram with vertices $z_0, z_0 + \omega_1, z_0 + \omega_1 + \omega_2, z_0 + \omega_2$, the vertex z_0, and the two sides through z_0 (see Figure 22.1).

22.03. THEOREM. If a periodic function is defined in a fundamental region, then it is defined over the whole unextended plane.

22.04. DEFINITION. A doubly periodic meromorphic function is said to be *elliptic*.

22.05. THEOREM. If $f_1(z), f_2(z)$ are elliptic with the same periods, then

$$f_1 + f_2, \quad f_1 f_2, \quad f_1/f_2, \quad cf_1 \tag{1}$$

are elliptic with at least the same periods, where c is a constant and none of the functions (1) is constant.

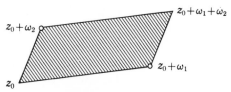

Figure 22.1

Proof: The functions (1) are certainly meromorphic. Again,

$$f_1(z + \omega) + f_2(z + \omega) = f_1(z) + f_2(z),$$
$$\text{etc.,}$$

and hence the functions (1) are also doubly periodic with at least the same periods, provided, of course, that these functions (1) are not constants.

22.06. THEOREM. If $f(z)$ is elliptic, then $f'(z)$ is elliptic with at least the same periods.

Proof: First of all, $f'(z)$ is meromorphic since the derivative of a meromorphic function is meromorphic.

Now we pick an arbitrary point z_0 where $f(z)$ is analytic and let

$$z_1 \equiv z_0 \bmod(\omega_1, \omega_2).$$

Then we have

$$\frac{f(z_0 + \Delta z) - f(z_0)}{\Delta z} = \frac{f(z_1 + \Delta z) - f(z_1)}{\Delta z}.$$

Taking the limit of both sides as $\Delta z \to 0$, we get

$$f'(z_0) = f'(z_1).$$

Hence $f'(z)$ has at least the same periods as $f(z)$. Moreover, $f'(z)$ can never be a constant c, since then we would have $f(z) = cz + d$, which is not elliptic. Hence the theorem.

22.07. DEFINITION. The *order* of an elliptic function is the number of poles in a fundamental region.

This definition is justifiable since (a) all fundamental regions contain the same number of poles, and (b) the poles are isolated and hence finite in number in a fundamental region.

22.08. THEOREM. There are no elliptic functions of zero order.

Proof: Suppose there are. Then there are no poles in the fundamental region, and $f(z)$, being meromorphic there, has no other singularities there, and hence is bounded there. Therefore $f(z)$ is bounded in the whole plane. Thus, by Liouville's Theorem, $f(z)$ is a constant. Hence $f(z)$ is not elliptic—a contradiction.

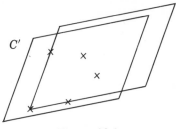

Figure 22.2

22.09.   COROLLARY.   Two elliptic functions with the same periods, same poles, and same principal parts differ by a constant.

22.10.   COROLLARY.   The quotient of two elliptic functions with the same periods, the same poles and orders, and the same zeros and orders is a constant.

22.11.   THEOREM.   The sum of the residues of an elliptic function in a fundamental region is zero.

Proof: As shown in Figure 22.2, mark all the poles in the fundamental region and then slightly displace the region, keeping its sides in the original directions, to the position C' so that all the marked poles lie in the *interior* of C'. Since the poles are isolated, this can be done. Then we have

$$\frac{1}{2\pi i}\int_{C'} f(z)dz = 0,$$

since the integral is equal but opposite in sign on the opposite sides of C', owing to the periodicity of $f(z)$.

22.12.   THEOREM.   There are no elliptic functions of the first order.

Proof: Suppose there are. There is, then, one pole in each fundamental region, and the residue of the function at that pole is, of course, different from zero (Art. 13.03, Cor.). But this contradicts Article 22.11. Hence the theorem.

22.13.   THEOREM.   If $f(z)$ is elliptic, then the number of poles in a fundamental region equals the number of zeros there.

Proof: Consider the function $f'(z)/f(z)$. This is the quotient of two elliptic functions, and hence is an elliptic function with at least the same periods as $f(z)$ (Art. 22.05). Now shift the fundamental region parallel to itself to position C' so that all the poles and zeros of the fundamental region lie in the *interior* of C'. Then we have (Art. 22.11)

$$\frac{1}{2\pi i}\int_{C'} \frac{f'(z)}{f(z)}\, dz = 0. \tag{1}$$

But, by Article 13.20, the value of the integral in (1) is the number of zeros minus the number of poles inside C'. Hence the theorem.

22.14. COROLLARY. If $f(z)$ is elliptic of order n, then $f(z)$ has n zeros in a fundamental region.

22.15. COROLLARY. If $f(z)$ is elliptic of order n, then it takes on every value c exactly n times in a fundamental region.

Proof: Apply Article 22.14 to the function $f(z) - c$.

22.16. NOTE. Notice that there has been an analogy between elliptic functions and rational functions, where for the latter the fundamental region may be considered as the whole plane. This analogy, however, breaks down in Article 22.18.

22.17. LEMMA. If $f(z)$ is meromorphic, then $zf'(z)/f(z)$ has a residue ka at a zero a of order k of $f(z)$, and a residue $-lb$ at a pole b of order l of $f(z)$.

Proof: (1) We have

$$f(z) = (z - a)^k \varphi(z), \quad \varphi(z) \text{ analytic at } a, \varphi(a) \neq 0.$$

Now,

$$f'(z) = k(z - a)^{k-1}\varphi(z) + (z - a)^k \varphi'(z).$$

Hence

$$\frac{zf'(z)}{f(z)} = \frac{kz}{z - a} + \frac{z\varphi'(z)}{\varphi(z)}. \tag{1}$$

This function has a pole of order 1 at $z = a$, and therefore the residue at $z = a$ is given by

$$r = \lim_{z \to a} (z - a) \frac{zf'(z)}{f(z)}$$

$$= \lim_{z \to a} \left\{ kz + z(z - a) \frac{\varphi'(z)}{\varphi(z)} \right\} = ka.$$

(2) We have

$$f(z) = \frac{\varphi(z)}{(z - b)^l}, \quad \varphi(z) \text{ analytic at } b, \varphi(b) \neq 0.$$

Now,

$$f'(z) = \frac{(z - b)^l \varphi'(z) - l(z - b)^{l-1}\varphi(z)}{(z - b)^{2l}}.$$

Hence

$$\frac{zf'(z)}{f(z)} = -\frac{lz}{z - b} + \frac{z\varphi'(z)}{\varphi(z)}.$$

This function has a pole of order 1 at $z = b$, and therefore the residue at $z = b$ is given by

$$r = \lim_{z \to b} \left\{ -lz + z(z - b) \frac{\varphi'(z)}{\varphi(z)} \right\} = -lb.$$

22.18. THEOREM.   If $f(z)$ is elliptic and has, in a fundamental region, zeros $a_1, a_2, \cdots, a_n$ of orders $k_1, k_2, \cdots, k_n$, and poles $b_1, b_2, \cdots, b_m$ of orders $l_1, l_2, \cdots, l_m$, then

$$\sum_1^n a_i k_i \equiv \sum_1^m b_i l_i \bmod(\omega_1, \omega_2).$$

Proof: Consider the function $zf'(z)/f(z)$. As shown in Figure 22.3, choose parallelogram C' congruent and parallel to the fundamental region and containing all the zeros $a_1, \cdots, a_n$ and all the poles $b_1, \cdots, b_m$ in its *interior*. Let the vertices of C' be $z_1, z_1 + \omega_1, z_1 + \omega_1 + \omega_2, z_1 + \omega_2$. Then we have, by Article 22.17,

$$\frac{1}{2\pi i} \int_{C'} \frac{zf'(z)}{f(z)} \, dz = \sum_1^n k_i a_i - \sum_1^m l_i b_i. \tag{1}$$

But, again,

$$\int_{C'} = \int_{z_1}^{z_1 + \omega_1} + \int_{z_1 + \omega_1}^{z_1 + \omega_1 + \omega_2} + \int_{z_1 + \omega_1 + \omega_2}^{z_1 + \omega_2} + \int_{z_1 + \omega_2}^{z_1} . \tag{2}$$

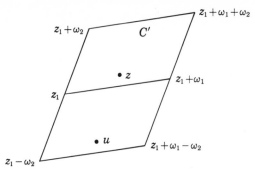

Figure 22.3

Now, owing to the periodicity of $f(z)$, we have

$$\int_{z_1}^{z_1+\omega_1} \frac{zf'(z)}{f(z)}\, dz - \int_{z_1+\omega_2}^{z_1+\omega_1+\omega_2} \frac{zf'(z)}{f(z)}\, dz$$

$$= \int_{z_1}^{z_1+\omega_1} \frac{zf'(z)}{f(z)}\, dz - \int_{z_1}^{z_1+\omega_1} (u+\omega_2)\frac{f'(u+\omega_2)}{f(u+\omega_2)}\, du$$

(making the transformation $z = u + \omega_2$)

$$= \int_{z_1}^{z_1+\omega_1} \frac{zf'(z)}{f(z)}\, dz - \int_{z_1}^{z_1+\omega_1} \frac{uf'(u+\omega_2)}{f(u+\omega_2)}\, du - \omega_2 \int_{z_1}^{z_1+\omega_1} \frac{f'(u+\omega_2)}{f(u+\omega_2)}\, du$$

$$= \int_{z_1}^{z_1+\omega_1} \frac{zf'(z)}{f(z)}\, dz - \int_{z_1}^{z_1+\omega_1} \frac{uf'(u)}{f(u)}\, du - \omega_2 \int_{z_1}^{z_1+\omega_1} \frac{f'(u)}{f(u)}\, du$$

(because of the periodicity of $f(z)$ and $f'(z)$)

$$= \int_{z_1}^{z_1+\omega_1} \frac{zf'(z)}{f(z)}\, dz - \int_{z_1}^{z_1+\omega_1} \frac{zf'(z)}{f(z)}\, dz - \omega_2 \int_{z_1}^{z_1+\omega_1} \frac{f'(z)}{f(z)}\, dz$$

(calling the variable under the integral sign, z)

$$= -\omega_2 \int_{z_1}^{z_1+\omega_1} \frac{f'(z)}{f(z)}\, dz$$

$$= -\omega_2 \log f(z)\Big|_{z_1}^{z_1+\omega_1}$$

$$= -\omega_2 \log \frac{f(z_1+\omega_1)}{f(z_1)}$$

$$= -\omega_2 \log(1)$$

$$= -\omega_2(2m_2\pi i).$$

Similarly, we have

$$\int_{z_1+\omega_1}^{z_1+\omega_1+\omega_2} - \int_{z_1}^{z_1+\omega_2} = -\omega_1(2m_1\pi i).$$

Hence, returning to (2), we have

$$\frac{1}{2\pi i}\int_{C'} \frac{zf'(z)}{f(z)}\,dz = 2m_1\omega_1 - 2m_2\omega_2. \qquad (3)$$

This, with (1), proves the theorem.

THE WEIERSTRASS $\wp$ FUNCTION

22.19. NOTATION.   Take any two complex numbers ω_1, ω_2 such that $I(\omega_2/\omega_1) > 0$ and draw the parallelogram network determined by ω_1, ω_2. Number the vertices of these parallelograms as shown in Figure 22.4, and let Ω_n be the point with the number n.

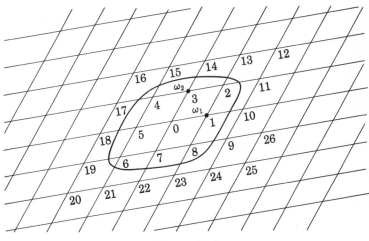

Figure 22.4

22.20. THEOREM. $\sum\limits_{n=1}^{\infty} 1/|\Omega_n|^n$ converges for $p = 3, 4, 5, \cdots$.

Proof: Let l be the shortest distance from 0 to a side of parallelogram 2468. Then

$$\sum_{1}^{\infty} \frac{1}{|\Omega_n|^p} \ll \frac{8}{l^p} + \frac{2 \cdot 8}{(2l)^p} + \cdots + \frac{k \cdot 8}{(kl)^p} + \cdots$$

$$= \sum_{k=1}^{\infty} 8/k^{p-1}l^p$$

$$= \frac{8}{l^p} \sum_{1}^{\infty} \frac{1}{k^{p-1}},$$

which converges for $p = 3, 4, 5, \cdots$.

22.21. THEOREM. $\displaystyle\sum_{n=0}^{\infty} 1/(z - \Omega_n)^p$ converges absolutely and uniformly for $z \neq \Omega_n$ and $p = 3, 4, 5, \cdots$.

Proof: Since

$$\lim_{n \to \infty} |\Omega_n| = \infty,$$

we have, for any given $z \neq \Omega_n$,

$$\lim_{n \to \infty} \left| \frac{\Omega_n}{z - \Omega_n} \right|^p = 1.$$

Therefore

$$\frac{|\Omega_n|^p}{|z - \Omega_n|^p} < 2, \text{ for } n > N, \text{ say.}$$

That is,

$$\frac{1}{|z - \Omega_n|^p} < \frac{2}{|\Omega_n|}, \quad n > N,$$

or

$$\sum_{N}^{\infty} 1/(z - \Omega_n)^p \ll \sum_{N}^{\infty} 2/|\Omega_n|^p,$$

which converges (Art. 22.20) for $p = 3, 4, 5, \cdots$.

22.22. THEOREM.   The function

$$f_p(z) \equiv \sum_{0}^{\infty} 1/(z - \Omega_n)^p, \quad p = 3, 4, 5, \cdots,$$

is meromorphic, its only poles being at the points

$$z = \Omega_n, (n = 0, 1, 2, \cdots),$$

and its principal parts at these poles being $1/(z - \Omega_n)^p$.

Proof: Choose a region R arbitrarily large but lying between two concentric sets of parallelograms (see Figure 22.4). Now, by Article 22.21,

$$\sum_0^\infty 1/(z - \Omega_n)^p, \quad p = 3, 4, 5, \cdots$$

converges uniformly for $z \neq \Omega_n$, and hence converges uniformly in R and therefore represents an analytic function there except for the points Ω_n. But R was arbitrarily large. Hence the series represents a function analytic in the unextended plane except for the points Ω_n.

22.23. THEOREM. $f_p(z)$, $(p = 3, 4, 5, \cdots)$, is elliptic of order p with periods ω_1, ω_2.

Proof: (1) We have already shown that $f_p(z)$ is meromorphic (Art. 22.22).

(2) We have

$$f_p(z + \omega_1) = \sum_0^\infty 1/(z - \Omega_n + \omega_1)^p = f_p(z),$$

because $\Omega_n - \omega_1$ takes in all the vertices as $n \to \infty$. That is,

$$\sum_0^\infty 1/(z - \Omega_n + \omega_1)^p$$

is the series $\sum_0^\infty 1/(z - \Omega_n)^p$ with the terms rearranged. But, by Article 22.21, the latter series converges absolutely, and hence its terms may be rearranged without affecting its sum. Similarly,

$$f_p(z + \omega_2) = f_p(z).$$

Hence ω_1 and ω_2 are certainly periods of $f_p(z)$. Thus $f_p(z)$ is doubly periodic, and therefore, by part (1), elliptic.

(3) There are no smaller periods than ω_1 and ω_2. For suppose there are. Then the fundamental parallelogram would be smaller. But then there would not be enough poles to go around, for there is only one pole (of pth order) in each parallelogram determined by ω_1, ω_2 (by Art. 22.22). Hence the parallelograms determined by ω_1, ω_2 are fundamental and $f_p(z)$ is of order p.

22.24. THEOREM. $f_p(-z) = (-1)^p f_p(z)$, $(z \neq \Omega_n)$.

Proof: We have

$$f_p(z) = \frac{1}{z^p} + \sum_1^\infty \frac{1}{(z - \Omega_n)^p}. \tag{1}$$

But

$$\sum_1^\infty \frac{1}{(z + \Omega_n)^p} = \sum_1^\infty \frac{1}{(z - \Omega_n)^p}, \tag{2}$$

for each side of (2) takes in all the vertices Ω_n, and since the series on the left converges absolutely for $z \neq \Omega_n$, its terms may be rearranged to give that on the right. Hence, because of (2), (1) may be written as

$$f_p(z) = \frac{1}{z^p} + \frac{1}{2}\sum_1^\infty \frac{1}{(z - \Omega_n)^p} + \frac{1}{2}\sum_1^\infty \frac{1}{(z + \Omega_n)^p}.$$

Hence

$$f_p(-z) = \frac{1}{(-z)^p} + \frac{1}{2}\sum_1^\infty \frac{1}{(-z - \Omega_n)^p} + \frac{1}{2}\sum_1^\infty \frac{1}{(-z + \Omega_n)^p}$$

$$= (-1)^p\left\{\frac{1}{z^p} + \frac{1}{2}\sum_1^\infty \frac{1}{(z + \Omega_n)^p} + \frac{1}{2}\sum_1^\infty \frac{1}{(z - \Omega_n)^p}\right\}$$

$$= (-1)^p f_p(z).$$

22.25. THEOREM. If z_a, z_b are symmetric in a point $\frac{1}{2}(n_1\omega_1 + n_2\omega_2)$, and if $z_a \not\equiv 0$, $z_b \not\equiv 0$, $\mathrm{mod}(\omega_1, \omega_2)$, then $f_p(z_a) = (-1)^p f_p(z_b)$.

Proof: We have

$$\tfrac{1}{2}(z_a + z_b) = \tfrac{1}{2}(n_1\omega_1 + n_2\omega_2),$$

or

$$z_a \equiv -z_b \,\mathrm{mod}(\omega_1, \omega_2).$$

Therefore

$$f_p(z_a) \equiv f_p(-z_b)$$
$$= (-1)f_p(z_b) \qquad \text{by Art. 22.24.}$$

Note: Article 22.24 is essentially a special case of this article.

22.26. COROLLARY. If p is odd, then $f_p(z)$ has zeros at the points $\omega_1/2$, $\omega_2/2$, $(\omega_1 + \omega_2)/2$, and all congruent points.

Proof: Let z_a and z_b be symmetric in one of the points $\omega_1/2$, $\omega_2/2$, $(\omega_1 + \omega_2)/2$. Then, by Article 25.25, since p is odd,

$$f_p(z_a) = -f_p(z_b).$$

Let z_a, and hence also z_b, $\rightarrow \omega_1/2$, $\omega_2/2$, or $(\omega_1 + \omega_2)/2$, whichever is the center of symmetry. Then

$$f_p(\omega_1/2) = -f_p(\omega_1/2), \text{ etc.}$$

Hence $\omega_1/2$, $\omega_2/2$, $(\omega_1 + \omega_2)/2$ are zeros of $f_p(z)$.

22.27.   DEFINITION.   Let us define

$$F(z) \equiv \int_a^z f_3(z)dz, \quad a \equiv 0 \bmod(\omega_1, \omega_2),$$

where the path of integration does not pass through a vertex. Then it may be shown that

(a) $F(z)$ is analytic at $z \neq \Omega_n$;

(b) $F(z)$ has a pole of order 2 at Ω_n, and a principal part there of $-1/2(z - \Omega_n)^2$;

(c) $F(z)$ is even, $F(z) = F(-z)$;

(d) ω_1 and ω_2 are primitive periods of $F(z)$.

Hence $F(z)$ is an elliptic function of the second order.

22.28.   THEOREM. $-2[F(z) + k] = \dfrac{1}{z^2} + \displaystyle\sum_1^\infty \left[\dfrac{1}{(z - \Omega_n)^2} - \dfrac{1}{\Omega_n^2} \right],$

where k is a constant.

Proof:

$$F(z) = \int_a^z f_3(z)dz$$

$$= \int_a^z \left[f_3(z) - \frac{1}{z^3} \right] dz + \int_a^z \frac{1}{z^3} dz$$

$$= \int_0^z \left[f_3(z) - \frac{1}{z^3} \right] dz - \int_0^a \left[f_3(z) - \frac{1}{z^3} \right] dz + \int_a^z \frac{1}{z^3} dz$$

$$= \int_0^z \sum_1^\infty \frac{dz}{(z - \Omega_n)^3} - k - \frac{1}{2z^2},$$

where

$$k = \int_0^a \left[f_3(z) - \frac{1}{z^3} \right] dz + \frac{1}{2a^2}.$$

Therefore

$$F(z) = -\sum_1^\infty \left[\frac{1}{2(z - \Omega_n)^2} - \frac{1}{2\Omega_n^2} \right] - k - \frac{1}{2z^2}.$$

(We may integrate the series term by term since the series converges uniformly.)

22.29.   DEFINITION.   The function

$$\wp(z) \equiv \frac{1}{z^2} + \sum_{1}^{\infty} \left[\frac{1}{(z - \Omega_n)^2} - \frac{1}{\Omega_n^2} \right]$$

is known as the *Weierstrass p function.*

22.30.   THEOREM. $\wp'(z) = -2f_3(z)$.

Proof:

$$\wp(z) = -2F'(z) = -2f_3(z).$$

22.31.   THEOREM. $\displaystyle\lim_{z \to 0} \left[\wp(z) - \frac{1}{z^2} \right] = 0$.

22.32.   PROPERTIES.

$$\wp(z)$$

(1) Meromorphic.
(2) Elliptic of order 2.
(3) Even. $\left.\vphantom{\begin{array}{c}1\\2\\3\\4\\5\end{array}}\right\}$ Art. 25.27
(4) Poles at $z = \Omega_n$ of order 2.
(5) Principal part at pole $= 1/(z - \Omega_n)^2$
(6) Has double values at $\omega_1/2$, $\omega_2/2$, $(\omega_1 + \omega_2)/2$ and congruent points [by (7) below].
(7) Primitive periods ω_1, ω_2.

$$\wp'(z)$$

(1) Meromorphic.
(2) Elliptic of order 3.
(3) Primitive periods ω_1, ω_2. $\left.\vphantom{\begin{array}{c}1\\2\\3\\4\\5\\6\end{array}}\right\}$ Art. 25.30
(4) Odd.
(5) Poles at $z = \Omega_n$ of order 3.
(6) Principal part at pole $= -2/(z - \Omega_n)^3$.
(7) Zeros at $\omega_1/2$, $\omega_2/2$, $(\omega_1 + \omega_2)/2$ and congruent points (Art. 22.26).

22.33.   THEOREM. $\wp'^2 - 4\wp^3 + 20c\wp + 28d = 0$, for

$$z \not\equiv 0 \bmod(\omega_1, \omega_2)$$

and where *c* and *d* are some constants.

Proof: By a Laurent expansion about 0, and since $\wp$ is even, we have

$$\wp(z) = \frac{1}{z^2} + k + cz^2 + dz^4 + \cdots.$$

But since, by Article 22.31,

$$\wp(z) - \frac{1}{z^2}\Bigg|_{z=0} = 0,$$

we have that $k = 0$. Hence

$$\wp'(z) = -\frac{2}{z^3} + 2cz + 4dz^3 + \cdots.$$

Therefore

$$[\wp'(z)]^2 = \frac{4}{z^6} - \frac{8c}{z^2} - 16d + (\quad)z^2 + \cdots. \tag{1}$$

Again,

$$[\wp(z)]^3 = \frac{1}{z^6} + \frac{3c}{z^2} + 3d + (\quad)z^2 + \cdots. \tag{2}$$

Hence

$$\wp'^2 + 4\wp^3 + 20c\,\wp + 28d = (\quad)z^2 + \cdots. \tag{3}$$

Now, the left side of (3) is elliptic (since its terms are) and hence being analytic at $z = 0$ [as is shown by the right side of (3)], it is analytic at all the vertices. Hence it is analytic over the whole plane, for, by Article 22.32, the vertices are the only candidates for singularities. Hence, by Liouville's Theorem, the left side of (3) is constant, the constant being determined as 0 from the right side of (3) by setting specifically $z = 0$. Hence the theorem.

22.34. THEOREM. $\quad g_2 \equiv 20c = 3 \cdot 4 \cdot 5 \sum_1^\infty 1/\Omega_n^4,$

$$g_3 \equiv 28d = 4 \cdot 5 \cdot 7 \sum_1^\infty 1/\Omega_n^6.$$

Proof: Setting

$$\varphi(z) \equiv \wp(z) - \frac{1}{z^2} = \sum_1^\infty \left[\frac{1}{(z - \Omega_n)^2} - \frac{1}{\Omega_n^2}\right],$$

we have

$$\varphi''(z) = 3! \sum_1^\infty 1/(z - \Omega_n)^4,$$

$$\varphi''''(z) = 5! \sum_1^\infty 1/(z - \Omega_n)^6.$$

Now,

$$c = \frac{\varphi''(0)}{2!} = 3 \sum_1^\infty 1/\Omega_n^4,$$

$$d = \frac{\varphi''''(0)}{4!} = 5 \sum_1^\infty 1/\Omega_n^6.$$

Hence the theorem.

22.35.   DEFINITION.   We set $\zeta'(z) \equiv - \wp(z)$, where

$$\lim_{z \to 0} [\zeta(z) - 1/z] = 0.$$

22.36.   THEOREM. $\zeta(z) = \dfrac{1}{z} + \displaystyle\sum_1^\infty \left[\dfrac{1}{z - \Omega_n} - \dfrac{z}{\Omega_n^2} + \dfrac{1}{\Omega_n} \right].$

Proof: We have, by Articles 22.35 and 22.29,

$$\zeta(z) = - \int_0^z \wp(z)dz = \frac{1}{z} + \sum_1^\infty \left[\frac{1}{z - \Omega_n} - \frac{z}{\Omega_n^2} + \frac{1}{\Omega_n} \right] + C.$$

Applying the second part of Article 22.35, we find that $C = 0$.

22.37.   PROPERTIES OF $\zeta(z)$.

(1) Meromorphic.
(2) Poles of first order, residues $= 1$, at Ω_n.
(3) Odd (integration of an even series with constant of integration zero is an odd series).

22.38.   DEFINITION.   We set $\sigma'(z)/\sigma(z) = \zeta(z)$, where

$$\lim_{z \to 0} \frac{\sigma(z)}{z} = 1.$$

22.39. **THEOREM.** $\sigma(z) = ze^{\int_0^z [\zeta(z) - 1/z]dz}$.

Proof: From Article 22.38,

$$\sigma(z) = e^{\int \zeta(z)dz}$$

$$= e^{\int_0^z [\zeta(z) - 1/z]dz + \log z + C}$$

$$= zke^{\int_0^z [\zeta(z) - 1/z]dz}, \quad k = e^C.$$

Now, by the second part of Article 22.38, it follows that $k = 1$. Hence the theorem.

22.40. PROPERTIES OF $\sigma(z)$.

(1) Meromorphic (by Art. 22.39).
(2) Entire with first-order zeros at Ω_n, no other zeros (see below).
(3) Odd (see below).

Proof: For

$$\zeta(z) = 1/(z - \Omega_n) + A(z),$$

where $A(z)$ is analytic at Ω_n by (2) of Article 22.37. Therefore

$$\int \zeta(z)dz = \log(z - \Omega_n) + A_1(z),$$

where $A_1(z)$ is analytic at Ω_n. Hence

$$e^{\int \zeta(z)dz} = (z - \Omega_n)A_2(z),$$

where $A_2(z)$ is analytic at Ω_n and $A_2(\Omega_n) \neq 0$. Hence we have part (2) above. Finally, $\sigma(z)$ is odd because $\zeta(z) - 1/z$ is odd; hence

$$\int_0^z [\zeta(z) - 1/z]dz$$

is even; hence $e^{\int_0^z}$ is even; and hence $ze^{\int_0^z}$ is odd.

22.41. **THEOREM.** $\zeta(z + \omega_1) - \zeta(z) = \eta_1$, a constant,
$\zeta(z + \omega_2) - \zeta(z) = \eta_2$, a constant.

Proof: Since ω_1 is a period of $\wp(z)$, we have

$$\wp(z + \omega_1) - \wp(z) = 0.$$

Integrating, we get the required results, etc.

22.42.   THEOREM.
$$\frac{\sigma(z + \omega_1)}{\sigma(z)} = -e^{\eta_1(z + \omega_1/2)},$$

$$\frac{\sigma(z + \omega_2)}{\sigma(z)} = -e^{\eta_2(z + \omega_2/2)}.$$

Proof: We have

$$\sigma(z) = e^{\int \zeta(z)dz} \quad \text{and} \quad \zeta(z + \omega_1) - \zeta(z) = \eta_1.$$

Now we set

$$\xi(z) = \int \zeta(z)dz.$$

Then

$$\xi(z + \omega_1) - \xi(z) = \eta_1 z + c_1,$$

and

$$\frac{\sigma(z + \omega_1)}{\sigma(z)} = e^{\xi(z+\omega_1) - \xi(z)}$$

$$= e^{\eta_1 z + c_1}$$

$$= k_1 e^{\eta_1 z}, \quad k_1 = e^{c_1}. \tag{1}$$

We set $z = -\omega_1/2$. Then

$$\frac{\sigma(\omega_1/2)}{\sigma(-\omega_1/2)} = -1 = k_1 e^{-\eta_1\omega_1/2}, \qquad \text{since } \sigma \text{ is odd,}$$

and hence

$$k_1 = -e^{\eta_1\omega_1/2}.$$

Therefore, from (1),

$$\frac{\sigma(z + \omega_1)}{\sigma(z)} = -e^{\eta_1(z + \omega_1/2)}.$$

Similarly,

$$\frac{\sigma(z + \omega_2)}{\sigma(z)} = -e^{\eta_2(z + \omega_2/2)}.$$

22.43.   THEOREM.

$$\text{(a) } \wp(z) = \frac{1}{z^2} + * + (\quad)z^2 + \cdots,$$

$$\text{(b) } \zeta(z) = \frac{1}{z} + *z + (\quad)z^3 + \cdots,$$

$$\text{(c) } \sigma(z) = z + *z^3 + (\quad)z^5 + \cdots,$$

where $* = 0$ in all three cases.

Proof: Case (a) was proven in Article 22.33; Case (b) is established by integrating Case (a); and Case (c) is established by equating coefficients in $\sigma'(z)/\sigma(z) = \zeta(z)$.

22.44. THEOREM. $\varphi(z) \equiv \dfrac{\sigma(z - z')\sigma(z + z')}{\sigma^2(z)\sigma^2(z')}$, where z' is a constant $\not\equiv 0 \mod(\omega_1, \omega_2)$, is elliptic of order 2 with primitive periods ω_1, ω_2.

Proof: Applying Article 22.42, we have

$$\varphi(z + \omega_1) = \frac{\sigma(z - z')e^{\eta_1(z - z' + \omega_1/2)}\,\sigma(z + z')e^{\eta_1(z + z' + \omega_2/2)}}{\sigma^2(z)e^{2\eta_1(z + \omega_1/2)}\sigma^2(z')}$$

$$= \frac{\sigma(z - z')\sigma(z + z')}{\sigma^2(z)\sigma^2(z')}$$

$$= \varphi(z).$$

Similarly,

$$\varphi(z + \omega_2) = \varphi(z).$$

Hence $\varphi(z)$ is doubly periodic with periods ω_1, ω_2. Moreover, $\varphi(z)$ is meromorphic, being the ratio of meromorphic functions. Hence $\varphi(z)$ is certainly elliptic. Now, since $z' \not\equiv 0 \mod(\omega_1, \omega_2)$, then (by Art. 22.40) $\sigma^2(z') \neq 0$ and σ is entire. Hence $\sigma(z - z') \neq \infty$, $\sigma(z + z') \neq \infty$. Hence $\varphi(z)$ is of order 2, having poles at Ω_n of second order. Hence, also, ω_1 and ω_2 are primitive periods, for otherwise there would not be enough poles to go around.

22.45. THEOREM. $\wp(z) - \wp(z') = -\dfrac{\sigma(z - z')\sigma(z + z')}{\sigma^2(z)\sigma^2(z')}.$

Proof:

$$\sigma(z + z') = \sigma(z') + \sigma'(z')z + \frac{\sigma''(z')}{2!}z^2 + \cdots$$

$$\sigma(z - z') = -\sigma(z') + \sigma'(z')z - \frac{\sigma''(z')}{2!}z^2 + \cdots \qquad \text{since } \sigma \text{ is odd.}$$

Therefore

$$\sigma(z + z')\sigma(z - z')$$

$$= -\sigma^2(z') + \{[\sigma'(z')]^2 - \sigma(z')\sigma''(z')\}z^2 + (\quad)z^4 + \cdots.$$

And from Case (c) of Article 22.43,

$$\sigma^2(z)\sigma^2(z') = \sigma^2(z')z^2 + (\quad)z^6 + \cdots.$$

Therefore

$$\frac{\sigma(z+z')\sigma(z-z')}{\sigma^2(z)\sigma^2(z')} = -\frac{1}{z^2} + \frac{[\sigma'(z')]^2 - \sigma(z')\sigma''(z')}{\sigma^2(z')} + (\quad)z^2 + \cdots.$$

Now,

$$-\wp(z) = \zeta'(z) = \frac{\sigma(z)\sigma''(z) - [\sigma'(z)]^2}{\sigma^2(z')}.$$

Hence

$$\frac{\sigma(z+z')\sigma(z-z')}{\sigma^2(z)\sigma^2(z')} = -\frac{1}{z^2} + \wp(z') + (\quad)z^2 + \cdots,$$

and

$$\varphi(z) + \wp(z) - \wp(z') = (\quad)z^2 + \cdots. \tag{1}$$

Now, the left side of (1) is elliptic with primitive periods ω_1, ω_2, since each of its terms is. But the left side is analytic at $z = 0$, since the right side is. Hence the left side is analytic over the whole plane, and hence is, by Liouville's Theorem, a constant. The value of this constant is 0, being determined by setting $z = 0$ in the right side. Hence

$$\varphi(z) + \wp(z) - \wp(z') = 0.$$

This proves the theorem.

22.46.   **THEOREM.** $\zeta(u+v) = \zeta(u) + \zeta(v) + \dfrac{1}{2}\dfrac{\wp'(u) - \wp'(v)}{\wp(u) - \wp(v)}.$

Proof: From Article 22.45 we get, by calculation,

$$\frac{\wp'(u)}{\wp(u) - \wp(v)} = \frac{\sigma'(u-v)}{\sigma(u-v)} + \frac{\sigma'(u+v)}{\sigma(u+v)} - \frac{2\sigma'(u)}{\sigma(u)}, \tag{1}$$

and

$$-\frac{\wp'(v)}{\wp(u) - \wp(v)} = -\frac{\sigma'(u-v)}{\sigma(u-v)} + \frac{\sigma'(u+v)}{\sigma(u+v)} - \frac{2\sigma'(v)}{\sigma(v)}. \tag{2}$$

Adding (1) and (2), we have

$$\frac{\wp'(u) - \wp'(v)}{\wp(u) - \wp(v)} = 2\zeta(u+v) - 2\zeta(u) - 2\zeta(v),$$

by Article 22.37. Hence the theorem.

22.47. THEOREM.

$$\wp(u + v) = -\wp(u) - \wp(v) + \frac{1}{4}\left[\frac{\wp'(u) - \wp'(v)}{\wp(u) - \wp(v)}\right]^2.$$

Proof: Differentiating the result of Article 22.46, w.r.t. u, we get, by Article 22.35,

$$-\wp(u + v)$$
$$= -\wp(u) + \frac{1}{2}\frac{\{\wp(u) - \wp(v)\}\wp''(u) - \{\wp'(u) - \wp'(v)\}\wp'(u)}{\{\wp(u) - \wp(v)\}^2}. \quad (1)$$

Similarly, differentiating w.r.t. v, we get

$$-\wp(u + v)$$
$$= -\wp(v) + \frac{1}{2}\frac{-\{\wp(u) - \wp(v)\}\wp''(v) + \{\wp'(u) - \wp'(v)\}\wp'(v)}{\{\wp(u) - \wp(v)\}^2}. \quad (2)$$

Adding (1) and (2), we have

$$2\wp(u + v)$$
$$= \wp(u) + \wp(v) - \frac{1}{2}\frac{6\{\wp(u)-\wp(v)\}^2\{\wp(u)+\wp(v)\} - \{\wp'(u)-\wp'(v)\}^2}{\{\wp(u)-\wp(v)\}^2}, \quad (3)$$

for, by Article 22.33, differentiating w.r.t. u and v, we have

$$2\wp''(u) = 12\wp^2(u) - g_2,$$
$$2\wp''(v) = 12\wp^2(v) - g_2.$$

Hence, subtracting, we have

$$\wp''(u) - \wp''(v) = 6\{\wp^2(u) - \wp^2(v)\}.$$

Continuing with (3), we have

$$2\wp(u + v) = \wp(u) + \wp(v) - 3\{\wp(u) + \wp(v)\} + \frac{1}{2}\left[\frac{\wp'(u) - \wp'(v)}{\wp(u) - \wp(v)}\right]^2,$$

whence the theorem.

22.48. THEOREM.

$$\wp(u + v) + \wp(u) + \wp(v) = [\zeta(u + v) - \zeta(u) - \zeta(v)]^2.$$

Proof: Follows from Articles 22.46 and 22.47.

22.49. THEOREM.   If $f(z)$ is any elliptic function of order $n(\geq 2)$ with primitive periods ω_1, ω_2 with zeros and poles at the points

$$a_1, a_2, \cdots, a_n,$$
$$b_1, b_2, \cdots, b_n$$

in the fundamental parallelogram ($\sum a = \sum b + \Omega$), then

$$f(z) = C \frac{\prod\limits_{k=1}^{n} \sigma(z - a_k)}{\prod\limits_{k=1}^{n-1} \sigma(z - b_k)\sigma(z - b_n - \Omega)},$$

where C is a constant.

Proof: Consider the function

$$\varphi(z) \equiv \frac{\prod\limits_{1}^{n} \sigma(z - a_k)}{\prod\limits_{1}^{n-1} \sigma(z - b_k)\sigma(z - b_n - \Omega)}.$$

Then

$$\varphi(z + \omega_1) = \frac{(-1)^n \prod\limits_{1}^{n} \sigma(z - a_k)e^{n\eta_1(z+\omega_1/2)+\eta_1\sum\limits_{1}^{n}a_k}}{(-1)^n \prod\limits_{1}^{n-1} \sigma(z - b_k)e^{n\eta_1(z+\omega_1/2)+\eta_1\sum\limits_{1}^{n}b_k+\eta_1\Omega}\sigma(z - b_n - \Omega)}$$

$$= \varphi(z).$$

Similarly,

$$\varphi(z + \omega_2) = \varphi(z).$$

Hence $\varphi(z)$ is doubly periodic with periods ω_1, ω_2. Moreover, $\varphi(z)$ has the required zeros and poles. Hence $f(z)/\varphi(z)$ has removable singularities at the vertices. Hence $f(z)/\varphi(z)$ is analytic over the whole plane and hence is a constant C. Thus the theorem.

22.50. THEOREM.   Any elliptic function is a rational function of $\wp$ and a finite number of its derivatives.

Index